Great Lakes in My World
Alliance for the Great Lakes, Chicago 60602
© 2005 by the Alliance for the Great Lakes
All rights reserved. Published 2005, reprinted 2008, 2010
Printed in the United States of America
10 9 8 7 6 5 4 3 2 1

ISBN: 0-9770212-0-3

The Alliance for the Great Lakes gratefully acknowledges support for this project from
the Wege Foundation, Rockwell Automation, Environmental Protection Agency - Region 5,
Kraft Foods, West Michigan Coastal Kayakers Association and Gravity Tank, Inc.

| Wege Foundation | Rockwell Automation | Environmental Protection Agency, Region 5 | Kraft Foods | West Michigan Coastal Kayakers Association | Gravity Tank, Inc. |

Library of Congress Control Number 2005932120

A Great Lakes educator's guide with 64 Great Lakes Creature Cards and an accompanying
compact disc with supplemental materials

This book is printed on totally chlorine free, recycled paper using soy inks.

Great Lakes in My World was funded in part by the United States Environmental Protection Agency (EPA) through grant number
NE 96545101 with Alliance for the Great Lakes. The contents of this document do not necessarily reflect the views and policies
of the United States Environmental Protection Agency, nor does mention of trade names or commercial products constitute
endorsement or recommendation for use.

Formed in 1970, the Alliance for the Great Lakes (formerly the Lake Michigan Federation) is the oldest independent citizens' organization in North America. Our mission is to conserve and restore the world's largest freshwater resource using policy, education and local efforts, ensuring a healthy Great Lakes and clean water for generations of people and wildlife.

Staff

Joel Brammeier
PRESIDENT & CEO
Todd Brennan
OUTREACH COORDINATOR, WISCONSIN
Susan Campbell
MANAGER, COMMUNICATIONS PROGRAM
Frances Canonizado
OUTREACH COORDINATOR, ILLINOIS AND INDIANA
Abigail Crisostomo
PROGRAM ASSOCIATE
Jamie Cross
MANAGER, ADOPT-A-BEACH
Judy Freed
MANAGER, MARKETING PROGRAM
Ed Glatfelter
DIRECTOR, WATER CONSERVATION PROGRAM
Janet Hanley
MANAGER, FINANCIAL OPERATIONS
Jennifer Jazwiec
MANAGER, CHICAGO OFFICE
Angela Larsen
MANAGER, COASTAL PROJECT
Katie Larson
EDUCATION COORDINATOR
Michelle Liebetreu
GRANT MANAGER
April Mather
OUTREACH COORDINATOR, OHIO
Carolyn Scholz
DIRECTOR, INDIVIDUAL PHILANTHROPY
Jonah Smith
DIRECTOR, SUSTAINABLE BUSINESS PROGRAM
Stephanie Smith
DIRECTOR, EDUCATION PROGRAM
Janet Taylor
ADMINISTRATIVE ASSISTANT, GRAND HAVEN OFFICE
Elizabeth Teague
ASSOCIATE, MEMBERSHIP/SUSTAINABLE
BUSINESS PROGRAMS
Lyman C. Welch
MANAGER, WATER QUALITY PROGRAM

Board of Directors

Jack Bails, Chairman
Lori Colman, Vice Chairman, Development
Matt Brett, Vice Chairman, Policy
Beverly McClellan, Secretary
Buzz Patterson, Treasurer
Joel Brammeier, President & CEO
Lisa Yee-Litzenberg, ex officio
Jim Ridgway, ex officio
Gary Ballesteros
Kate Bartter
Sue Conatser
Jonathan Cooper
Paul Culhane
Dave Dempsey
David Keller
Deborah Loeser
Larry MacDonald
Peter Marks
David C. McClellan
Benjamin Mills
Jo-Elle Mogerman
Sarah Nerenberg
Tina Rongers
Mark Shadle
Bill Sheldrake
Unmi Song
Bob Taft
Lee Botts, emeritus
Henry T. Chandler, emeritus
James Griffith, emeritus

Great Lakes in My World

PROJECT COORDINATOR
Stephanie Smith
CURRICULUM DEVELOPERS
Anne Richardson
Stephanie Smith
EDITOR
Sarah Surroz
PROJECT ASSISTANTS
Amy Colonna
Tori Kleinbort
Katie Larson
CURRICULUM AND ASSESSMENT
CONSULTANT
Anna Kraftson
ART DIRECTOR
Robert Zolna
robert.zolna@gmail.com
GRAPHIC DESIGNERS
Curriculum
Robert Zolna
Creature Cards
Moritsugu Kariya
moritsugu.kariya@gmail.com
ASSISTANTS
Ric Edinberg
Imtiaz Musaliar
Felicia Zusman
ILLUSTRATOR
Sara Jenner
sarajenner@hotmail.com
SOUND
Jerry "Butch" Curry
bcsounddesign@netzero.com

For general inquiries, contact the Alliance for the Great Lakes at:
chicago@greatlakes.org or 312-939-0838
michigan@greatlakes.org or 616-850-0745

For inquiries regarding the curriculum, e-mail or call:
education@greatlakes.org or 312-939-0838

Acknowledgements

We thank the following educators for lending their expertise to the field-testing, evaluating and advising of this curriculum:

Shelly Bender, Second Chance High School, *Chicago, IL*
Cindy Byers, Rosholt Middle School, *Rosholt, WI*
Kelly Cook, James Madison Memorial High School, *Madison, WI*
Nicole Cook, Kennedy Elementary, *Hastings, MN*
Jane Curran, Cesar E. Chavez Upper Grade Center, *Chicago, IL*
Shari Dann, Michigan State University, *East Lansing, MI*
MaryBeth Dechant, John G. Shedd Aquarium, *Chicago, IL*
Marti Dekker, Woodbridge Elementary School, *Zeeland, MI*
Phyllis Edinberg, retired teacher, *Worcester, MA*
Rachel Egan, Madison Metropolitan School District, *Madison, WI*

Kathryn Eggers, Peggy Notebaert Nature Museum, *Chicago, IL*
Rosanne Fortner, The Ohio State University, *Columbus, OH*
Jeanine Staab Gelhaus, Medford Area Middle School, *Medford, WI*
Tammy Gerend, Sheboygan Falls Middle School, *Sheboygan Falls, WI*
Christy Gerlach, Indiana Dunes National Lakeshore, *Porter, IN*
Boyd Gilbert, Tolleston Middle School, *Valparaiso, IN*
Sarah Gilbert, Americorps, *Valparaiso, IN*
Katherine Gillespie, Frank O'Bannon Elementary School, *Hammond, IN*
Robin Goettel, Illinois-Indiana Sea Grant, *Urbana, IL*
Nancy Gonzalez, Barker Woods, *Michigan City, IN*

Julie Grecian, Earthforce, *Chicago, IL*
Rachel Gross, John G. Shedd Aquarium, *Chicago, IL*
Jeanette Hamman, Richard Yates School, *Chicago, IL*
Kelly Holtzman, Oconomowoc High School, *Oconomowoc, WI*
Jan Hosier, Hoosier Riverwatch, *Indianapolis, IN*
Al Hovey, retired teacher, *Waukesha, WI*
Anna Kraftson, Queen of Peace High School, *Burbank, IL*
Valerie Keener, Illinois Department of Natural Resources, *Springfield, IL*
Jaejung Kim, Education Consultant, *Chicago, IL*
Linda Kirchner, Longfellow Elementary School, *Clintonville, WI*

Dave Krebs, Muskegon Intermediate School District, *Muskegon, MI*
Maggie Krochalk, educator, *Milwaukee, WI*
Betty Krygsheld, Lansing Christian School, *Lansing, IL*
Ben Lafontaine, Morton West High School, *Berwyn, IL*
Nancy Lynch, St. Catherine of Siena, *Ogden Dunes, IN*
Mary Kane Mather, Ph.D., *Grand Rapids, MI*
Jessica McParlane, *student, Michigan State University, East Lansing, MI*
Rick Meyer, Pine River Backus High School, *Pine River, MN*
Kate Morgan, Pier Wisconsin, *Milwaukee, WI*
Paul Nelson, Wausau West High School, *Wausau, WI*

Patricia Pennell, West Michigan Environmental Action Council, *Grand Rapids, MI*
Robin Podell, Le Mans Academy, *Rolling Prairie, IN*
Lillian Primer, Clintonville Middle School, *Clintonville, WI*
Tom Ruiz, Guion Creek Middle School, *Indianapolis, IN*
Laurie Schaefer, Wisconsin Hills Middle School, *Brookfield, WI*
Michael Schaefer, Francis W. Parker School, *Chicago, IL*
Wayne Schimpf, Von Steuben High School, *Chicago, IL*
Wendy Smith, Great Lakes Center for Research and Education, *Porter, IN*
Ann Soderman, educator, *Pardeeville, WI*
Valerie Stone, educator, *Greenfield, WI*

Kim Swift, Indiana Dunes National Lakeshore, *Porter, IN*
Dawn Tennant, Mishicot High School, *Mishicot, WI*
Elma Thiele, Richardson Wildlife Sanctuary, *Chesterton, IN*
Cynthia Thomashow, Antioch New England Graduate School, *Keene, NH*
Joyce Tuharsky, Grand Rapids Hebrew Academy *Grand Rapids, MI*
Dave Tupa, educator, *Egg Harbor, WI*
Kathy Veenstra, Central Elementary School, *Muskegon, MI*
Lori Voelker, Fritsche Middle School, *Milwaukee, WI*
Anne Wasserman, Evanston Home Educators, *Evanston, IL*
Deb Wearne-Neurohr, Portage Jr. High, *Portage, WI*

Peter Wilkin, Purdue University, *Westville, IN*
Paul Wilsmann, educator, *New Berlin, WI*
Dennis Yockers, University of Wisconsin at Steven's Point, *Steven's Point, WI*
Nadine Zelley, Outreach Educator, *Chicago, IL*

We thank the following for their research and technical review of this curriculum:

Joel Brammeier, Alliance for the Great Lakes, *Chicago, IL*
Elizabeth Brockwell-Tillman, P.J. Hoffmaster State Park, Gillette Sand Dune Visitor Center, *Muskegon, MI*
Michael Chrzastowski, Illinois State Geological Survey, *Champaign, IL*
Cyndi Duda, U.S. Fish and Wildlife Service, *Barrington, IL*
Ed Glatfelter, Alliance of the Great Lakes, *Chicago, IL*
Ralph Grundel, U.S. Geological Survey, *Porter, IN*
Randy Knutson, Indiana Dune National Lakeshore, National Park Service, *Porter, IN*
James Kuch, Research Volunteer, *Grand Haven, MI*
Joy Marberger, Great Lakes Center for Research and Education, *Porter, IN*
Dan Mason, Indiana Dune National Lakeshore, National Park Service, *Porter, IN*

Nancy Matthews, Kenosha Public Museum, *Kenosha, WI*
Tina Meyer, Research Volunteer, *Chicago, IL*
Cheryl Mendoza, Alliance for the Great Lakes, *Grand Haven, MI*
Jamie Morton, Alliance for the Great Lakes, *Grand Haven, MI*
Thomas Nalepa, NOAA, *Ann Arbor, MI*
Laurel O'Sullivan, Natural Resources Defense Council, *Chicago, IL*
Simon Otto, Tribal Elder, Historian, Storyteller, *Petoskey, MI*
Don Quintenz, Schlitz Audubon Nature Center, *Milwaukee, WI*
Carolyn Rock, Whitefish Dunes State Park, *Sturgeon Bay, WI*
Carey Rogers, National Wildlife Federation, *Ann Arbor, MI*

Nicole Rom, National Wildlife Federation, *Ann Arbor, MI*
Derek Strohl, Wisconsin Wetlands Association, *Madison, WI*
Rochelle Sturtevant, NOAA, Great Lakes Environmental Research Laboratory, *Ann Arbor, MI*
Steve Sullivan, Peggy Notebaert Nature Museum Collections, *Chicago, IL*
Janet Vail, Annis Water Resource Institute, Grand Valley State University, *Muskegon, MI*
Lyman Welch, Alliance for the Great Lakes, *Chicago, IL*
Tom Wessels, Antioch New England Graduate School, *Keene, NH*

We thank the following organizations for providing specimens for Great Lakes Creature Card illustrations:

Indiana Dunes National Lakeshore Herbarium, *Porter, IN*
Peggy Notebaert Nature Museum Collections, *Chicago, IL*

We thank the Alliance for the Great Lakes Education Advisory Group for providing guidance on this project:

Megan Gavin, Environmental Protection Agency, Region 5, *Chicago, IL*
Julie Grecian, Earthforce, *Chicago, IL*
Matthew Hayden, Hayden Graham, LLC, *Madison, WI*
Anna Kraftson, Queen of Peace High School, *Burbank, IL*
Jill Ryan, Great Lakes Aquatic Habitat Network and Fund, Tip of the Mitt Watershed Council, *Petoskey, MI*
Janet Vail, Annis Water Resource Institute, Grand Valley State University, *Muskegon, MI*
Kathy Veenstra, Central Elementary School, *Muskegon, MI*
Dennis Yockers, University of Wisconsin at Steven's Point, *Steven's Point, WI*

Table of Contents

Acknowledgements

We thank the following educators for lending their expertise to the field-testing, evaluating and advising of this curriculum:

Shelly Bender, Second Chance High School, *Chicago, IL*
Cindy Byers, Rosholt Middle School, *Rosholt, WI*
Kelly Cook, James Madison Memorial High School, *Madison, WI*
Nicole Cook, Kennedy Elementary, *Hastings, MN*
Jane Curran, Cesar E. Chavez Upper Grade Center, *Chicago, IL*
Shari Dann, Michigan State University, *East Lansing, MI*
MaryBeth Dechant, John G. Shedd Aquarium, *Chicago, IL*
Marti Dekker, Woodbridge Elementary School, *Zeeland, MI*
Phyllis Edinberg, retired teacher, *Worcester, MA*
Rachel Egan, Madison Metropolitan School District, *Madison, WI*

Kathryn Eggers, Peggy Notebaert Nature Museum, *Chicago, IL*
Rosanne Fortner, The Ohio State University, *Columbus, OH*
Jeanine Staab Gelhaus, Medford Area Middle School, *Medford, WI*
Tammy Gerend, Sheboygan Falls Middle School, *Sheboygan Falls, WI*
Christy Gerlach, Indiana Dunes National Lakeshore, *Porter, IN*
Boyd Gilbert, Tolleston Middle School, *Valparaiso, IN*
Sarah Gilbert, Americorps, *Valparaiso, IN*
Katherine Gillespie, Frank O'Bannon Elementary School, *Hammond, IN*
Robin Goettel, Illinois-Indiana Sea Grant, *Urbana, IL*
Nancy Gonzalez, Barker Woods, *Michigan City, IN*

Julie Grecian, Earthforce, *Chicago, IL*
Rachel Gross, John G. Shedd Aquarium, *Chicago, IL*
Jeanette Hamman, Richard Yates School, *Chicago, IL*
Kelly Holtzman, Oconomowoc High School, *Oconomowoc, WI*
Jan Hosier, Hoosier Riverwatch, *Indianapolis, IN*
Al Hovey, retired teacher, *Waukesha, WI*
Anna Kraftson, Queen of Peace High School, *Burbank, IL*
Valerie Keener, Illinois Department of Natural Resources, *Springfield, IL*
Jaejung Kim, Education Consultant, *Chicago, IL*
Linda Kirchner, Longfellow Elementary School, *Clintonville, WI*

Dave Krebs, Muskegon Intermediate School District, *Muskegon, MI*
Maggie Krochalk, educator, *Milwaukee, WI*
Betty Krygsheld, Lansing Christian School, *Lansing, IL*
Ben Lafontaine, Morton West High School, *Berwyn, IL*
Nancy Lynch, St. Catherine of Siena, *Ogden Dunes, IN*
Mary Kane Mather, Ph.D., *Grand Rapids, OH*
Jessica McParlane, student, Michigan State University, *East Lansing, MI*
Rick Meyer, Pine River Backus High School, *Pine River, MN*
Kate Morgan, Pier Wisconsin, *Milwaukee, WI*
Paul Nelson, Wausau West High School, *Wausau, WI*

Patricia Pennell, West Michigan Environmental Action Council, *Grand Rapids, MI*
Robin Podell, Le Mans Academy, *Rolling Prairie, IN*
Lillian Primer, Clintonville Middle School, *Clintonville, WI*
Tom Ruiz, Guion Creek Middle School, *Indianapolis, IN*
Laurie Schaefer, Wisconsin Hills Middle School, *Brookfield, WI*
Michael Schaefer, Francis W. Parker School, *Chicago, IL*
Wayne Schimpf, Von Steuben High School, *Chicago, IL*
Wendy Smith, Great Lakes Center for Research and Education, *Porter, IN*
Ann Soderman, educator, *Pardeeville, WI*
Valerie Stone, educator, *Greenfield, WI*

Kim Swift, Indiana Dunes National Lakeshore, *Porter, IN*
Dawn Tennant, Mishicot High School, *Mishicot, WI*
Elma Thiele, Richardson Wildlife Sanctuary, *Chesterton, IN*
Cynthia Thomashow, Antioch New England Graduate School, *Keene, NH*
Joyce Tuharsky, Grand Rapids Hebrew Academy *Grand Rapids, MI*
Dave Tupa, educator, *Egg Harbor, WI*
Kathy Veenstra, Central Elementary School, *Muskegon, MI*
Lori Voelker, Fritsche Middle School, *Milwaukee, WI*
Anne Wasserman, Evanston Home Educators, *Evanston, IL*
Deb Wearne-Neurohr, Portage Jr. High, *Portage, WI*

Peter Wilkin, Purdue University, *Westville, IN*
Paul Wilsmann, educator, *New Berlin, WI*
Dennis Yockers, University of Wisconsin at Steven's Point, *Steven's Point, WI*
Nadine Zelley, Outreach Educator, *Chicago, IL*

We thank the following for their research and technical review of this curriculum:

Joel Brammeier, Alliance for the Great Lakes, *Chicago, IL*
Elizabeth Brockwell-Tillman, P.J. Hoffmaster State Park, Gillette Sand Dune Visitor Center, *Muskegon, MI*
Michael Chrzastowski, Illinois State Geological Survey, *Champaign, IL*
Cyndi Duda, U.S. Fish and Wildlife Service, *Barrington, IL*
Ed Glatfelter, Alliance of the Great Lakes, *Chicago, IL*
Ralph Grundel, U.S. Geological Survey, *Porter, IN*
Randy Knutson, Indiana Dune National Lakeshore, National Park Service, *Porter, IN*
James Kuch, Research Volunteer, *Grand Haven, MI*
Joy Marberger, Great Lakes Center for Research and Education, *Porter, IN*
Dan Mason, Indiana Dune National Lakeshore, National Park Service, *Porter, IN*

Nancy Matthews, Kenosha Public Museum, *Kenosha, WI*
Tina Meyer, Research Volunteer, *Chicago, IL*
Cheryl Mendoza, Alliance for the Great Lakes, *Grand Haven, MI*
Jamie Morton, Alliance for the Great Lakes, *Grand Haven, MI*
Thomas Nalepa, NOAA, *Ann Arbor, MI*
Laurel O'Sullivan, Natural Resources Defense Council, *Chicago, IL*
Simon Otto, Tribal Elder, Historian, Storyteller, *Petoskey, MI*
Don Quintenz, Schlitz Audubon Nature Center, *Milwaukee, WI*
Carolyn Rock, Whitefish Dunes State Park, *Sturgeon Bay, WI*
Carey Rogers, National Wildlife Federation, *Ann Arbor, MI*

Nicole Rom, National Wildlife Federation, *Ann Arbor, MI*
Derek Strohl, Wisconsin Wetlands Association, *Madison, WI*
Rochelle Sturtevant, NOAA, Great Lakes Environmental Research Laboratory, *Ann Arbor, MI*
Steve Sullivan, Peggy Notebaert Nature Museum Collections, *Chicago, IL*
Janet Vail, Annis Water Resource Institute, Grand Valley State University, *Muskegon, MI*
Lyman Welch, Alliance for the Great Lakes, *Chicago, IL*
Tom Wessels, Antioch New England Graduate School, *Keene, NH*

We thank the following organizations for providing specimens for Great Lakes Creature Card illustrations:

Indiana Dunes National Lakeshore Herbarium, *Porter, IN*
Peggy Notebaert Nature Museum Collections, *Chicago, IL*

We thank the Alliance for the Great Lakes Education Advisory Group for providing guidance on this project:

Megan Gavin, Environmental Protection Agency, Region 5, *Chicago, IL*
Julie Grecian, Earthforce, *Chicago, IL*
Matthew Hayden, Hayden Graham, LLC, *Madison, WI*
Anna Kraftson, Queen of Peace High School, *Burbank, IL*
Jill Ryan, Great Lakes Aquatic Habitat Network and Fund, Tip of the Mitt Watershed Council, *Petoskey, MI*
Janet Vail, Annis Water Resource Institute, Grand Valley State University, *Muskegon, MI*
Kathy Veenstra, Central Elementary School, *Muskegon, MI*
Dennis Yockers, University of Wisconsin at Steven's Point, *Steven's Point, WI*

Table of Contents

Introduction i

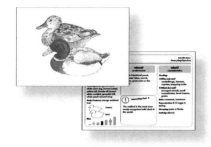  

4

Creature Cards
illustrations and information on 64 notable plants and animals

How to use the Creature Cards

These 64 cards of plants and animals are used in a variety of the activities. See the list provided with the Creature Cards for specifics. You may also use them as flashcards, for background information, as a tool for charades or have students sort them into various groups (by type, kingdom, class, habitat, role in food web, etc.). With two sets, students can play a variety of card games such as Memory, Go-Fish, Old Maid or Rummy.

We value your thoughts and feedback on Great Lakes in My World. Please let us know about any oversights, errors or omissions you find, or if there are things you or your students particularly like.

Send your comments to: education@greatlakes.org

5

Resource List
additional resources to supplement the activities

What you'll find on the Resource List

For additional background and support materials, this is a great collection of helpful websites, organizations, agencies, books, etc. Use this list to find resources for students' research or additional background for units and activities.

6

CD Supplement
additional resources to supplement the activities

What you'll find on the CD

+ **Sounds of the Great Lakes** - Pre-recorded sounds can be used with the activity Sound Picture and other activities that benefit from the sounds of the Great Lakes as background atmosphere
+ **Images of the Great Lakes** - These provide visual context for activities when a field trip is not possible
+ **Media Articles** - You'll need these for certain activities with the older grades.
+ **State Standards Chart** - Use the chart for your state to identify the standards that each activity addresses.
+ **Activity Matrix** - Use this list to identify, at a glance, the activities designed for each grade level, from kindergarten through eighth grade.
+ **Journal Pages** - In addition to the printed set in the curriculum book
+ **Assessment Rubrics** - Use the benchmarks provided for each activity to help you evaluate students' progress.
+ **Set of Creature Cards** - An extra set that can be printed out
+ **Resource List** - For additional background and support materials, this is a great collection of helpful websites, agencies, books, etc.

Some Notes on Our Philosophy

Every educator has his or her own style of teaching, and we've designed this program with that in mind. Likewise, every student has his or her own style of learning, and we've given great consideration to that, too. Here is some brief background on the key teaching theories employed in this curriculum. We hope you find it helpful.

➜ A SENSE OF PLACE

At the root of a flourishing relationship between a child and the Great Lakes ecosystem is the ability to acknowledge and build upon connections with places. "If you don't know where you are, you don't know who you are," says author Wendell Berry. We encourage students to explore their personal connection to the landscape. Ecosystems evoke feelings. Acknowledging that a place holds meaning, and inquiring about its special characteristics, gives new definition and importance to the word "home."

Through these activities, students ask questions that explore the science, history, beauty and mystery of the Great Lakes watershed. This moves students toward developing a greater sense of place—a connection to the lake through new awareness, reflection and experience. As students build relationships with the ecosystem, they gain a new understanding that can inspire a lifetime of learning and care.

➜ INQUIRY-BASED ACTIVITIES

This curriculum encourages students of all ages to learn through asking questions and finding answers. Students are challenged to formulate their own questions and find ways to answer them. In order to answer their questions, students must come to understand the concepts and material involved. They develop essential problem-solving skills.

Inquiry-based learning can be challenging to plan, as questions and solutions are driven by the students. This curriculum supports teachers in their planning by constructing an inquiry-driven learning process and by suggesting projects and models students are likely to come up with.

➜ A POSITIVE FOCUS

Environmental issues can be daunting to students of all ages. According to educator David Sobel, author of "Beyond Ecophobia: Reclaiming the Heart in Nature Education," when children are confronted by environmental issues, they may become overwhelmed and turned off. An ethic of care is more likely to develop if young children are allowed to first find joy in the natural world, especially if it is in a local context. As their world view expands, from local to regional to global, students will have an easier time making connections.

NOTE: In presenting an issue to students, it is important that they are old enough to understand both the concepts and their own ability to make positive change. For this reason, we encourage you to follow our grade level recommendations.

➜ A PROBLEM-SOLVING APPROACH

When students are old enough to address environmental issues, a problem-solving approach can turn negative topics into positive experiences.

In these activities, students learn what they can do to keep their local ecosystem healthy. They become both researcher and problem-solver, and by doing so they become empowered to take action that can impact the future of their own community. This is known as "authentic learning." Unlike simulated problems, real issues provide truly meaningful experiences for students. Student involvement in local issues can lead to mutually beneficial partnerships with the community, and can even lead to revitalization projects.

NOTE: When presenting issues to students, endeavor to provide balanced and complete information. Informed decisions take effort, and here is an opportunity for students to discover the difference between a superficial review and a deep exploration.

➜ SERVICE LEARNING

Several activities in the Human Communities Unit use service learning—a method by which students develop new skills through participating in a community service project that is integrated into the curriculum. These are thoughtfully organized activities that support an academic curriculum while meeting actual community needs.

➜ LEARNING FOR UNDERSTANDING

Though these activities teach material specific to the Great Lakes, their broader aim is for students to understand core principles that they can apply to other ecosystems. Assessments reflect this emphasis on understanding the big-picture concepts.

Unit 1
Lakes

? essential questions

- **How does the lake ecosystem work?**
- **How am I connected to the lake?**
- **What are some issues that impact the lake?**

The yellow perch (Perca flavescens), an important part of the Great Lakes food web and a popular fish for humans to eat, prefers plankton-rich water. The invasive zebra mussel filters plankton to eat, which negatively impacts the yellow perch and many other species.

unit overview

Students experience and discuss their connections to the Great Lakes. They explore life in a watershed, then investigate the diversity of life within the ecosystem, starting with the microscopic species that make up the base of the lake food web. Students learn about other lake species as they experiment with models of food webs, nutrient cycles and energy flows. Students each choose a species to research through the course of the unit. Other activities investigate some of the issues that impact the lake food web, such as invasive species and mercury pollution. The questions students ask and the information they gather will inform their final project, a model of a Great Lakes food web that demonstrates this complex interdependent system.

concepts

O A complex system is made up of interdependent parts that follow specific patterns, but may adjust over time. The Great Lakes ecosystem is driven by the flow of energy.

O The lake food web is made up of diverse and interdependent species. The system functions as nutrients cycle between organisms and energy flows through the web.

O The lake ecosystem is impacted by the introduction of new species and substances that accumulate within individual organisms, affecting the food web as a whole.

unit activities

| CONNECT | EXPLORE | INVESTIGATE |

1 | Lake Connection   P. 3
GRADE LEVEL K-8 (modifications for 4-8)
Recognize connections to the lake by quickly recording feelings on paper, then analyzing the spontaneous feelings that emerged.

2 | I Am a Camera   P. 8
GRADE LEVEL K-4
Students acknowledge their connection to the lake by taking mental "pictures" and translating them into artwork.

3 | Maps of Home   P. 11
GRADE LEVEL 3-6
Students draw maps of their neighborhoods, including the nearest Great Lake, then compare these to professional maps. Using maps, students determine the best way to get from school to the lake, and discuss the location of the lake in relation to the rest of the United States.

4 | Watershed Orientation   P. 15
GRADE LEVEL 4-8
Students orient themselves to the Great Lakes using maps and learn about watersheds, including point and nonpoint source pollution, by building a model.

5 | Satisfy Your Curiosity   P. 20
GRADE LEVEL K-8 (modifications included)
Students formulate questions on select Great Lakes species and research answers throughout this unit. Information gathered through research can be used to complete the final unit project.

6 | Eco-Language   P. 24
GRADE LEVEL 4-8
Students learn definitions of common food web terms and discuss examples of each one through story writing, illustration, and presentation.

7 | A Closer Look   P. 29
GRADE LEVEL 3-6
(additional journal pages for K-2)
Students formulate questions about microscopic lake organisms and answer their questions through observation and research.

8 | Fish Observation   P. 34
GRADE LEVEL 3-6 (modifications for K-2)
Students observe and compare 2 Great Lakes fish species, either in class or through a trip to an aquarium, and discuss structure, function and the significance of their differences.

9 | Web of Life   P. 39
GRADE LEVEL K-3
Students make a web of connections between Great Lakes organisms and discuss the idea of a food web.

10 | Tangled Web   P. 42
GRADE LEVEL 4-8
Students make a yarn web of connections between Great Lakes species, discuss the significance of the complexity of the web, and discover the impacts of changes to the web.

11 | What's New?   P. 45
GRADE LEVEL 3-6
Students play a game that demonstrates the impact of suddenly introducing a new species to an ecosystem.

12 | Great Lakes Relay   P. 50
GRADE LEVEL 4-8
Students take part in a Great Lakes food web relay race, passing nutrients and energy between species. Students compare the relay outcomes and discuss how nutrients cycle and energy flows through food webs.

13 | Invasive Issues   P. 56
GRADE LEVEL 6-8
Students research and present findings on invasive species, then research and write about possible solutions.

14 | Moving Mercury   P. 63
GRADE LEVEL 4-8
Students learn about bioaccumulation and its harmful effects on the food web through the example of mercury in the aquatic ecosystem.

15 | Solubility   P. 68
GRADE LEVEL 6-8
Students learn about water and fat solubility through a demonstration and discussion. This activity prepares students for "It Adds Up and Up."

16 | It Adds Up and Up   P. 71
GRADE LEVEL 6-8
Students discuss mercury issues and carry out calculations to further understand biomagnification of mercury within the Great Lakes.

Final Project

17 | Building a Web   P. 81
GRADE LEVEL K-8
As a class, students create a food web model that includes their research organism and additional details they have learned. Students may be assessed individually based on their ideas and contributions.

CONNECT

1 | Lake Connection

30 - 45 minutes

Developmental Modifications: Use additional 4-8 journal page. Set the stage for respectful listening and honest sharing.

summary

Recognize connections to the lake by quickly recording feelings on paper, then analyzing the spontaneous feelings that emerged.

subjects

Science, Language Arts

standards

This Great Lakes in My World activity is aligned to the Common Core State Standards and to state learning standards in:

Illinois
Indiana
Michigan
Minnesota
New York
Ohio
Pennsylvania
Wisconsin

This alignment is available on your Great Lakes in My World CD in the "Standards" folder and on-line at http://www.greatlakes.org/ GLiMWstandards.

objectives

Describe how people feel about the Great Lakes.

prerequisite

None

vocabulary

Abstract: a type of art that depicts the essential nature of something without using literal pictorial representation; frequently depicts a quality or emotion without showing any concrete object

Representational: a type of art that presents concrete objects with a realistic graphic representation

materials

- Journals
- Pencils
- Example sketches
- Images on CD

setting

INDOORS   OUTDOORS

Lake is preferable. Can be done indoors with visual aids

background

Emotion Sketches (from *Drawing on the Artist Within*, by Betty Edwards) are quick abstract drawings of ideas or feelings. These sketches are spontaneous, rather than carefully conceived drawings. No prior planning is involved.

The following sketches are examples of happiness, surprise, joy, peace, relaxation and fear. While the drawings are not necessarily of recognizable objects, although some are, the ideas are represented through line, placement and movement.

Source: Edwards, Betty, *Drawing on the Artist Within: An Inspirational and Practical Guide to Increasing Your Creative Powers*, Simon & Schuster Books, 1987.

Happiness

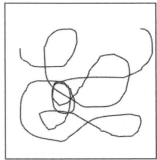

Surprise

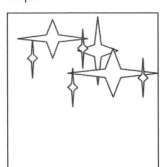

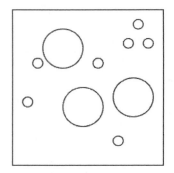

Chicago Park District Camper Sketches

procedure

1. You may choose to show or not to show the example pictures.

2. If you show the students the pictures, ask students what about the picture shows the feeling described.

3. Or, show the students the pictures without words and ask them if they can guess what the artist was feeling while making these drawings. It does not matter whether the students guess correctly. Explain that they can guess the artist's emotion in the pictures without the pictures being representational. Explain that they will be able to make pictures (different from these) that show feelings.

4. Have students sketch (30 second - 1 minute) on how they are feeling right now.

5. Have students sketch (30 second - 1 minute) their perceptions of the lake. If students are not at the lake, show them a photograph from the Great Lakes in My World compact disc or ask what students feel when they think of the lake, if they have been there before. They may also draw based on preconceived notions, depending on what information you would like to elicit.

6. Students should not take time to think before drawing, but just begin instantly. This is a spontaneous process. Students should be experiencing feelings and drawing in the same moment. They may draw anything that comes into their minds.

7. Have students consider individually: Are there any feelings or ideas connected with your sketches that you identify? Students may write one word on their pictures to label the emotions.

8. Have students free write or draw (10-15 minutes) about their connection to the lake using these questions: What draws you to the lake? How do you feel when you are near the lake? How do you interact with the lake?

wrap-up

1. The sharing process must be handled delicately, as students are sensitive about their feelings. Set the stage for respectful listening and honest sharing. Sharing in a small group or with a partner may make students more comfortable. Ask the students what they can do to help create a productive and comfortable sharing discussion. Sharing is voluntary. It is important during the sharing time to reserve judgment on the student responses.

2. Ask students to share their drawings with the group. Discuss personal stories and feelings about the lake. If sharing is difficult, students may prefer to give examples of things at the lake that evoke different emotions, e.g., animals, other people, water or ask for an example of something that makes people feel peaceful. *Answers may include the wind or the water.* Ask for an example of something that makes people feel fear. *Answers might include deep water, drowning or getting lost.* Ask more questions based on students' answers. For example: What is it about the wind that is peaceful? Ask how the weather or season could affect someone's mood at the lake.

3. Read the poem Every Day New and discuss the different ways it describes the lake. What kind of emotions does the poem evoke for students? Ask students how they would describe the lake based on the field trip or a photo.

Every Day New

Glimmering, shimmering, endless and blue,
thrashing and crashing,
it's every day new.

Sometimes it's gray with a glimmer of light.
Sometimes it shines with the full moon at night,
painting the water all yellow and black.
Sunrise comes up and the blueness comes back.
Polishes pebbles and
plays with the sand,
changing the look of the shore and the land.

Howling with grief through a cold wintry gale,
lapping in summer, so clear and so pale.
Sometimes so sharp, like a streak in the sky,
sometimes so muted, a color gone shy.
Drifts in the winter like scenes from the moon,
melts in the spring sun, but never too soon.
Sunken ship treasures and eerie night ghosts
known for their visits on every lake coast.

So many secrets, so vast and so deep,
secrets that only a Great Lake could keep.

Source: Great Lakes Rhythm and Rhyme, by Denise Rodgers, available through River Road Publications
http://www.riverroadpublications.com/

extension

Have students write their own poems that describe the Great Lakes.

assessment

Rubric on page 83

1 | Lake Connection

GRADE LEVEL
K-8

journal pages

FIRST NAME																	
LAST NAME																	

Connection Sketches

[1] DRAW: How do you feel right now?

DESCRIBING WORD
....

[2] DRAW: How do you feel about the lake?

DESCRIBING WORD
....

APPROVED BY	

1 | Lake Connection

GRADE LEVEL
4-8

FIRST NAME																				
LAST NAME																				

[1] Connection Free-Write

What attracts you to the lake? How do you feel when you are near the lake? How do you interact with the lake?

APPROVED BY

2 | I Am a Camera

GRADE LEVEL

K-4

45 minutes

Developmental Modifications: This activity can be used for older students to help them think about perspective and angles in learning to draw.

summary

Students acknowledge their connection to the lake by taking mental "pictures" and translating them into artwork.

subjects

Art, Language Arts

standards

This Great Lakes in My World activity is aligned to the Common Core State Standards and to state learning standards in:

Illinois
Indiana
Michigan
Minnesota
New York
Ohio
Pennsylvania
Wisconsin

This alignment is available on your Great Lakes in My World CD in the "Standards" folder and on-line at http://www.greatlakes.org/GLiMWstandards.

objectives

- Describe the significance of at least one part of the lake ecosystem.
- Create a piece of artwork that represents part of the Great Lakes ecosystem.

materials

- Journals
- Pencils
- Erasers
- Art supplies

prerequisite

None

vocabulary

None

setting

OUTDOORS

background

Encourage students to think about what is special or important about the Great Lakes and the area where they live by focusing on specific aspects. Consider plants, animals or objects of beauty and interest to record in memory and translate on to paper.

procedure

1. Ask students why they think it is important to take pictures. If age-appropriate, ask students to identify the main parts of a camera. Explain the basic mechanism of how a camera works.

2. Pair students and have them pick which of the two will be the camera first. The person who is not the camera will be the photographer. The job of the camera is to use his/her eyes like a lens and his/her eyelids like a shutter. His/her brain acts as the film.

3. The photographer takes the "camera" with eyes closed or open, depending on the age and comfort level of students, to the spot where he/she wants to take a picture. *Tell students to be careful when leading someone with closed eyes.* The photographer carefully positions the camera for the photograph and tells the camera how far away the subject is. The photographer can ask the camera to move until the proper angle is achieved.

4. Now it's time to take a picture. The photographer will gently squeeze the shoulder of the camera to open the shutter. When the squeeze is released, the shutter must close. The camera should have several seconds to "record" the image. The photographer may take up to three pictures before taking the camera back to the starting point and telling the camera to open his/her eyes. The camera should attempt to find the location for each shot taken.

5. The students switch places and repeat the process. After both students have been a camera, each student should decide on a favorite picture that they took as camera. Then they should "develop" the film by going to that location to draw it. If there was something moving in the picture, it may be necessary to draw that part from memory. Students should sign and date their own pictures.

wrap-up

1. Ask students and partners to discuss how the image is similar or different from what the photographer imagined when the "picture" was taken.

2. Have students write or talk about why they chose to draw this image. What about it is important to them?

3. Have students present their pictures to the class. Students explain the part the subject of her/his picture plays in the lake ecosystem.

4. As a class, discuss what sorts of plants an animals live in and around the Great Lakes.

extension

Students can continue to work with their drawings by choosing an aspect of the scene to paint, color or sculpt in clay. This activity can be done for other aspects of the lake ecosystem as well, e.g., wetlands and sand dunes.

Contributing Author: Cora Thiele

assessment

Rubric on page 83

2 | I Am a Camera

GRADE LEVEL
K-4

journal pages

FIRST NAME																			
LAST NAME																			

Develop your film here.

APPROVED BY

CONNECT

3 | Maps of Home

GRADE LEVEL
3-6

60 minutes

summary

Students draw maps of their neighborhoods, including the nearest Great Lake, then compare these to professional maps. Using maps, students determine the best way to get from school to the lake, and discuss the location of the lake in relation to the rest of the United States.

objectives

- Assess personal perspectives of neighborhoods in relation to the lake.
- Explain where the lake is in relation to the school.
- Sharpen observations about surroundings.

prerequisite

None

vocabulary

None

setting

INDOORS

subjects

Geography, Social Studies

standards

This Great Lakes in My World activity is aligned to the Common Core State Standards and to state learning standards in:

Illinois
Indiana
Michigan
Minnesota
New York
Ohio
Pennsylvania
Wisconsin

This alignment is available on your Great Lakes in My World CD in the "Standards" folder and on-line at http://www.greatlakes.org/GLiMWstandards.

materials

- Maps of local area that include the nearest Great Lake detailed enough to show street names
- One large map of the United States
- Journals
- Pencils, crayons and markers.

background

The Great Lakes are bordered by eight United States and two Canadian provinces: Michigan, Wisconsin, Minnesota, Illinois, Indiana, Ohio, New York, Pennsylvania, Quebec and Ontario. Learning about where we live helps us to understand who we are. In this activity, students will be looking at traditional maps and making "sense of place maps." About "sense of place maps:" Educator David Sobel says, "Mapmaking, in the broad sense of the word is as important to making us human as language, music, art and mathematics. Just as young children have an innate tendency to speak, sing, draw and count, they also tend to make maps….The stories of their lives are folded into the niches of their neighborhoods; their maps are the weaving together of inner emotion and external forays." (*Mapmaking with Children: Sense of Place Education for the Elementary Years*, David Sobel, Heinneman 1998.)

procedure

Part One: Place Maps

1. Pass out art supplies to students.
2. Ask students to imagine their neighborhoods. They should think about where the following things are located in relation to each other: their school, home and the lake.
3. In their journals, students will create "sense of place maps" of their neighborhoods, including the above-mentioned places and other places they want to include. They may think of the maps more as pictures or representations of their neighborhoods than maps. It also helps to pretend they are flying above the area like a bird. What will they see when they look down?
4. These maps do not have to be exact, to scale or artistic. There is no right or wrong way to make these maps. Things that are more important to students may naturally be more prominent in their maps. They may go into as much detail as they like and time allows. Students should include several landmarks that they think are important. They may also include natural objects and draw plants and animals or their habitats.

wrap-up

1. Display the place maps in the classroom. Allow students to present their maps to large or small groups. Ask students about the prominent features in their maps. Why are these things important?
2. Ask students where they think the lake is, and how far it is from their school and homes. Ask students if they have been to the lake. Ask if they consider the lake to be a part of their neighborhoods. Why or why not?

procedure

Part Two: Looking at Local Maps

1. Break students into groups of four. Pass out one map of the local area to each group. As a class, review some basic map reading skills: how to use the key, the scale, and the cardinal directions.
2. In their groups, have students circle the following things on their map: the school, their homes, their local Great Lake and the local park.
   In their groups, have students answer the questions in their journals.

extension

When you take a field trip to the lake, have the students figure out how to get there. Measure the distance en route and time how long it takes to get there.

wrap-up

1. Discuss the following: Where is the lake? How can you get there from school or home? Have you ever been to the lake? If so, how did you get there?
2. As a class, look at a large map of North America. What states/provinces does your Great Lake border? How many states/provinces border on the Great Lakes? How big is your Great Lake?
3. Choose a city in the United States. Calculate its distance from the Great Lakes. Compare this with the distance from the lake to your school.
4. Look again at the place maps. Were students' perceptions of their proximity to the lake correct? How does the location of the lake influence experiences with it? If some place maps include plants, animals or their habitats, discuss why they are not included on the local maps that you looked at. Why do students think indications of plant and animal life should or should not be included on maps?

assessment

Rubric on page 83

3 | Maps of Home

GRADE LEVEL
3-6

| FIRST NAME | | | | | | | | | | | | | | | | | | | |
| LAST NAME | | | | | | | | | | | | | | | | | | | |

[1] Draw a map of your neighborhood.

Include: HOME, SCHOOL, YOUR GREAT LAKE

| APPROVED BY | |

3 | Maps of Home

journal pages

| FIRST NAME | | | | | | | | | | | | | | | | | | | |
| LAST NAME | | | | | | | | | | | | | | | | | | | |

[1] Which way do you go to get from school to the lake? (circle one)

NORTH   SOUTH   EAST   WEST

[2] Describe the route from your school to the lake.

....
....
....
....
....
....

[3] How do you get to the lake from school or home? (circle one)

WALK   BUS   TRAIN   CAR

[4] What makes living near a Great Lake interesting?

....
....
....
....
....
....
....
....
....

| APPROVED BY | |

EXPLORE

4 | Watershed Orientation

GRADE LEVEL
4-8

60 minutes

summary

Students orient themselves to the Great Lakes using maps and learn about watersheds, including point and nonpoint source pollution, by building a model.

objectives

- Identify the Great Lakes watershed on a map.
- Describe a watershed.
- Locate local watershed(s) on a map.
- Discuss point and nonpoint source pollution.

prerequisite

Lake Connection, Maps of Home

vocabulary

Watershed: all the land that drains into a particular river, lake or other body of water
Basin: synonym for watershed
Great Lakes basin or watershed: all the land draining into the five Great Lakes

setting

Indoors – or an outdoor sandbox or sandy area of a park, playground, or beach.

INDOORS

subjects

Environmental Science, Geology, Geography

standards

This Great Lakes in My World activity is aligned to the Common Core State Standards and to state learning standards in:

Illinois
Indiana
Michigan
Minnesota
New York
Ohio
Pennsylvania
Wisconsin

This alignment is available on your Great Lakes in My World CD in the "Standards" folder and on-line at http://www.greatlakes.org/GLiMWstandards.

materials

- 4 spray bottles
- Journals
- Pencils
- Plastic tarp/tablecloth
- Plastic bags
- Highlighters
- 5 toothpicks
- Food coloring

- Maps: world map; Great Lakes watersheds map (one for each student plus one for the classroom); local watershed map (one for each student)

background

A watershed is the area of land drained by a body of water. For example, all of the water that falls in the Great Lakes basin eventually drains into one of the Great Lakes. All land is a part of a watershed. Watersheds are nested within each other. The United States could be divided into Atlantic and Pacific watersheds, then into smaller watersheds of rivers and lakes and then even smaller watersheds of the tributaries of rivers. The Great Lakes basin is the land that makes up the Great Lakes watershed. Within the basin, each lake has its own watershed (see map). Within the lake watersheds are smaller watersheds of land that drain into rivers.

Point source pollution is when pollutants enter the waterway though a specific entry point, such as a drainpipe draining directly into a river or lake. Industrial water discharges and sewage treatment plants are the main culprits of this type of pollution. Point source pollutants can include many different organic and inorganic substances, including human waste and toxic metals. Point source pollution can be traced to a specific discharge point and owner; therefore, it has been the easiest source of pollution to control and regulate, although it continues to be a problem.

In contrast, nonpoint source (or NPS) pollution comes from many different diffuse sources and is extremely difficult to regulate and control, which makes it a hazard facing the Great Lakes today.

NPS pollution is mainly caused by runoff, when rain and snowmelt move over the land, picking up pollutants along the way and eventually dumping the pollutants into rivers and lakes. Some common NPS pollutants include fertilizers and pesticides from agricultural lands and homeowners; oil, grease and salt from highways; sediment from construction sites and eroding shorelines; and animal and human waste.

Atmospheric pollution (or air deposition), which comes from the sky, is another form of nonpoint source pollution. As water moves through the hydrologic cycle, it falls as rain or snow and then evaporates into the air from land and surface water. Pollutants emitted into the air, such as through smoke stacks, follow this same path, and can be carried through the atmosphere and deposited into waterways hundreds of miles away from its source. Acid rain is a well-known form of atmospheric pollution.

The major sources of atmospheric pollution include coal-burning energy plants and waste incinerators. The combustion of fossil fuels and waste (such as from hospitals) produces large amounts of mercury in the air, a toxic chemical that is fatal to humans and animals in large quantities. Phosphorus and polychlorinated biphenyls (PCBs) are also transported to waterways via air deposition.

....

procedure

What is a watershed?

1. Clear a space large enough for the plastic tarp/tablecloth and all of the students to stand around it.

2. Option 1: Have students use a plastic tarp. Plastic bags and other items can be bunched underneath the tarp to form its shape.

   Option 2: Have students use sand in a sandbox or kiddie pool filled with sand. Allow students to form a landscape. The landscape should have a lot of variety, using mountains, ridges, plains and depressions.

3. Choose three places on the landscape to sprinkle water, simulating rain. Mark them with toothpicks. Ask students to guess where the water will go when sprinkled on the landscape. Have them draw arrows on the tarp or in the sand to mark the water flow. At each of the marked locations, use spray bottles or sprinkling cans with colored water (add food coloring) to gently pour water over the landscape. Students should watch carefully to see where the water goes. Did it follow their arrows? Why did the water flow the way it did? *Water will flow down hills and collect in basins. If you chose to use sand, some of the water will sink in. This mimics water flow in the natural world. Gravity is the force affecting this flow.*

4. Have students point out bodies of water and rivers that formed. Explain that the area drained by a body of water is called a watershed. Have students find the watershed for the larger bodies of water in their landscape. Ask students if they notice anything about water poured over the tops of their mountains or ridges. *Water poured over the top of a point will probably flow in both directions, into different watersheds. These points mark the boundaries between watersheds.* Students can outline the watershed boundaries in the sand, or on the tarp with markers. Consider using cocoa powder instead of colored water or food that will melt or has colors that will run (chocolate chips, or other candy) to place in the landscape and simulate pollution and animal waste in the ecosystem. You can also make marks with dots of food coloring or markers that are not waterproof to indicate pesticides and insecticides. Re-spray the landscape and have the students observe and discuss what happens.

5. Ask students to think of watersheds in the natural landscape. What body of water is nearby? What land do they think is a part of its watershed? Are they standing in a watershed now? *Every place is in a watershed!* Tell students that they will look at maps to find their watersheds. If desired, have students sketch the landscape they've created.

procedure continued

Where are the watersheds?

1. Hang a world map in the classroom. Ask students to find the Great Lakes on it. Wait until everyone thinks they can find them, then ask a volunteer to point them out. Ask students to describe the characteristics that make the Great Lakes easy to find. *The lakes are very large (the largest source of freshwater in the United States). What shapes can the students find? Lake Superior looks like the head of a wolf, and Lake Michigan looks like a mitten.*

2. Now show students a map of the Great Lakes watershed or basin. Explain that all of the water in this area of land ultimately drains into one of the Great Lakes.

3. Ask students to find their town and decide which lake watershed it is in or figure out how far they live from a Great Lake's watershed. Explain that all of the water that falls on the ground or runs through the rivers in their town ultimately drains into that lake. Have students mark their watershed on the map with a highlighter. Now find your smaller watershed. The lake watershed is made up of wetlands, rivers, and streams that have their own watersheds.

Optional for grades 4-8: watersheds online

1. You may do this research in advance or with the class. Go to http://cfpub.epa.gov/surf/locate/index.cfm to locate your watershed and find out information about it.

2. Have students mark their watershed on a Great Lakes map with a highlighter. These maps are not very detailed, so you may wish to use them in conjunction with more detailed maps of your area. Comparing the two maps, have students find their watershed on the more detailed map. This will give students a better orientation-they can look for their school and homes on the map as well. Topographic maps are great for this.

3. To find out more about your watershed, click on: *Environmental Websites Involving This Watershed.* Scroll through the list of web sites and look for a general site about your watershed. Click on the link. The screen will say: *You are now exiting the EPA web server.* Click on the blue link. If you do not find a general web site about your watershed, try www.great-lakes.net.

wrap-up

1. Hang one watershed map in the classroom for students to look at while they are studying the Great Lakes.

2. Discuss what it means to live in a watershed and some of the responsible behaviors people can choose to keep the watershed healthy. *Suggestions might include picking up after pets, using environmentally friendly products for yards, parks, car washing and cleaning supplies.*

3. In their journals, have students draw a picture of their local watershed and answer the questions.

4. Students in grades 6-8 can write a short essay explaining what a watershed is, the connection between their local watershed and the Great Lakes, and what is important to know about living in a watershed.

assessment

Rubric on page 83

 We value your thoughts and feedback on Great Lakes in My World. Please let us know about any oversights, errors or omissions you find, or if there are things you or your students particularly like.

Send your comments to: education@greatlakes.org

The Great Lakes Watershed

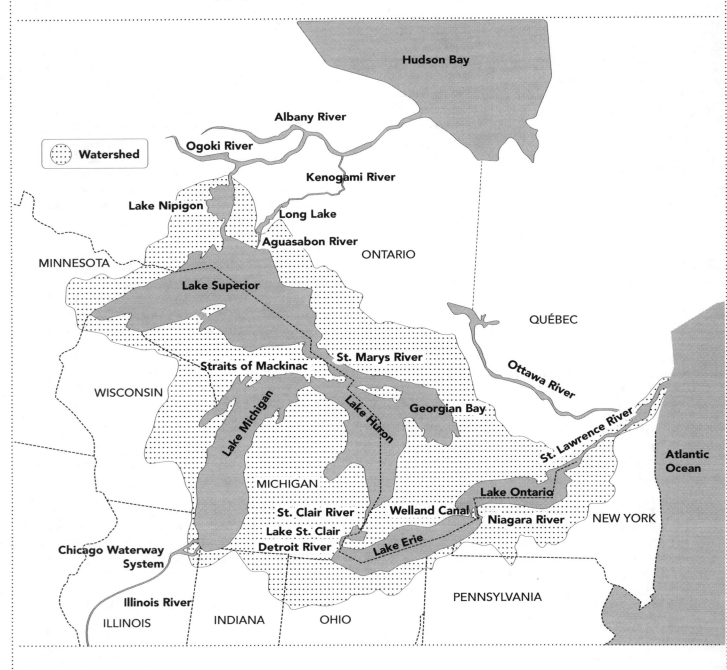

Hudson Bay

Albany River

Ogoki River

Kenogami River

Lake Nipigon

Long Lake

Aguasabon River

ONTARIO

MINNESOTA

Lake Superior

QUÉBEC

St. Marys River

Straits of Mackinac

Ottawa River

WISCONSIN

Georgian Bay

Lake Michigan

Lake Huron

St. Lawrence River

Atlantic Ocean

MICHIGAN

Lake Ontario

St. Clair River

Welland Canal

Niagara River

NEW YORK

Lake St. Clair

Detroit River

Lake Erie

Chicago Waterway System

Illinois River

PENNSYLVANIA

ILLINOIS

INDIANA

OHIO

- Watershed

4 | Watershed Orientation

GRADE LEVEL
4-8

journal pages

FIRST NAME																		
LAST NAME																		

[1] Your teacher will tell you to draw a map of either: your local watershed, your Great Lake and its watershed or the classroom demonstration. Draw arrows to show where the water drains.

[2] Describe the water flow in a watershed.

[3] What are the problems associated with point and nonpoint source pollution?

[4] What can you do to decrease problems with pollution in your watershed?

APPROVED BY	

EXPLORE

GRADE LEVEL

5 | Satisfy Your Curiosity

K-8

 Ongoing

Developmental Modifications: K-3: At this age level, appropriate research includes observation, credible picture books, simple research sources and talking with experts.

summary

Students formulate questions on select Great Lakes species and research answers throughout the Lake Ecology Unit. Information gathered can be used to complete the final unit project.

objectives

- Formulate questions and conduct research.
- Show how organisms fit into the Great Lakes food web.
- Develop an understanding of organisms and their environments.
- Present to class on one Great Lakes organism.

prerequisite

Eco-Language

vocabulary

None

setting

INDOORS   OUTDOORS

subjects

Biology, Ecology

standards

This Great Lakes in My World activity is aligned to the Common Core State Standards and to state learning standards in:

Illinois
Indiana
Michigan
Minnesota
New York
Ohio
Pennsylvania
Wisconsin

This alignment is available on your Great Lakes in My World CD in the "Standards" folder and on-line at http://www.greatlakes.org/ GLiMWstandards.

materials

- Creature Cards
- Research materials
- Resource people
- Multiple copies of Journal Page 23 (several per student)

background

Select information on select species can be found on the Creature Cards. Research can be done through observation, the internet, community speakers, books, and field trips. Local nature centers and museums may be willing to work with students on their research. They may also have observable specimens. See the resource list for specific titles.

procedure

1. Students choose one of the Great Lakes species (from the Creature Cards) to research. Throughout the unit, students will be responsible for gathering information pertaining to their organism. Use multiple copies of the journal pages for students to record their research.

2. Give students the following question that they will try to answer about their species: What is my species' habitat? Write the question on the board and have students copy the question into their journals. Explain that the students will also create their own questions to answer about their organisms.

3. Students individually think of questions they would like to answer. Remind students that they are creating research questions, which do not have a "yes or no" answer. Help younger students to write their questions in their journals.

4. Students think about what they already know about their organisms. They should write or draw these things in their journals.

5. At the end of each activity, have students use new ideas, observations, or knowledge to create questions about their organisms and conduct research to find the answers. At least half of the questions should pertain to the species' role in the food web. Some questions may ask about other species and their relationship to the chosen plant or animal, or physical and behavioral adaptations. Students should keep in mind that their species may use more than one habitat or ecosystem. For example, lake sturgeon swim from the lake into rivers to spawn.

6. Help younger students formulate questions. For example, before reading to the class or having students read on their own, a teacher might ask students for one thing they might learn from the book, phrase it in a question and then have students explain the answer to their question at the end.

   Before observing a species, a teacher might ask students: what is one part of this organism's body that helps it to survive? Students would sketch their organism and label the adaptation they find, then explain their observation to the class (i.e.: a student might point out that the wings of a dragonfly help it to fly quickly.).

wrap-up

1. Students should record all questions, findings, and sources on the Satisfy Your Curiosity journal pages. The first page is intended for initial research and the second page can be used for follow-up after applicable activities. Students should have a copy of this page to fill out for every activity that might aid their research.

2. For each entry, students may write or draw answers in their journals.

3. Students present their species and research to the class.

assessment

Rubric on page 84

5 | Satisfy Your Curiosity

GRADE LEVEL
K-8

journal pages

FIRST NAME																					
LAST NAME																					

[1] Species Name

....

....

[2] I KNOW:

....

....

....

....

....

....

....

....

[3] I WANT TO LEARN:

....

....

....

....

....

....

....

....

[4] I LEARNED:

....

....

....

....

....

....

....

....

APPROVED BY	

5 | Satisfy Your Curiosity

GRADE LEVEL
K-8

journal pages

FIRST NAME																							
LAST NAME																							

My species is..

[1] Question: ....

....

Answer: ....

....

Information source: ....

[2] Question: ....

....

Answer: ....

....

Information source: ....

[3] Question: ....

....

Answer: ....

....

Information source: ....

[4] Question: ....

....

Answer: ....

....

Information source: ....

APPROVED BY	

EXPLORE

6 | Eco-Language

GRADE LEVEL

4-8

60 minutes

Developmental Modification: Select a few key words and have younger students illustrate food web examples to accompany the definitions.

summary

Students learn definitions of common food web terms and discuss examples of each one through story writing, illustration, and presentation.

objectives

- Define terms related to food webs and ecology.
- Provide examples of food web terms specific to the Great Lakes.

prerequisite

Lake Connection, I Am A Camera, Maps of Home

vocabulary

Ecology: the study of relationships between organisms and their environments
Ecosystem: a system made up of an ecological community and its environment especially under natural conditions

Others included in activity

setting

INDOORS

subjects

Biology, Ecology, Environmental Science

standards

This Great Lakes in My World activity is aligned to the Common Core State Standards and to state learning standards in:

Illinois
Indiana
Michigan
Minnesota
New York
Ohio
Pennsylvania
Wisconsin

This alignment is available on your Great Lakes in My World CD in the "Standards" folder and on-line at http://www.greatlakes.org/ GLiMWstandards.

materials

- Chalkboard
- Pencils
- Journals
- Creature Cards

background

Below is a list of terms and examples you will need for this activity:

Ecology: The study of relationships between organisms and their environments.

Food Chain: The path of food consumption from plants to plant-eaters to meat-eaters to decomposers.

Food Web: Set of interconnected food chains within an ecosystem through which nutrients flow and energy is transferred. All living things belong to a food web.

Trophic Levels: Each level of consumption in a food chain. Energy is transformed and nutrients flow from one level to the next. Energy is given off as heat through respiration in each transformation.

Predators: Animals that hunt other animals, e.g., hawk, lake trout.

Prey: Animals that are hunted, e.g., mouse, chub.

Producers: Organisms that can produce their own food through photosynthesis; all green plants, e.g., trees, algae.

Consumers: Organisms that eat other organisms because they cannot produce their own food, e.g. trout, chub.

Decomposers: Organisms that eat dead organisms, e.g., fungus, bacteria.

Herbivores: Animals that eat only plants, e.g., deer or microscopic zooplankton, e.g., daphnia and diporeia.

Omnivores: Animals that eat both plants and animals, e.g., raccoon, herring gull.

Carnivores: Animals that eat only other animals, e.g., hawk, lake trout.

Energy: The capacity of matter to do work; usable power. Most energy on earth comes from the sun. Energy allows organisms to reproduce, mend wounds and battle illness.

procedure

1. Tell students they will learn some of the terms used in the field of ecology and will illustrate them and use them to write a descriptive essay. Define the word "ecology," and let them know that as they study this concept, they will focus on the flow of energy through an ecosystem. Explain that energy flows through an ecosystem when organisms feed off each other, so knowing about eating relationships is essential.

2. Ask students for their ideas on the roles plants and animals play in the world. Let them know that common ants, for instance, play a large role in seed dispersal and soil aeration. They also play a large role in food webs, eating various plants and animals, and getting eaten in return. Direct the students' thoughts to aquatic species, and solicit ideas on food web roles for creatures that live in the Great Lakes. Use this to begin to assess what students know about food web terminology.

3. Tell students they will create short stories or essays using "eco-language" that exemplify the roles plants and animals play. Written pieces must each use the same list of words and offer examples for each eco-language term. Students may use Creature Cards for reference.

4. Introduce and discuss the vocabulary terms. This is just a basic introduction. Deeper understanding of these concepts should come through the completion of the activities in this unit.

5. Define and provide examples of each of the terms. Point out that something could be a predator, consumer and carnivore.

6. Students should include the definition and an example for each term in their journal pages. Students may illustrate the examples if time allows.

wrap-up

1. Have students read their to each other work and discuss what they like and/or would improve upon.

assessment

Rubric on page 85

6 | Eco-Language

FIRST NAME																			
LAST NAME																			

Write a definition and include a Great Lakes example for each word. If time, draw a picture from the Great Lakes that describes each one. Be creative.

Food Web

Trophic Levels

Producer

Consumer

Predator

Prey

APPROVED BY	

6 | Eco-Language

FIRST NAME																				
LAST NAME																				

Decomposer	Herbivore

Omnivore	Carnivore

Energy	Ecosystem

APPROVED BY	

6 | Eco-Language

| FIRST NAME | | | | | | | | | | | | | | | | | | | | | |
| LAST NAME | | | | | | | | | | | | | | | | | | | | | |

[1] Write a story using the vocabulary words.

| APPROVED BY | |

EXPLORE

7 | A Closer Look

GRADE LEVEL

3-6

1½ hours minimum

Developmental Modifications: For younger students, use K-2 Journal Pages. Students' questions might focus on how the organisms move or what they look like. Be sure to wrap-up by having students do a Plankton Dance. To do this, have all of the students stand up and move like the organisms they saw under the microscopes.

summary

Students formulate questions about microscopic lake organisms and answer their questions through observation and research.

objectives

- Describe microscopic lake organisms.
- Explain the role of microscopic organisms in the lake food web.

prerequisite

Lake Connection, Maps of Home, Eco-Language

vocabulary

Plankton: the small floating or swimming animal and plant life of a body of water

setting

INDOORS   OUTDOORS

Indoors and Lake

subjects

Biology

standards

This Great Lakes in My World activity is aligned to the Common Core State Standards and to state learning standards in:

Illinois
Indiana
Michigan
Minnesota
New York
Ohio
Pennsylvania
Wisconsin

This alignment is available on your Great Lakes in My World CD in the "Standards" folder and on-line at http://www.greatlakes.org/GLiMWstandards.

materials

Plankton net, jars with lids, microscopes (at least 100x), videoscope or projecting microscopes if available, slides, cover slips, eye droppers, journals, pencils, water spray bottles

background

Some of the organisms that might be found are:

Euglenoids: Organisms that contain chlorophyll, but have both plant and animal characteristics.
Algae: Plant-like organisms that contain chlorophyll and produce their own food through photosynthesis.

Bacteria: Organisms that break down detritus for food; some (Cyanobacteria) contain chlorophyll.
Zooplankton: Microscopic animals.
Phytoplankton: Microscopic plants
Diatoms: Microscopic plants containing chlorophyll and a glassy silica shell.

procedure

1. Before class: collect Great Lakes water and plankton samples. To order a plankton net, see: http://www.wildco.com and go to either Plankton Equipment and Nets (look for Tow Nets) or Fieldmaster Student Sampling (Fieldmaster Plankton Nets).
   We recommend searching here for products:
   https://wildco.com/index.php?cPath=12_46&osCsid=d29337250cf6df3537dc8e5156149775
   or here: https://wildco.com/index.php?cPath=12_44&osCsid=d29337250cf6df3537dc8e5156149775

   If taking water samples is not possible at all, order pre-made slides of Great Lakes water samples.

A – Indoors

2. Discuss the process of scientific research with the class and explain that aquatic scientists collect water samples to observe microscopic creatures and attempt to answer questions they have formulated. This is what the class will be doing. Discuss the importance of microorganisms and show the students pictures from the Creature Cards that students can sketch into their journals.

3. Have students formulate three questions about microscopic creatures living in the lake. At least one question should relate to organisms' roles in the food web. Some questions might include:
   * *What are they shaped like?*
   * *Can they move? If so, how?*
   * *Are they interacting with each other? In what way?*
   * *Where do they fit into the lake food web?*

Satisfy Your Curiosity QUESTION IDEAS

* *How do these species relate to mine?*
* *How is this species similar or different to mine?*
* *What might their interactions be (if any) in the food web?*
* *Do these species have any indirect impact on my organism? For example, the amount of algae in the lake influences the amount of food available for species at every trophic level in the food web.*

B – At the lake

It is best to do this with the class, but can be done ahead of time if a field trip is not possible. This field trip may be combined with connection activities and species observation.

2. Ask a couple of students to wade knee-deep into the water. They should place the plankton nets into the water and hold the tops open while walking along the shore for about 20 feet.

3. Take the plankton nets out of the water and spray the plankton net with the spray bottle to dislodge any stuck plankton so that it will fall into the plastic bottle at the bottom.

4. Empty the contents into jars with lids for transport back to the classroom.

Back in the classroom...

5. Place a drop of water from the jars on each microscope slide with a slide cover.

6. Break students into pairs or small groups (depending on number of microscopes) and give each a slide to view. Note: As organisms move around in their water drop, slides may have to be moved around to follow them.

wrap-up

1. In their journals, students should draw what they see and attempt to answer the questions they have formulated.
2. Look at the Creature Cards for help identifying the species.
3. Any questions that cannot be answered through observation may be researched through books, and the internet.

4. Groups should share their findings with the class so all students have the same information.
5. Discuss what the food web would be like without microorganisms. What role do they play? *They are essential to the functioning of the Great Lakes ecosystem.*

assessment

Rubric on page 85

7 | A Closer Look

journal pages

FIRST NAME																			
LAST NAME																			

[1] Write three questions about Great Lakes microscopic organisms:

a. ....
....
....

b. ....
....
....

c. ....
....
....

[2] Draw a microscopic plant or animal from one of the Creature Cards.

Species Name ....

APPROVED BY	

7 | A Closer Look

GRADE LEVEL
3-6

journal pages

FIRST NAME																				
LAST NAME																				

[3] Draw what you see under the microscope.

Species name: ....

[4] Answer your three questions.

a. ....

....

....

b. ....

....

....

c. ....

....

....

APPROVED BY

7 | A Closer Look

GRADE LEVEL
K-2

journal ≡ pages

FIRST NAME																			
LAST NAME																			

[1] Draw what you see under the microscope or on the Creature Cards.

Name of plant or animal: ....

[2] Answer these questions:

a. What colors do you see? ....

....

....

....

b. What is most interesting about this tiny plant or animal? ....

....

....

....

....

APPROVED BY	

EXPLORE

8 | Fish Observation

GRADE LEVEL

3-6

90 minutes

Developmental Modifications: Although students may have many questions, help them develop questions they can answer through observation. Students should focus more on comparisons and less on organism structure and function.

summary

Students observe and compare two Great Lakes fish species, either in class or through a trip to an aquarium, and discuss structure, function and the significance of their differences.

objectives

- List basic need of organisms.
- Describe a Great Lakes fish.
- Explain the similarities and differences between two Great Lakes fish and their roles in the food web.
- Discuss the significance of structure and function with regard to a fish.
- Explain the importance of having different types of fish in the Great Lakes.

prerequisite

Eco-Language and A Closer Look

vocabulary

Forage fish: eat phytoplankton and zooplankton; serve as prey for larger predators such as lake trout and whitefish; include smaller fish such as herring, alewives, chubs and smelt producers to higher trophic levels

Predator: an animal that lives by killing and eating other animals

Structure: arrangement or relationship of elements (as particles, parts, or organs) in a substance, body, or system

Function: natural or proper action of a bodily part in a living thing

setting

Classroom or aquarium field trip

INDOORS   OUTDOORS

subjects

Ecology, Biology

standards

This Great Lakes in My World activity is aligned to the Common Core State Standards and to state learning standards in:

Illinois
Indiana
Michigan
Minnesota
New York
Ohio
Pennsylvania
Wisconsin

This alignment is available on your Great Lakes in My World CD in the "Standards" folder and on-line at http://www.greatlakes.org/GLiMWstandards.

materials

- A live fish is required, ideally one per four students.
- Journals
- Pencils
- Ruler
- Tape measure or ruler
- Chalkboard
- Creature Cards

background

It is best if the fish are species found in the Great Lakes. Some ideas for this activity:

- Buy several minnows from a local bait shop.
- Take a field trip to a local aquarium or nature center.
- Ask a local nature center if they could bring a live fish to your classroom.
- The U.S. Department of Fish and Wildlife has live fish to share in classrooms.

Never release a plant or animal that is not from the area into the local ecosystem. This could cause serious problems for the native Great Lakes plants and animals. If you are not set-up for live animals in your classroom, consider showing a video that shows different fish. Formulate a plan for caring for any living creature in your classroom, as well as a long-term teaching/learning plan that involves the plant/animal.

procedure

Day 1 Observation

1. Ask students when they have seen a fish: fishing, grocery store, aquarium, on a plate. Ask students what they know about Great Lakes fish (there are over 180 species!). Ask students what fish and other organisms need to survive. Discuss basic requirements of living things.

2. Tell students they will be observing a fish and discussing Great Lakes fish. Discuss rules for visits with live animals:

- The animal is a living thing and has feelings: please be respectful.
- Wild animals are afraid of people. Since this is a scary experience for the animal, stay quiet and calm.
- Never touch an animal near its face.
- If students are to touch the fish, make sure they have wet hands and touch one at a time with one finger only. Wash hands before and after touching the fish.
- Do not tap on the glass: it's loud in there.

3. In small groups, formulate three questions about the fish that may be answerable through observation. Some questions might be:

- *What does it look like?*
- *How does it breathe?*
- *How does it move?*
- *What is it doing?*
- *How big is it?*
- *What does it eat?*

4. Have groups observe the fish. In their journals, students should make drawings of the fish. Holding the ruler up to the tank, measure (as best possible) the length and height of the fish and record measurements with the drawings. In their journals, students should answer the questions they formulated.

wrap-up

1. Discuss as a class:

- *What did you think of the fish?*
- *What was interesting about it?*
- *What other fish have you seen before? How was it similar or different?*
- *What was your favorite thing about the fish?*

 We value your thoughts and feedback on Great Lakes in My World. Please let us know about any oversights, errors or omissions you find, or if there are things you or your students particularly like.

Send your comments to: education@greatlakes.org

procedure

Day 2 Observation

1. Review fish Creature Cards and discuss as a class:

   - Which type of fish did we observe? *Is it a predator fish or a forage fish?*
   - What fish from the Creature Cards are like this one?
   - What leads you to this conclusion? *The size of the body and the shape of the mouth should give some clues about what this fish eats and to what other fish it is similar.*
   - What does this fish eat? *Does it eat the kind of microorganisms we saw in "A Closer Look" activity? If this is a forage fish, then it is possible. Other animals that eat microorganisms are mussels and shrimp.*
   - How does the size of this fish compare with the size of the microorganisms? *The fish is much bigger-the microorganisms are so small that they cannot be seen with the naked eye. Even though they are so small, they are an important food source for many animals.*

2. Discuss structure and function as it applies to the fish. How does a fish's structure and function determine its behavior, motion, diet and habitat?

3. Look at a Creature Card fish (sturgeon, muskellunge, walleye, yellow perch, lake whitefish).

   - *Is it a predator or a forager?*
   - *What other fish are like this? Compare the observed fish with one of the Creature Cards fish. Draw a Venn diagram to illustrate how are they similar or different.*

4. On the chalkboard, draw a life-size picture of a sturgeon or muskellunge and have the students help you measure and mark the length of five feet on the board. Underneath, have students measure out and mark the length of the observed fish, and draw it.

> ### *Satisfy Your Curiosity* QUESTION IDEAS
>
> - *How are these species related to mine?*
> - *What are their similarities and differences?*
> - *What might their interactions be (if any) in the food web?*
> - *Do these species have any indirect impact on my organism? For example, the amount of forage fish a muskellunge eats may influence the amount of zooplankton in a lake or the amount of food available for other predators.*

wrap-up

Discuss and write in journals on the following questions.

1. How do the sizes of the two fish (live fish and Creature Card) compare?

2. What relationship do these two fish have (if any)? *For example, do they have a predator/prey relationship; do they share a similar food source, etc?*

3. What is the role of each one in the food web? *Predator, prey, scavenger, etc. Note that an animal could have more than one role, e.g., a muskellunge is a predator, carnivore and a consumer.*

4. Is one more important than the other? Why or why not? *No. Although the sizes of the two organisms may be very different, they each play a role in the food web. The microorganisms from the "A Closer Look" are extremely small, but are an important food source for other organisms. Likewise, each of these fish is an important food source, and they each play a role by eating other organisms.*

5. What would the lake be like if all of the organisms looked the same and had the same roles in the food web? *The food web wouldn't work very well. It is important that there is diversity among the organisms so that one organism is food for another, and so on and that there are choices, depending on the availability of certain species.*

6. Why is it important to keep the Great Lakes fishery healthy? *Same reasons, as well as for fishing, food.*

assessment

Rubric on page 85

8 | Fish Observation

GRADE LEVEL
3-6

FIRST NAME																						
LAST NAME																						

[1] Formulate three questions about the fish:

a. ....

....

....

b. ....

....

....

c. ....

....

....

[2] Draw the fish and label the length and height.

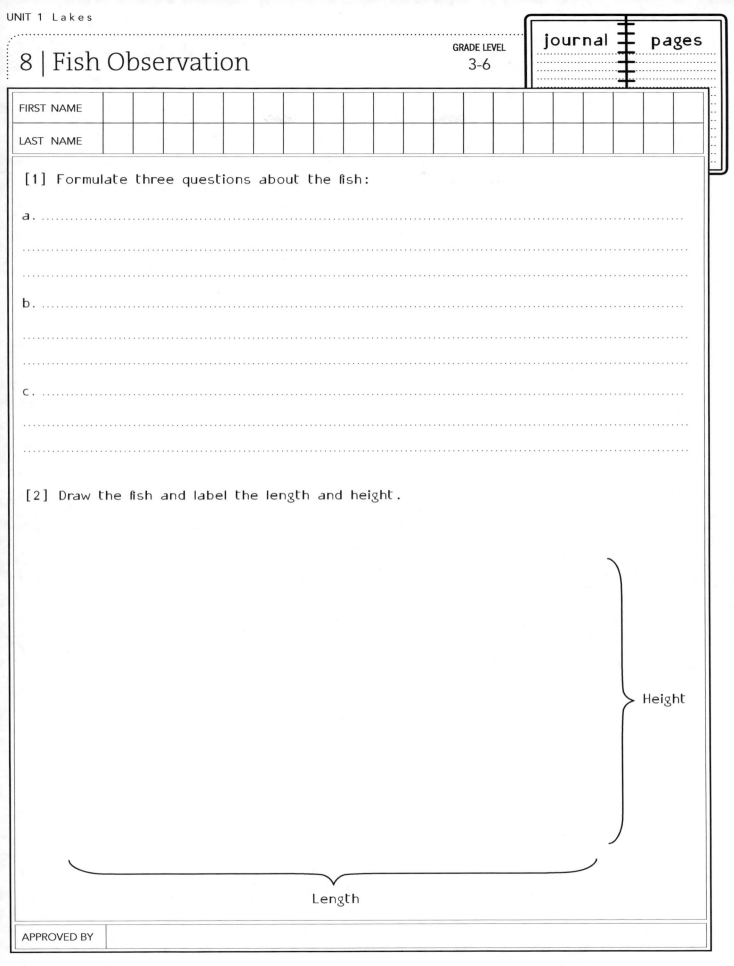

Height

Length

APPROVED BY	

8 | Fish Observation

FIRST NAME																					
LAST NAME																					

[3] Answer your three questions:

a. ....

....

....

b. ....

....

....

c. ....

....

....

[4] The observed fish is a: (circle one)   FORAGE FISH   PREDATOR FISH   SCAVENGER FISH

How do you Know?

....

....

....

What does it eat?

....

....

....

[5] What is the name of the Creature Card fish you are comparing to?

This fish is a: (circle one)   FORAGE FISH   PREDATOR FISH   SCAVENGER FISH

a. How do you Know?

....

....

....

b. What does it eat?

....

....

....

APPROVED BY	

EXPLORE

9 | Web of Life

GRADE LEVEL

K-3

45 minutes

summary

Students make a web of connections between Great Lakes organisms and discuss the idea of a food web.

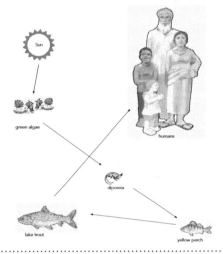

objectives

- Describe a food web.
- List connections between Great Lakes organisms in a food web.

prerequisite

Lake Connection, A Closer Look

vocabulary

Food chain: a series of organisms in which each uses the next usually lower member of the series as a food source
Food web: the whole group of interacting food chains in a living community

setting

INDOORS   OUTDOORS

subjects

Ecology

standards

This Great Lakes in My World activity is aligned to the Common Core State Standards and to state learning standards in:

Illinois
Indiana
Michigan
Minnesota
New York
Ohio
Pennsylvania
Wisconsin

This alignment is available on your Great Lakes in My World CD in the "Standards" folder and on-line at http://www.greatlakes.org/GLiMWstandards.

materials

- Creature Cards with asterisks*
- Photocopied food chain species (1 set per student)
- Ball of yarn
- Masking tape

background

Food chains that show feeding relationships in an ecosystem are part of large and complex food webs. By exploring these relationships, students become familiar with the concept of food webs, as well as the different plants and animals that inhabit the Great Lakes. Information on eating habits can be found on the backs of the Creature Cards.

procedure

1. Discuss food chains by talking about the food eaten by humans. For example, if we eat a fish, that fish has possibly eaten a smaller fish, which ate microscopic zooplankton, which ate microscopic phytoplankton, which gained its energy from the sun. Have students trace back an element from their lunches in order to see how these connections apply. Show students Creature Cards listed above that make up a food chain (an example: sunlight (not a card), green algae, diporeia, yellow perch, lake trout, humans). Diagram this for students.

2. Have students complete the journal page and/or give students photocopied Creature Cards to color and glue on a page. Have them add lines to show which creatures eat each other.

3. Choose organisms from the Creature Cards that are best connected in a food web. The plants and animals with an asterisk (*) are best suited for this activity. This can be done in two small groups, each supervised by adults, which will make the activity move more quickly. Pass out one card to each student. Have students hold the cards so that everyone can see the pictures. Have students act like their species for 10 seconds to create an "instant Great Lake."

4. Have students sit in a circle and announce the names of their organisms. Make sure everyone understands what all of the organisms are.

5. Holding the ball of yarn, tell students that you represent the sun. You will give your energy to one of the plants (e.g., algae) by holding onto the end of the yarn and passing the ball to a student with a plant card. When a student receives the ball of yarn, she/he should hold onto one end, and pass the ball to a student with the card of a species that her/his organism could eat OR be eaten by. It is VERY IMPORTANT that students realize that it can go to the species that eats their creature OR to a species their creature eats. Otherwise, a food web will not be successfully created. For example, the algae could pass the yarn to a zooplankton, who could pass it to a forage fish, and so on. Likewise, the fish could pass it back to something else it eats. Students look at the backs of their cards to determine what the species eats or is eaten by. Pass the yarn until it has reached everyone at least once. This may involve some problem-solving. A web will form between the students. Some species may be included more than once. Continue the game to find new connections.

6. Have a student give a light tug on his/her piece of the yarn. Have students "tug back" when they feel the tug, raising their hands as they tug for a visual on the web interconnections. For each species, at least two others will feel a tug on the yarn. Soon all students will be gently tugging with one hand raised, which demonstrates that the food web is all connected. If one species feels a tug from another, it means these are especially important to each other in the food web.

Satisfy Your Curiosity QUESTION IDEAS

- *Where does my species fit into the food web?*
- *What eats my species?*
- *What does my species eat?*
- *What other organisms are impacted by my species?*

---

wrap-up

Discuss

1. What did the yarn look like after it had been passed to everyone? *A web.*

2. Why did it look like this instead of a straight line or circle? *The food web connections are complex, like a web.*

3. Ask one student to drop their piece of the yarn. Pretend this species is no longer a part of the food web because it has died off or left to live elsewhere. Have the other students re-tighten the web to adjust for the change. When one student dropped the yarn, what happened? *The rest of the species adjusted, and the web did not fall apart.* Explain that this worked because there are so many organisms in the web.

4. Now, have everyone drop their yarn except for three students. Now what will happen? *It is a lot harder to readjust this time, because there are fewer organisms left.*

5. A food web is healthier when it is more complex and when there are a variety of species present. Like students, most animals eat more than one type of food. A web with many types of species gives them food choices. If the web is not very complex it is harder to adjust to changes.

6. Why is it important that there are so many different types of organisms in the food web? *The high number of types of species keeps a healthy web and allows for food choices.*

7. If students have not completed the journal page, have them do so. Use the diagram to show how three to five organisms need each other to live.

assessment

Rubric on page 85

9 | Web of Life

FIRST NAME																		
LAST NAME																		

CONNECT the parts of the lake food web.

Sun

green algae

humans

diporeia

lake trout

yellow perch

APPROVED BY	

10 | Tangled Web

45 minutes

summary

Students make a yarn web of connections between Great Lakes species, discuss the significance of the complexity of the web and discover the impacts of changes to the web.

objectives

- List five to eight connections between Great Lakes organisms in a food web.
- Explain the impacts of changes in a Great Lakes food web.
- Diagram a small food web.

prerequisite

Lake Connection, Eco-Language, Fish Observation, A Closer Look

vocabulary

Food web: the whole group of interacting food chains in a living community

setting

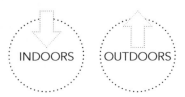

INDOORS   OUTDOORS

subjects

Ecology, Environmental Science

standards

This Great Lakes in My World activity is aligned to the Common Core State Standards and to state learning standards in:

Illinois
Indiana
Michigan
Minnesota
New York
Ohio
Pennsylvania
Wisconsin

This alignment is available on your Great Lakes in My World CD in the "Standards" folder and on-line at http://www.greatlakes.org/ GLiMWstandards.

resources

Food Web sites:

Environmental Protection Agency
www.epa.gov/glnpo/atlas/
images/big05.gif
Michigan Sea Grant
http://www.glwi.uwm.edu/
ourwaters/documents/
FoodWebWeb.pdf
Michigan Tech
www.techalive.mtu.edu/meec/
module08/FoodWeb.htm

materials

- Creature Cards with asterisk (*)
- Ball of yarn
- Masking tape

background

Food chains that show feeding relationships in an ecosystem are part of large and complex food webs. By exploring these relationships, students become familiar with the concept of food webs, as well as the different plants and animals that inhabit the Great Lakes. Information on eating habits can be found on the backs of the Creature Cards.

procedure

1. Have students brainstorm a list of species in the lake. Use the Creature Cards to help guide their responses. Give each student one Creature Card. Using those from the aquatic ecosystem will work best (with asterisks). *Include organisms students have learned about in the two previous activities.*

2. Have students hold the cards or attach them to their shirts with masking tape so that everyone can see the pictures. Have students sit in a circle and announce the names of their organisms.

3. Holding the ball of yarn, tell students that you represent the sun. You will give your energy to one of the plants, e.g., algae, by holding onto the end of the yarn and passing the ball to a student with a plant card. When a student receives the ball of yarn, she or he should hold onto one end, and pass the ball to a student with the card of an organism that his/her organism could eat OR be eaten by. For example, the algae could pass the yarn to a zooplankton, who could pass it to a forage fish or vice versa. Students should look at the backs of their Creature Cards to determine what the organism eats or is eaten by. Continue passing the yarn until it has reached everyone at least once. Continue the game as long as you can find new connections. Since each student is holding onto a piece of the yarn, a web should be forming between the students.

4. It is very important that each time the yarn is passed, students realize that it can go to the organism that eats their creature OR to an organism their species eats. Otherwise, a food web will not be created. Some creatures may be included more than once. Make sure all creatures become part of the web. This may involve some problem-solving.

5. At this point, give a hypothetical situation (positive or negative) that affects a species. For example, if the lake trout have been over-fished, have the "lake trout" give a light tug on his/her piece of the yarn. Have students "tug back" when they feel the tug, raising their hands as they tug for a visual of the web interconnections. For each species, at least two others will feel a tug on the yarn and eventually everyone will. You can also have the "lake trout" drop the yarn and have the rest of the class readjust the web to account for the change. Other scenarios could include: (+) a comeback in the yellow perch population, wetland habitat restoration, or (-) a wetland is filled, impacting species who spawn in the wetland; mercury has entered the lake, causing aquatic birds to die; or zebra mussels have entered the food web, reducing the amount of food available for native fish.

6. Discuss:
   - What did the yarn look like after it had been passed to everyone? *A web.*
   - Why did it look like this instead of a straight line or circle? *The food web connections are complex, like a web.*
   - What happened when one organism dropped the yarn? Did the web stay the same, fall apart completely, or something else? *The rest of the web had to readjust. Other organisms were impacted, but the whole web did not collapse because it is complex enough that it can change and still survive.*

7. What would happen if more and more scenarios were introduced, eliminating more parts of the food web? *The food web would ultimately look a lot different from the way it looked originally, and would be more simplified. Food webs that lack complexity are not as resilient to change as those with a diverse group of organisms.*

Satisfy Your Curiosity QUESTION IDEAS

- *Where does my species fit into the food web?*
- *What eats my species?*
- *What does my species eat?*
- *What other organisms does my species impact?*

---

wrap-up

Use the journal pages for the following:

1. Food Web Diagram: Have each student create a food web diagram that includes five to eight organisms. The food web should include several food chains. Use arrows to indicate who eats who, and include all types (decomposers, producers, herbivores, omnivores, carnivores, scavengers). Students may need to ask questions of others who had different Creature Cards.

2. Have each student write a brief essay that articulates how his/her organism fits into the food web. In the essay, the student should explain the effect of changes in the food web, and begin to draw conclusions about what happens to a food web when species are eliminated.

---

assessment

Rubric on page 86

10 | Tangled Web

GRADE LEVEL
4-8

FIRST NAME																			
LAST NAME																			

[1] Draw a picture of a lake food web. Include 5-8 species in your picture, and arrows to show how they are connected.

[2] Write about how your organism fits into the food web. Explain the impact changes have on the food web. Draw conclusions about what happens to a food web when species are reduced or increased.

APPROVED BY

EXPLORE

11 | What's New?

GRADE LEVEL

3-6

45 minutes

summary

Students play a game that demonstrates the impact of suddenly introducing a new species to an ecosystem.

objectives

- Define invasive species.
- Explain the impact of invasive species on the food web.

prerequisite

Web of Life or Tangled Web

vocabulary

Invasive species: plant or animal that enters an ecosystem to which it is not native and competes with one or more native species for food, shelter and/or reproductive opportunities

setting

INDOORS

subjects

Ecology, Environmental Science

standards

This Great Lakes in My World activity is aligned to the Common Core State Standards and to state learning standards in:

Illinois
Indiana
Michigan
Minnesota
New York
Ohio
Pennsylvania
Wisconsin

This alignment is available on your Great Lakes in My World CD in the "Standards" folder and on-line at http://www.greatlakes.org/ GLiMWstandards.

materials

- Four decks of playing cards
- Creature Cards
- Journals
- Pencils

background

Invasive species arrive, often accidentally, from their native ecosystem to a new ecosystem. There are hundreds of examples of invasive species (also known as exotic or non-native species) around the world. An "introduced species" is one that has been intentionally brought from their native ecosystem to a new one. When a new species is introduced into an ecosystem, the balance is altered and competition is high until a new balance is achieved. Many times invasive or introduced species cannot survive in these new ecosystems or become a non-threatening part of the ecosystem. However, if the new species is successful, one or more native species populations can suffer, altering the ecosystem.

Invasive species arrive in new ecosystems by a variety of means and for different reasons. In the Great Lakes Chinook and Coho salmon, were introduced to increase the diversity of catch for the sport fishing industry. Because salmon live in salty to brackish water for most of their lives and spawn in the same place they were born, they do not breed when transported to a new environment. There is simply no way for them to find the same region of a river or lake where they were born, thus they do not reproduce. Instead, the population continues to exist as a result of manual repopulation by those in the fishery industry.

Generally, invasive species can cause significant change to their newly adopted ecosystems. According to the United Nations Convention on Biological Diversity about 1.4 trillion dollars a year is spent globally to control invasive species and to help repair the damage they cause.

Within the Great Lakes region, commercial shipping has been responsible for over 60% of invasive species that have arrived since 1960. Two species, which are assumed to have been transported here in the ballast water of commercial ships, are quagga and zebra mussels. These "successful" invaders altered the balance within the Great Lakes ecosystem by competing with native mussels for resources. As a result of this competition, the native mussel population has plummeted. Another great example is the round goby, which was introduced into the St. Claire River in 1990 (probably in ship ballast water). This aggressive fish competes with native fish for prime spawning sites, causing problems for the mottled sculpin, logperch and darters. The introduction of the Goby has changer the ecosystem, as the native species mentioned are bottom dwellers, an important part of the food web. This poses threats to a number of species in the food web, as they are interdependent. On an economic level, it poses a threat to the fishing industry that depends on the abundance of certain fish.

The Great Lakes states continue to seek solutions to preventing new invasive species from establishing themselves in the ecosystem. The possibility of Asian carp in the Great Lakes has significantly escalated prevention discussions. Known to batter boaters and even knock them into the water at the sound of a passing motor, the fish are voracious filter feeders that can grow to more than 4 feet long, weigh up to 100 pounds and quickly dominate a body of water by gobbling up the same food that sustains native fish populations. Once established in the Great Lakes, the fish could devastate the region's $7 billion fishing industry and permanently alter how recreational boaters, anglers and tourists use and enjoy the lakes and their tributaries.

Asian carp are just one of many nuisance plant and animal species that have moved or are poised to move between the Great Lakes and Mississippi River basins via the manmade Chicago Waterway System that has connected the basins for over 100 years. Other non-native species introduced into the Great Lakes are: rusty crayfish, spiny water flea, common carp, Eurasian ruffe, sea lamprey, zebra mussel, Eurasian water milfoil and quagga mussel.

....

procedure

1. Introduce the concept of invasive species and explain it. Tell the students they'll play a game to illustrate it. Break the class into four small groups. Pass out a deck of cards to each group. Tell the groups that they will each play a different card game and they should not share what they are doing with the other group. If it helps, one group may be located in the hallway or a different room.

2. Two groups will play Old Maid and two groups will play Go Fish.

3. Old Maid Rules:
   • Cards are passed out to players until the deck is gone. One joker is in the deck.
   • The joker is the "old maid." Players do not reveal their hands to each other.
   • The object of the game is to run out of cards and not end up with the "old maid."
   • Players take turns taking one card from the hand of another player (any player).
   • If a player has a match of numbers or faces in his/her hand, she/he should put down the match, face up.
   • Play continues until all but one run out of cards, and one player is left with the "old maid."

procedure continued

4. Go Fish rules:
   - Seven cards are passed out to each player. The remainder of the deck is placed in the middle, face down.
   - The object of the game is to get the most matches.
   - Players take turns asking another player (any player) for specific number or face cards in order to find matches.
   - For instance, a player asks any other player, "Do you have a queen?"
   - If the player has the card, she/he turns it over to the asker. If not, she/he says "Go fish," and the asker takes one card from the remaining deck.
   - Whenever a player has a match, she/he should put it down.

   Play continues until everyone runs out of cards, and then players count their matches.

5. Once the groups understand the rules, select two students from each group to trade places with students from a group playing a different game. These transferring students should go into the new group playing by the rules of their "home" game, without knowing the rules of the new game. If a student knows what the other game is, she/he should pretend not to know the rules.

6. The groups should be instructed to go on playing their games and not change the rules to accommodate the newcomers. With the newcomers, the games will change. These students are playing by different rules, changing the dynamic of the group. Some of the players' situations may change or suffer because of the newcomers.

7. Stop the game about three minutes after the switch. Discuss as a class what the playing was like before the switch. Were the situations calm and the rules easy to understand? Then discuss what happened when the newcomers entered the group. The class should be able to understand that the dynamics changed. Explain that this is what happens when a species from one ecosystem is introduced into another-the species reproduces and causes change in the ecosystem. It takes a long time before the ecosystem reaches a balance again. Make sure students understand that invasive species are not "bad." They have a home in another ecosystem, which means they are used to living by different rules.

wrap-up

1. Show the class a map of the United States, and point out where the Great Lakes connect with rivers and canals that connect with the ocean.

2. Show how ships can come into the Great Lakes from the ocean with new organisms such as zebra mussels attached. Show how organisms such as carp can swim up the Mississippi River and other rivers into the Great Lakes.

3. Show students the Creature Cards of invasive species. Ask students where they think these species are originally from.

4. Ask students what they think about a new species entering the lake system. What do they think happens to the food web?

5. In their journals, students write about what happened during the game. Then, they should work in groups to investigate an invasive species from the Creature Cards. Have students think about what type of impact it has on the lake food web. Does it eat species that do not have a natural predator (i.e., another invasive species)? Does it eat something that is a food source for another species? Does it occupy the same habitat as another species? Students can find this information by looking at the Creature Cards. Then students should write in their journal pages about how the food web might change because of the introduction of this species. For a more detailed invasive species activity, see Invasive Issues.

assessment

Rubric on page 86

 We value your thoughts and feedback on Great Lakes in My World. Please let us know about any oversights, errors or omissions you find, or if there are things you or your students particularly like.

Send your comments to: education@greatlakes.org

11 | What's New?

FIRST NAME																				
LAST NAME																				

[1] Describe the game. How was it different after the switch?

Before there was a new player	After the new player arrived

[2] Which invasive species did you choose from the Creature Cards?

....

[3] In what way does this species interfere with a native species or cause problems for humans?

- It eats food that another species eats.
- It uses the same habitat space.
- Other:

....

[4] Name of native species impacted by the invasive species: ....

[5] List the names of at least two other species that are connected to the native organism you listed in #4 (predators, prey, etc.):

....

....

....

....

....

APPROVED BY	

11 | What's New?

FIRST NAME																						
LAST NAME																						

[6] Write two sentences about how the food web might change because of the introduction of the invasive species.

....

....

....

....

....

....

....

....

[7] Draw a picture of a lake food web. Include at least two invasive species.

APPROVED BY	

EXPLORE

12 | Great Lakes Relay

GRADE LEVEL

4-8

60 minutes

summary

Students take part in a Great Lakes food web relay race, passing nutrients and energy between species. Students compare the relay outcomes and discuss how nutrients cycle, and energy flows through food webs.

objectives

- Explain that nutrients cycle through a food web and are not lost when transferred from one organism to another.
- Explain that energy flows through a food web and some is lost when it is transformed from one organism to another.
- List species in a Great Lakes food web and explain their interdependence.

prerequisite

Tangled Web, Eco-Language, What's New?

vocabulary

Trophic level: various levels of the food web characterized by organisms which are the same number of steps removed from the primary producers
Food web: the whole group of interacting food chains in a living community

Others included in Background section

setting

OUTDOORS

subjects

Ecology, Environmental Science

standards

This Great Lakes in My World activity is aligned to the Common Core State Standards and to state learning standards in:

Illinois
Indiana
Michigan
Minnesota
New York
Ohio
Pennsylvania
Wisconsin

This alignment is available on your Great Lakes in My World CD in the "Standards" folder and on-line at http://www.greatlakes.org/GLiMWstandards.

materials

- One paper cup for each student
- Paper clips (a few)
- One marker for each student or group
- Bucket of water
- Name cards for each student

background

- *Energy*: the capacity to do work. In living things, energy is used for growth and reproduction, and is lost through excretion and respiration.
- *One Kilocalorie (Calorie)*: the amount of heat required to raise one liter of water one degree Celsius. Calories are used to measure the energy level in food. For example, if a candy bar has 200 calories, then when the candy is burned inside the body, the heat given off by the burning is enough to raise the temperature of 200 liters of water by one degree Celsius.
- *Nutrient Cycle*: the circular course traced by one of life's several essential substances as it moves through the food web. Carbon and nitrogen are examples of nutrients that move through a food web.

procedure

Part One: Nutrient Cycling Relay

1. Explain that the students will be learning that nutrients *cycle* and energy *flows* by doing a relay activity. Divide students into groups of five. Within each group, one student is algae, one is diporeia, one is a chub, one is a lake trout and one is bacteria and fungus. Each student should wear a card around their neck identifying their organism.
2. Briefly review the organisms so the students remember who eats whom. Information about many species can be found on the backs of the Creature Cards.
3. Groups should spread out along the length of the field, with the algae, bacteria and fungus, and chub on one side of the field and the diporeia and lake trout on the other side (about 10 meters away). Each student should have a paper cup and a marker. On the algae side of the field is a bucket of water representing nutrients in the lake water.
4. On GO, the algae dip their cups into the lake water to fill them about half way and mark the water line on the side of the cup with their marker. Then, they run or walk quickly down the field to the diporeia and pour the water into their cup.

Students should try not to spill the water!
- The diporeia then mark the water level on their own cups, run down the field to the chubs and pour the water into the chubs' cups.
- The chubs mark the water level on their cups, run down the field to the lake trout and pour the water in their cup.
- The lake trout mark the water level on their cup, and run down the field to the bacteria and fungus and pour the water into the trouts' cups.
- The bacteria and fungus mark their water level and pour their water back into the Lake Water bucket. Run the relay twice so that students can see the cycle happening.

5. Each time there is a water pass-off; it represents one species eating another. The nutrients, which are represented by the water, are passed from one species to the next through the food web. When an organism such as the lake trout dies, it passes its nutrients to the bacteria and fungus, who break down the detritus. Nutrients released during this process are absorbed by algae through the lake water.

wrap-up

1. All of the students should take their cups and place them together in groups with their organism, so that all chubs are together, etc. Look at the marks on the cups and compare water levels between each of the groups of organisms. Are they in similar places or different? *They should all be about the same - the algae all filled their cups halfway in the beginning, and none was lost.*
2. What does this mean? *Nutrients are not lost as they pass through the food chain. They continue to cycle through.*
3. Was there an end to the food chain or not? *No, it was a loop, or circle. Why is this significant? Nutrients are not just passed in one direction to a dead end at the top predator. Instead, they are cycled through the food web and reused again and again.*
4. Where do human nutrients come from? *Just Like other animals, we get our nutrients from the food we eat.*

assessment

Rubric on page 86

procedure continued

Part Two: Energy Flow Relay

1. Have students run around outside for a few minutes.

2. Have students feel the tops of their heads. They should feel warm. Running burns calories. The heat they feel coming from their bodies is energy that is being lost into space as a result of the energy transformation.

   It is OKAY that they are losing energy. According to the second law of thermodynamics, energy can be transformed from one state to another, but in the system in which this occurs, there is always a loss of energy. It is okay to use energy as long as we are not using more than is coming in. A system is stable or growing as long as the amount of energy used is equal to or less than the amount of energy entering the system.

3. Students should get back into their relay groups and original formations. This time, students should each punch a small hole in the bottom of their paper cups with a paper clip. They should each still have a marker.

4. The bucket of water at the algae end of the field represents the sun's energy this time. The water in the cups represents the energy of the organisms. The algae begin the relay by filling their cups (all the way this time) with water from the sunshine bucket. The relay continues in the same way as the first relay. The difference here is that the relay stops with the bacteria and fungus (they do not cycle back to the algae). This is because energy flows, but does not cycle.

5. Once the relay has begun, the algae continue to go back and fill their cups from the sun (as plants do in the real world) and pass it off to continue the relay. Thus, energy will continue to flow through the relay until the game is over. Each time water is passed into another cup, it represents an energy transformation as one animal eats another. As the students run across the field, they will be losing water from the bottom of their cups. This represents energy that is lost through respiration and excretion. Water that is left in the cups represents energy that is stored for growth and that can be passed on to the next organism.

> ### *Satisfy Your Curiosity* QUESTION IDEAS
>
> - *How does my organism's place in the food web (its trophic level) affect the nutrients and energy it receives?*
> - *If my species is high in the food web, how does it compensate for the reduced amount of energy it receives from its prey?*

wrap-up

1. Line up the cups by organism groups again and look at the marks. Which species had the most energy and which had the least? Why?
   The algae started with the most energy, then each time energy was transformed for a new organism, some was lost to respiration and excretion.

2. How do animals high in the food chain make up for this energy loss?
   Usually, animals higher in the food chain use less energy than animals lower in the food chain. Some eat more animals that are lower in the food chain. Also, if they eat animals two steps down on the food chain, they can get more energy for growth. For example, lake sturgeon are very large fish, but they eat small organisms, such as zooplankton, instead of fish. Saving energy this way allows them to grow larger than predator fish who eat forage fish.

3. Where does new energy come from?
   The sun.

4. How can we make sure that as much energy as possible enters the food chain? Make sure there are plenty of plants to convert the energy into food.
   Discuss again: It is okay to use energy as long as we are not using more than the plants are taking up from the sun. A system is stable or growing as long as the amount of energy used is equal to or less than the amount of energy entering the system.

assessment

Rubric on page ?

12 | Great Lakes Relay

GRADE LEVEL
4-8

FIRST NAME

LAST NAME

[1] Draw arrows between the organisms to show where the NUTRIENTS went. Color in the boxes to show how full of NUTRIENTS the cups were.

Sun

Nutrients in lake water

Algae

Bacteria and Fungus

Diporeia

Trout

Chub

APPROVED BY

12 | Great Lakes Relay

GRADE LEVEL
4-8

journal pages

FIRST NAME																					
LAST NAME																					

[1] Draw arrows between the organisms to show where the ENERGY went. Color in the boxes to show how full of ENERGY the cups were.

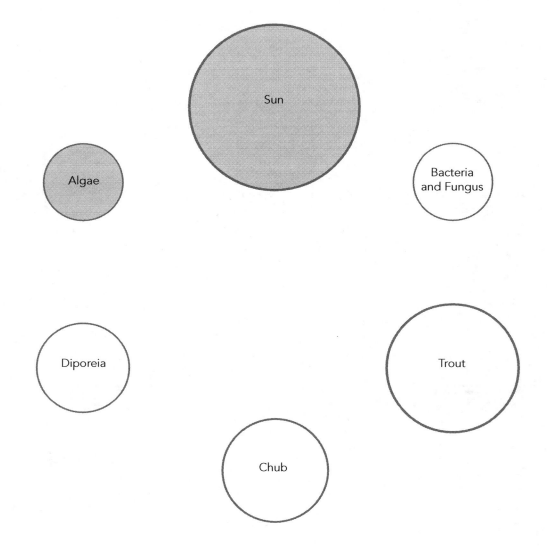

APPROVED BY

12 | Great Lakes Relay

GRADE LEVEL
4-8

FIRST NAME																					
LAST NAME																					

[1] Draw a picture of a lake food web. Choose at least three organisms that are not in the other two journal pages for this activity. Draw arrows to show how nutrients cycle and energy flows through this food web.

[2] Explain the difference between what happens to energy and what happens to nutrients in a food web.

....

....

....

....

....

....

....

....

APPROVED BY	

INVESTIGATE

13 | Invasive Issues

GRADE LEVEL
6-8

90 minutes

summary

Students research and present findings on invasive species, then research and write about possible solutions.

objectives

- Explain how specific invasive species have impacted the lake food web.
- Suggest possible solutions to problems caused by invasive species in the Great Lakes.

prerequisite

What's New?

vocabulary

Invasive species: plant or animal that enters an ecosystem to which it is not native and competes with one or more native species for food, shelter and/ or reproductive opportunities

Biodiversity: biological variety in an environment as indicated by numbers of different plants and animals

setting

INDOORS

subjects

Language Arts, Ecology

standards

This Great Lakes in My World activity is aligned to the Common Core State Standards and to state learning standards in:

Illinois
Indiana
Michigan
Minnesota
New York
Ohio
Pennsylvania
Wisconsin

This alignment is available on your Great Lakes in My World CD in the "Standards" folder and on-line at http://www.greatlakes.org/ GLiMWstandards.

materials

- Journals
- Pencils
- Poster board
- Markers
- Research materials

background

Please see the background section of the "What's New?" activity. The list of invasive species includes: rusty crayfish, spiny water flea, bighead and silver carp, Eurasian ruffe, sea lamprey, zebra mussel, Eurasian water milfoil and quagga mussel.

procedure

1. Introduce the activity by telling the class they're going to build upon what they've learned about invasive species. Create a large chart to hang on the wall that duplicates the one on the journal page for this activity. Break students into eight teams to research invasive species. Each team should choose one species.

2. Teams research the species to answer the questions in the chart. Students should record the research in their journals, then enter concise responses on the class and journal chart

3. Each team should give a five-minute presentation on their findings. Discuss the following questions as a class: What are the most common ways in which these species enter the Great Lakes? *Ballast water carried by ships, through canals made by humans.* What characteristics are shared by successful invasive species? What can happen when an invasive species successfully establishes itself in an ecosystem?

4. Discuss the changes that the lake food web has undergone as a result of the introduction of new species. How long do students think the food web will continue to change? *This answer is dependent on predator-prey relationships and on habitat requirements of the invasive and native species and how habitats change with invasive species.* Is the food web stable, or in balance right now with the invasive species? *No.* Will the food web become stable again over time? *Possibly- Right now, native organisms spend a lot of energy competing with new organisms for food and space. Over a very long period of time, organisms co-evolve so that they can live in balance and expend less energy competing with each other. In the meantime, the food web as we know it could change drastically and decrease in biodiversity.*

5. Students work in their groups to draw diagrams of the lake food web that include the invasive species.

wrap-up

1. Make clear the difference between the short- and long-term time scales. The imbalance in ecosystems caused by invasive species may be corrected through evolution, but this happens over a very long period of time (thousands of years). In the more immediate future, invasive species may do considerable damage to an ecosystem.

2. What is the answer? Do students think that the best solution to this problem is to let the food web take its own course in finding a new balance or to try to control the invasive species? What are the possible ways in which invasives could be controlled? *Preventative measures include things such as electric barriers or regulations on shipping ballast water. Measures to reduce existing numbers of invasives in the Great Lakes include selective poisoning, introducing predators and interfering with reproduction.*

3. Students should go back into their groups to research potential solutions to the damage caused by their species.

4. Have students begin research by looking for articles on their species on the following web site: http://www.glerl.noaa.gov/res/Programs/glansis/glansis.html. Each group should read at least two articles on their species and one article on another species.

5. After reading the articles and doing additional research as necessary, students should brainstorm a list of potential solutions. Have groups each choose one solution from their list on which to expand.

6. Students should each write a one-page essay in their journals explaining the impact of the invasive species they have chosen and a possible solution to the problem.

7. Student groups should each take five minutes to present their issue and proposed solution to the class.

extension

Turn essays into proposal letters to send to the officials best in a position to affect change. If you choose to do this, it is important to first discuss with students that while they are capable of making change, people are not always successful on their first attempt.

assessment

Rubric on page 87

Name	Latin Name	Origin	When Arrived in Great Lakes	How Arrived in Great Lakes	
alewife	*Alosa pseudoharengus*	Atlantic coast	Before 1931	Canals and the St. Lawrence River	
bighead and silver carp	*Hypophthalmichthys nobilis* and *Hypophthalmichthys molitrix*	Originally from China, now in Mississippi River	Not yet arrived; currently in upper Illinois River less than 55 miles from Lake Michigan; a permanent electric fish barrier is being constructed to prevent their advance towards Lake Michigan	Escaped into the Mississippi River from aquaculture facilities in the early 1990s when the facilities were flooded	
Eurasian ruffe*	*Gymnocephalus cernuus*	Northern Europe- Black and Caspian Seas	1980s	Arrived in ballast water from a ship	
Eurasian water milfoil	*Myriophyllum spicatum*	Europe, Asia and North Africa	1940s	Introduced as an aquarium plant	
Hydrilla	*Hydrilla verticillata*	Africa	1960	Aquarium trade	
purple loosetrife*	*Lythrum salicaria*	Northern Europe	Early 1900s	Intentionally imported for its beautiful flowers	
quagga mussel	*Dreissena bugensis*	Eurasia	1989	Arrived in ballast water from a ship	
round goby	*Neogobius melanostomus*	Black Sea	1986-1988	Arrived in a ship's ballast water brought into St. Clair River or Lake St. Clair	
rusty crayfish	*Orconectes rusticus*	Ohio River Basin	1960s	Used as bait by fishermen and released by science classes who had them as pets	
sea lamprey	*Petromyzon marinus*	Atlantic Ocean, St. Lawrence and Hudson Rivers and possibly Lake Ontario	Arrived in 1830s, established by 1938	Through the Welland Canal	
spiny water flea	*Bythotrephes cedarstromi*	Northern Europe	Lake Huron 1984, in all Great Lakes by 1987	Arrived in ballast water from a ship	
white perch*	*Morone americana*	Atlantic coast	1930s-1950s	Canals	
zebra mussel	*Dreissena polymorpha*	Caspian Sea region of Poland, Bulgaria and Russia	About 1985	Arrived in ballast water from a ship	

* = not a Creature Card

Habitat	Food Source	Impact on Food Web	Other Impact	Notes
Lakes and oceans	Phytoplankton, zooplankton, and small crustaceans	Competes for food	Large numbers die off, can clog water intake pipes and contaminate beaches	Thrived when sea lamprey ate the fish that prey upon it
Surface layers of open water	Plankton	Would likely compete for food with native fish; are large and consume large quantities of food	Have the potential of destroying the $1 billion commercial and recreational fishing industry on the Great Lakes	Silver carp species are bothered by boat motor noises and leap several feet out of the water, injuring boaters
Fresh and brackish waters, usually near river mouths	Highly variable diet including mollusks, insect larvae, small fish, and crustaceans	Aggressive competitor for food	Reproduces quickly; its not eaten because of spiny fins; has a variable diet	Tolerates varying water conditions
Full sunlight; lives in water to depths of 1-3m/ 3-9ft	Sunlight	Forms thick mats that choke out native vegetation	Disrupts water recreation	Thrives in warm water and spreads quickly
Any partially sub-merged body of water with a salinity level of less than 7%	Oxygen and sunlight	Forms tall and thick stalks and shade or choke out all native vegetation	Disrupts water recreation and grows until the surface	Reproduces at an incredibly fast rate
Moist to wet ground in prairies and streambanks	Sunlight	Destroys habitat for other wetland plants	Its roots choke waterways	
Freshwater lakes up to 33m/98ft	Plankton	Competes for food	See "zebra mussel"	Reproduces quickly; lives at greater depth than zebra mussels
Lake bottom; found in all Great Lakes and some nearby lakes	Small fish, zebra mussels, fish eggs	Compete with native sculpin for resources; reduces top predators by consuming their eggs		Reproduces quickly; is more likely to find prey than to become prey
Lakes, ponds, and streams in areas where there is debris on the bottom	Aquatic plants and insects, fish eggs, small fish	Displaces native crayfish; reduce the number and types of aquatic vegetation in invertebrates.		
Freshwater lakes and oceans	Lake trout	Upsets the ecosystem balance by removing top predators	Destroys fish by sucking blood and tissues	Had great impact on the commercial fishing industry of the 1950s
Throughout Great Lakes and some inland lakes	Plankton	Competes with small fish for food, but its spiny tail prevents it from being eaten		
Marine; spawn in coastal streams; now found in freshwater lakes	Eggs of walleye and white bass	Competes with yellow perch and other fish in shallow water; consumes eggs of other fish	Reduced number of walleye impacted fishing industry	
Freshwater; native to the Caspian and Black Seas; now in all Great Lakes and some inland lakes; depths of 2-7m/ 6-23 ft	Plankton	Competes for food by filtering large amounts of plankton, which has reduced this population	Accumulates on objects, such as boat hulls, and clogs water pipes	Increases water clarity through filter feeding, which increases algae growth and decreases abundance of plankton

13 | Invasive Issues

GRADE LEVEL
6-8

FIRST NAME

LAST NAME

[1] Species name: ....

[2] Species is from: ....

[3] When did it arrive in the Great Lakes? ....

[4] How was it introduced? ....
....

[5] What is its habitat? ....
....

[6] What is its food source? ....
....

[7] Describe its impact on the food web. ....
....
....
....

[8] Draw a diagram of the lake food web including the invasive species. Describe how the native species are impacted by the invasive species.

APPROVED BY

13 | Invasive Issues

FIRST NAME																						
LAST NAME																						

Titles, authors and dates of research articles:

1. ....

....

2. ....

....

3. ....

....

Brainstorm a list of potential solutions to the negative impact your species has had on the lake food web. This may include methods of preventing more of this species from entering the Great Lakes and/or methods of reducing numbers already in the lakes. Narrow down your list to one solution - circle this solution.

1. ....

....

2. ....

....

3. ....

....

Write!
On a separate sheet of paper, write a composition explaining the impact of the invasive species you have chosen, and a possible solution to the problem.

APPROVED BY	

13 | Invasive Issues

GRADE LEVEL
6-8

journal pages

FIRST NAME													
LAST NAME													

Fill in the row on the chart for the species your group chose.
During the presentations, fill in the rest of the chart.

SPECIES NAME	Originally from	Year it arrived in the Great Lakes	How it was Introduced	Habitat (shelter or space occupied)	Food Source	Impact on Lake Food Web

APPROVED BY

INVESTIGATE

14 | Moving Mercury

GRADE LEVEL

4-8

45 minutes

summary

Students learn about bioaccumulation and its harmful effect on the food web through the example of mercury in the aquatic ecosystem.

objectives

- Explain bioaccumulation.
- Trace mercury's path to the lake and through the food web.
- Create a concept map relating to mercury issues in the Great Lakes.
- List ways to help solve problems related to mercury bioaccumulation and biomagnification.

prerequisite

A Tangled Web, Great Lakes Relay

vocabulary

Bioaccumulation: the building up of a chemical in the tissues of an organism
Biomagnification: the large increase in the concentration of a chemical in an organism at the top trophic level of a food chain
Mercury: a silvery-white poisonous metallic element (Hg), liquid at room temperature and used in thermometers, barometers and batteries, and in the preparation of chemical pesticides
Primary consumer: an animal that gets its energy from plants (producers); an herbivore
Secondary consumer: a consumer that gets its energy from other consumers; a carnivore
Tertiary consumer: an animal that feeds on secondary consumers in a food chain, usually the top predators in an ecosystem or food chain
Predator: an animal that lives by killing and eating other animals

setting

INDOORS

subjects

Environmental Science, Human Health

standards

This Great Lakes in My World activity is aligned to the Common Core State Standards and to state learning standards in:

Illinois
Indiana
Michigan
Minnesota
New York
Ohio
Pennsylvania
Wisconsin

This alignment is available on your Great Lakes in My World CD in the "Standards" folder and on-line at http://www.greatlakes.org/ GLiMWstandards.

materials

- 10 very small clear containers (1-2 oz.)
- Water
- Five small clear containers (4-5 oz.)
- Three medium clear containers (8 oz.)
- One large clear container
- One small jar of glitter

background

When an unnecessary or unhealthy chemical bioaccumulates in a living creature, it can cause health problems. It can also be transferred to the animal that eats this organism.

There are several toxic chemicals that biomagnify in the Great Lakes food web. They include dioxin, polychlorinated biphenyls (PCBs), DDT and mercury. This activity focuses on mercury, as it continues to be a pressing issue in the Great Lakes watershed.

Mercury is a naturally occurring element. It becomes present in the environment through volcanoes and the weathering of rocks. However, most mercury in the environment is released into the atmosphere as a by-product of coal-fired power plants. Once in the air, it can attach to precipitation (rain, snow, sleet) and enter waterways via the water cycle.

Once in waterways, mercury transforms into methylmercury and is taken into the food chain by microorganisms. Methylmercury is a neurotoxin that can bioaccumulate. It can cause harm to organisms as it moves up the food chain, increasing in concentration with each contaminated organism ingested. Unlike other toxins (DDT, dioxin and PCB) which only accumulate in fatty tissues of organisms, mercury can also accumulates in muscle tissues. This means that there is no simple way to remove the mercury from the edible parts of the fish or other organisms. The longer an organism lives, the more contaminated food it eats, and the more toxins it accumulates. The increase of toxins found at the higher levels of the food chain is called biomagnification.* Mercury is a neurotoxin which damages or destroys nerve tissue.

Note: Although the concept of bioaccumulation is demonstrated by this activity, the amounts of the substance representing mercury are not intended to be true representations. For accurate measurements and amounts, see the activity: It Adds Up and Up.

Students are asked to make a concept map in this activity. A concept map is a type of diagram used for exploring knowledge, as well as, gathering and sharing information. A concept map consists of cells or circles that contain a concept, item or question and links. The links are labeled and show direction with an arrow. The labeled links explain the relationship between the cells. The arrow describes the direction of the relationship and reads like a sentence.

procedure

1. Ask students to make a food chain based on what they have eaten during the day. When discussing the food chains, ask students how they can tell if what they ate was grown/raised in a healthy way. *If it has a special label (e.g., organic, hormone free) or was grown/raised by themselves or someone they know. Otherwise, it is difficult to know what an animal or plant has ingested.*

2. Tell students you will be talking about mercury, a substance that is not able to be seen in the Great Lakes but is definitely present and can be unhealthy for living creatures. It is passed along a Great Lakes food web, from plant to animal to animal. First, how does it get into the lake? Ask students to list the different ways we get power to our homes. Focus on coal-fired power plants, which generate electricity. That is the major source of mercury in the environment. As you explain the path of mercury into the Great Lakes, have students create diagrams.

3. Explain the concept of bioaccumulation and how it affects a food web. Have students define bioaccumulation in the journal pages.

4. Point out the containers (each filled 1/3 full with water) and tell students these represent organisms in the food web. Show students the glitter and explain that it represents the mercury. Have the students decide (in small groups if time) on a plan that uses the containers and the mercury to demonstrate bioaccumulation. If students do not do it on their own, discuss how the containers can represent organisms in the food web (suggested names included). Guide them to come up with names for the 10 very small (1-2 oz.) containers (green algae), names for the five primary consumer jars (4-5 oz.) (diporeia), names for the three secondary consumer jars (8 oz.) (chub), and a name for the top predator jar (lake trout). If students come up with a different system, discuss it and use their idea, if it is accurate.

5. Demonstrate the food web and bioaccumulation in action by putting a pinch of glitter in the very small containers, small containers, and medium containers. Pour the contents of the very small containers into the five small containers. This represents producers being eaten by the consumers. Continue with the other containers, as each "organism" is "eaten." Some of the glitter may stay in the containers as you pour, which is fine as it can represent the mercury that is not accumulated, or is excreted by the animal.

6. Discuss what happened. Where did most of the glitter end up? What does this mean in a food web? *When a lot of the glitter/mercury ends up in the top predators, it can be described as "biomagnification."*

7. Have students diagram what they saw in the activity by creating a food web that shows mercury being passed along to each organism.

wrap-up

1. Have the students create a concept map using vocabulary from the activity: bioaccumulate, micro-organism, primary consumer, secondary consumer, top predator, biomagnify, mercury, coal-fired power plant.

2. Have students share their diagrams with each other.

3. Create a list of ways to help solve the problem of mercury in the environment. The list might include:

- *Properly recycle light bulbs.*
- *Don't buy products with mercury in them.*
- *Use less electricity, so less coal has to be burned (turn off the lights!).*
- *Educate others about the issue.*
- *Encourage alternative energy sources.*
- *Write letters requesting stronger emissions controls on power plants.*
- *Support public leaders who will back strong emissions controls.*

sources

This activity has been adapted with permission from Mercury in Schools:
http://www.mercuryinschools.uwex.edu/curriculum/index.htm

Mercury Contamination of Aquatic Ecosystems
   http://water.usgs.gov/wid/FS_216-95/FS_216-95.pdf
Food Watch
   http://www.foodandwaterwatch.org/

assessment

Rubric on page 87

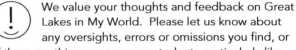

We value your thoughts and feedback on Great Lakes in My World. Please let us know about any oversights, errors or omissions you find, or if there are things you or your students particularly like.

Send your comments to: education@greatlakes.org

14 | Moving Mercury

GRADE LEVEL
4-8

FIRST NAME																					
LAST NAME																					

[1] Create a diagram that shows how mercury enters the Great Lakes.

[2] Explain bioaccumulation.

....

....

....

....

....

....

....

....

[3] Using the materials available, how would you design a demonstration that shows
    bioaccumulation?

....

....

....

....

....

....

....

....

....

APPROVED BY	

14 | Moving Mercury

GRADE LEVEL
4-8

journal ⫸ pages

FIRST NAME																			
LAST NAME																			

[4] Diagram a food web that show mercury being passed along.

[5] Create a concept map that shows the relationship between the following words: bioaccumulate, micro-organism, secondary consumer, tertiary consumer, top predator, biomagnify, mercury, coal-fired power plant. Use arrows and additional words to explain your ideas.

[6] MaKe a list of ways to help solve the problem of mercury in the environment.

....

....

....

....

....

....

APPROVED BY	

15 | Solubility

30 minutes

summary

Students learn about water and fat solubility through a demonstration and discussion. This activity prepares students for "It Adds Up and Up."

objectives

- Explain solubility and the difference between matter that is soluble in water versus soluble in fat.

prerequisite

Moving Mercury

vocabulary

Dissolve: to pass into, or "melt" into, a solution in a way that the entire solution is uniform in its makeup

setting

INDOORS

subjects

Environmental Science, Physical Science

standards

This Great Lakes in My World activity is aligned to the Common Core State Standards and to state learning standards in:

Illinois
Indiana
Michigan
Minnesota
New York
Ohio
Pennsylvania
Wisconsin

This alignment is available on your Great Lakes in My World CD in the "Standards" folder and on-line at http://www.greatlakes.org/GLiMWstandards.

materials

- Three beakers of water
- One pad of butter
- One teaspoon sugar
- One teaspoon sand
- Journals
- Pencils

background

Solubility: the ability of a substance to become dissolved in another substance.

Parts Per Million: a unit of concentration often used when measuring levels of toxins in air, water or body fluids. For example, if a fish has three ppm of mercury, that means if the fish is divided into one million parts, three of those parts are made up of mercury. For example, one part per million is equivalent to one drop of chocolate in 16 gallons of milk. For further information on "parts per million," see "It Adds Up and Up."

procedure

1. Define "dissolve" and ask the students what they think will happen (form a hypothesis) when the butter, sand, and sugar are each added to a separate beaker of water and stirred. Students write their hypothesis in their journals.

2. Demonstrate with volunteers or have students come up with the procedure by discussing different ways to use the materials provided: Mix the butter in one beaker. *It will not dissolve.* Mix the sugar in the next beaker. *It will dissolve.* Mix the sand in the last beaker. *It will not dissolve.*

3. Define solubility. Ask students which substances were soluble in water and which were not. Students should record the results in their journals. Explain that some things are soluble in water, some are not, and some materials are soluble in other substances, such as fat. Some things that are soluble in fat are certain vitamins (A, E and D). These vitamins stay in the body in the fat tissues, rather than getting flushed out with water in urine and sweat.

wrap-up

1. Why is this significant? *Mercury, a harmful contaminant in the Great Lakes is not soluble in water. Instead, it dissolves in fat and muscle tissue. It is extracted from the lake water through food consumption, but is not flushed out of the body in urine.*

2. Where do you think fat-soluble pollutants turn up in lake organisms? *In the fat. Fat-soluble contaminants may become concentrated in fatty substances in plants and animals. Thus, they end up in higher concentrations in the belly fat and under the skin of such fatty fish as lake trout, salmon and chubs.*

3. Why can't mercury be washed out by blood or urine? *It won't dissolve in these watery fluids. A water-soluble contaminant might flush out in the urine fairly soon after the animal is exposed. However, fat-soluble substances do not. They tend to build up in fat tissues and are not released unless the fish uses its own fat tissues as an energy source. Mercury is stored in both the fat and muscle tissue of organisms.*

4. How are anglers told about contaminants in fish they are trying to catch? *When anglers buy their fishing licenses, they should receive information about fish consumption advisories.*

5. Trout and salmon have more fat in their bodies than whitefish, perch, and smelt. Why might the amount of body fat have something to do with parts per million of a fat-soluble pollutant in a fish? *The greater the amount of fat, the greater the concentration of fat-soluble pollutants.*

assessment

Rubric on page 88

source

This activity has been adapted with permission from The Life of the Lakes: A Guide to Great Lakes Fishery Education Materials, Michigan Sea Grant Extension, Michigan State University, by Shari L. Dann

15 | Solubility

FIRST NAME																							
LAST NAME																							

[1] What do you think will happen when the butter, sand and sugar are each added to a beaker of water? Write your hypothesis for each one.

Butter: ....

....

Sand: ....

....

Sugar: ....

....

[2] Results: What actually happened? Were your hypotheses correct or not?

Butter: ....

....

Sand: ....

....

Sugar: ....

....

[3] Why does it pose a problem for animals if mercury is in the Great Lakes? How does this relate to your experiment?

....

....

....

....

....

....

....

....

APPROVED BY	

16 | It Adds Up and Up

GRADE LEVEL
6-8

90 minutes minimum

summary

Students discuss mercury issues and carry out calculations to further understand biomagnification of mercury within the Great Lakes.

objectives

- Explain bioaccumulation and biomagnification, and their significance with regard to mercury pollution in Lake Michigan.
- Discuss the causes and effects of this pollution and how it relates to humans.
- Use math to show that a very small amount of pollution can be magnified through the food chain to a very high level of toxicity.

prerequisite

Solubility and Moving Mercury

vocabulary

Neurotoxin: substance that has the ability to damage or destroy nerve tissues

Bioaccumulation: process through which organisms accumulate toxins in their bodies from their environment; if an environment is polluted, organisms can absorb the toxins by eating other contaminated organisms; heavy metal pollutants such as mercury are not flushed out of the system with other fluids, and therefore accumulate over time

Biomagnification: process through which toxins move through a food chain and are magnified at each higher trophic level

setting

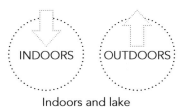
INDOORS   OUTDOORS

Indoors and lake

subjects

Environmental Science, Ecology, Math

standards

This Great Lakes in My World activity is aligned to the Common Core State Standards and to state learning standards in:

Illinois
Indiana
Michigan
Minnesota
New York
Ohio
Pennsylvania
Wisconsin

This alignment is available on your Great Lakes in My World CD in the "Standards" folder and on-line at http://www.greatlakes.org/ GLiMWstandards.

materials

Creature Cards
- Journals
- Pencils
- Tape measure
- Two grains of sand
- Red permanent marker
- 1,000 cm³ box filled with sand (standard tissue box, which is 11cm x 11cm, filled to 8.26cm high)
- Calculators
- Yarn or stakes
- Scissors
- News articles (on compact disc)
- Chalkboard

background

Overview of mercury

Mercury occurs naturally in the environment and is released into the air by coal-fired power plants and waste incinerators. When it falls onto surface waters, bacteria in the water cause a chemical change that transforms the mercury into methylmercury, a neurotoxin, which is absorbed by fish as they eat aquatic organisms.

What is Mercury (Hg)?

Mercury occurs naturally in coal and mineral ores. It makes up a very small percentage of the earth's crust (approx. .00003%). Mercury combines with sulfur to form more than 25 different minerals. The symbol for the element mercury is Hg.

How Does Mercury Enter the Environment?

Mercury is released into the environment by both natural and anthropogenic (caused by human activity) sources. It is estimated that about 11,000 metric tons of mercury are released annually to the air, soil, and water through human activity. Most mercury is released into the environment through coal-fired power plants. Other sources include: mining, smelting and manufacturing activities.

Once released into the environment, mercury is easily transported through the air. Mercury attaches itself to rain drops (precipitation) in the atmosphere and eventually can end up in the lake. When it gets into lakes, bacteria in the water, combined with small amounts of oxygen, can change it into methylmercury. Methylmercury gets into the bottom sediments (sand and mud) in lakes and is taken up by the algae and phytoplankton. This is then eaten by bottom-feeding fish, and then makes its way up the food web. Fish (or humans) cannot ingest mercury from the water, only by eating the affected plants or animals.

What is the Problem?

Mercury is toxic and never leaves the environment once it gets in. It easily transforms into methylmercury, which is very dangerous for people to consume. Mercury is one of the single biggest environmental threats to the Great Lakes. This is because the Great Lakes are a virtually closed ecosystem. It takes 100 years for a drop of rainwater to leave Lake Michigan once it enters, longer for Lake Superior!

Mercury is harmful to people. 1/70 of a teaspoon of mercury can contaminate a 25-acre lake to the point the fish are unsafe to eat. It is a neurotoxin.

For more information look at: http://www.epa.gov/captrade.

What is Being Done?

To assess health risks, the EPA developed a reference dose that is a scientifically justifiable maximum level of exposure to protect public health from toxic effects of mercury. This means that women of childbearing age and children under the age of 15 should limit their consumption of fish in mercury-contaminated water to one serving per week.

What can individuals do about the mercury problem?

- Conserve electricity so that coal-fired power plants do not release so much mercury into the atmosphere.

- Stop buying products that contain mercury. Products include thermometers, shoes that glow in the dark and certain types of batteries and light switches.

- Don't eat fish that come from an area in which there is a "fish consumption advisory" based on mercury. Currently, all Great Lakes are under such an advisory. Limit consumption of Great Lakes fish to once/week or once/month.

- Recycle old batteries by taking them to a recycling facility. If left in your garbage they go to a landfill and the mercury in them is released into the environment.

- Regular household light-bulbs, including Compact Fluorescent Light-bulbs CFLs, should be recycled. If left in your garbage they go to a landfill, like old batteries, and the mercury in them is released into the environment. Look at http://www.ehow.com/how_2164166_recycle-light-bulbs.html for more information.

Sand: A grain of sand is approximately 1 cubic millimeter. One million grains of sand fit into a 10 cm x 10 cm x 10 cm box (or a standard tissue box, which is 11 cm x 11 cm, filled to 8.26 cm high). Ten billion grains of sand fit into 10 cubic meters, which is a space approximately 1 ft x 16.5 ft x 16.5 ft (.33 m x 5.5 m x 5.5 m).

procedure

Preparation: Color two grains of sand with a red permanent marker.

A) Beach Field Trip: (this can be done as its own trip or as part of a previous field trip)
Demonstrate: How much is one part per million? How much is one part in 10 billion?

1. Fill a 10cm x 10cm x 10cm box with sand. Show the students one of the red grains of sand and place it in the box. Tell the students there are 1 million grains of sand in this box and that one of them is red. This is one part per million red.

2. Explain that toxins in water are usually measured in parts per million (ppm). This is because toxins are usually present in minute quantities.

3. Using the tape measure, have the students mark off a square on the beach that measures 16.5 feet on each side. Use the yarn or stakes to mark the corners (sticks or rocks may be used to hold the yarn in place).

4. Have the students close their eyes while you hide the other red grain of sand in the area they have marked off.

5. Tell the students that they have 10 minutes to look within this area, to a depth of one foot for the red grain of sand. There are 10 billion grains of sand in this area, so this sand is one part per 10 billion red.

6. After 10 minutes, stop looking for the red grain of sand. Ask whether it was easy or hard to find the red grain and why. *Since there is so much sand, it is too hard to find the red grain. One part per million is a very small amount, and one part in 10 billion is very, very small.*

7. Explain that they will study a hypothetical situation in which the water has been polluted with mercury. They'll pretend algae from the water has one part in 10 billion mercury, like the sand example.

8. Help students understand that in this simulation, for every 10 billion parts of algae, one part is contaminated with mercury, like the sand grain. Allow time for questions and clarification. More examples may be helpful. For example, in a city with a population of one million, if one person is blue and the rest are yellow, then the city is 1 ppm blue. If 12 people in that city are blue, then the city is 12 ppm blue.

9. Ask the students what they think about this amount of mercury in the lake (1 part per 10 billion or .0001 ppm). Do they think this very small amount could be enough to harm organisms? They will find out in the next part of the activity!

B) Food Chain Calculations: This part of the activity can be done indoors.

1. Divide the class into groups of three. Each student is assigned an organism: within each group there should be a diporeia, a yellow perch and a lake trout. Give each group a copy of her/his respective Creature Card.

2. Review the roles that each organism plays in the food chain.

3. Within their groups, students must come up with the essential components needed to calculate the ppm of mercury that could be in their organism's body. *The components needed are 1) weight of prey, 2) weight of predator, 3) number of prey eaten, and 4) ppm (by weight) of mercury present in the prey.*

4. Once students have come up with the correct components, allow time for groups to try to work out an equation that would calculate the ppm of mercury in their organism. Ask students whether they would all be able to calculate their ppm at the same time, or if they would need information from each other before they could do their own calculations. The correct equation is:

$$\frac{\text{Weight of prey (oz)}}{1} \otimes \frac{\text{Methylmercury ppm in prey}}{1} \otimes \frac{\text{Number of prey eaten}}{\text{Weight of predator (oz)}} = x$$

5. Now divide the class into three groups by organism. One group is diporeia (zooplankton), one is yellow perch (forage fish), and one is lake trout (predator fish). Pass out a chart to each student.

6. Explain that the lake has been contaminated with mercury. Briefly discuss where it comes from, why, and what impact this has on people. In a hypothetical situation, the algae sampled from the lake is .0001 ppm mercury. This is the same as 1 part in 10 billion, like the grain of sand on the beach.

7. Each group is responsible for calculating the mercury (in ppm) in their organisms, based on its weight and how much it eats.

8. Tell students at the end of this lesson, they will write a story about it. (Detailed in the wrap-up section)

procedure continued

9. Using the formula, have students calculate their parts per million of methylmercury. The diporeia will have to go first and give their answer to the yellow perch, who will go next, and give their answer to the lake trout for use in their calculations. It may be helpful to do the calculations on the board, having the group members plug in the appropriate numbers and calculate the answers. Students write the ppm answers on their charts and discuss the questions beneath it.

10. Discuss the following:
    - What do you think regarding the amount of mercury it takes to impact fish and the humans that eat it? *A very small amount of mercury can be enough to make larger fish toxic to humans.*
    - How is such a small amount of mercury magnified as it moves through the food chain? *At each trophic level, organisms eat more over a longer period of time, causing them to accumulate toxins at high levels.*

C) News Articles (on compact disc):

1. Pass out one of the news articles to each of the three groups. Articles can also be read as homework, prior to food chain calculations.

2. Allow 20 minutes for students to read the articles, then have each write three sentences on the main argument and supporting points.

3. Now switch the groups so students are back in their original groups of three, with each student representing a different organism.

4. Allow students 15 minutes (five minutes per student) to teach the others about the articles, using the three-sentence summary.

5. As a class, discuss the articles with the questions from the journal pages. These can be answered in class or as homework.

Answer key for Journal Pages

Biomagnification in the Food Chain Chart 1
Lake trout: 10 ppm
Yellow perch: 1 ppm
Diporeia: .01 ppm

[6] Zooplankton example answers only:
.01 oz, .0001 ppm, 1000 number of prey/ .1 oz, .01 ppm

[7]
Yes, has less than 3 ppm methylmercury (1 ppm)

[8]
No, has more than 3 ppm methylmercury (10 ppm)

Biomagnification in the Food Chain Chart 2
Lake trout: 5 ppm
Smelt: .5 ppm
Mysis: .005 ppm

[9]
.01 oz, .00005 ppm, 1000 number of prey/ .1 oz, .005 ppm

[10]
.1 oz, .005 ppm, 10,000 number of prey/ 10 oz, .5 ppm

[11]
10 oz, .5ppm, 100 number of prey/ 100 oz, 5 ppm

[12]
All safe except lake trout (5 ppm)

wrap-up

1. Ask each student to write a story describing a simple lake food chain and the biomagnification of a fat-soluble toxin within that food chain. Their understanding of the concept of biomagnification should be apparent in their writing. Students should include two to three action steps in their stories to correct the problem.

extension

Take steps to reduce the amount of mercury in the lake:

Find out what is happening in your community about mercury pollution. Look at http://www.checkmylake.org/lake/ as a starting place for research. Decide as a class whether action needs to be taken on the situation in order to protect the lake and people living near it. Make a list of possible action steps. Perhaps choose some, as a group, to carry out.

assessment

Rubric on page 88

16 | It Adds Up and Up

GRADE LEVEL
6-8

FIRST NAME

LAST NAME

[1] What organism are you responsible for? ....

[2] What does this organism eat? ....

....

[3] What information do you need to calculate the ppm of mercury in the body of your organism? (four things)

a. ....

b. ....

c. ....

d. ....

[4] Use this space to try to figure out an equation for calculating the ppm of mercury in an organism.

[5] Write the correct equation here.

APPROVED BY

16 | It Adds Up and Up

GRADE LEVEL
6-8

FIRST NAME																		
LAST NAME																		

Biomagnification in the Food Chain

ORGANISM	MASS	# PREY EATEN	PPM METHYLMERCURY
Lake Trout (predator fish)	100 oz. (10 times the weight of yellow perch)	100 yellow perch	
Yellow Perch (forage fish)	10 oz. (100 times the weight of diporeia)	10,000 diporeia	
Diporeia (zooplankton)	.1 oz (10 times the weight of algae)	1,000 algae	
Algae	.01 oz	Not applicable	.0001

$$\frac{\text{Weight of Prey (oz)}}{1} \times \frac{\text{Methylmercury ppm in Prey}}{1} \times \frac{\text{Number of Prey Eaten}}{\text{Weight of Predator (oz)}} = X$$

[6] Now plug in the numbers:

$$\frac{\quad\quad oz}{1} \times \frac{\quad\quad ppm}{1} \times \frac{\quad\quad}{\quad\quad oz} = \frac{\quad\quad ppm}{\quad\quad}$$

The U.S. EPA (Environmental Protection Agency) has released a statement recommending people not eat any organisms with greater than 3 ppm methylmercury. Any concentration higher than this is harmful to humans.

[7] In the classroom example, would the yellow perch be safe for humans to eat? Why?

....

[8] What about the lake trout? Why? ....

....

APPROVED BY	

16 | It Adds Up and Up

GRADE LEVEL
6-8

journal ≡ pages

FIRST NAME																			
LAST NAME																			

Biomagnification in the Food Chain

ORGANISM	MASS	# PREY EATEN	PPM METHYLMERCURY
Lake Trout (predator fish)	100 oz. (10 times the weight of smelt)	100 smelt	
Smelt (forage fish)	10 oz. (100 times the weight of mysis)	10,000 mysis	
Mysis (zooplankton)	.1 oz (10 times the weight of algae)	1,000 algae	
Algae	.01 oz	- - -	.00005

$$\frac{\text{Weight of prey (oz)}}{1} \times \frac{\text{Methylmercury ppm in Prey}}{1} \times \frac{\text{Number of Prey Eaten}}{\text{Weight of Predator (oz)}} = X$$

[9] Now plug in the numbers: Solve for mercury ppm in zooplankton.

$$\frac{\quad\quad oz}{1} \times \frac{\quad\quad ppm}{1} \times \frac{\quad\quad}{\quad\quad oz} = \quad\quad ppm$$

[10] Solve for mercury ppm in forage fish.

$$\frac{\quad\quad oz}{1} \times \frac{\quad\quad ppm}{1} \times \frac{\quad\quad}{\quad\quad oz} = \quad\quad ppm$$

[11] Solve for mercury ppm in predator fish.

$$\frac{\quad\quad oz}{1} \times \frac{\quad\quad ppm}{1} \times \frac{\quad\quad}{\quad\quad oz} = \quad\quad ppm$$

[12] Are these organisms safe for humans to eat according to the U.S. EPA?

....

....

APPROVED BY	

16 | It Adds Up and Up

GRADE LEVEL
6-8

journal pages

FIRST NAME																			
LAST NAME																			

[1] News Article Title: ....

....

[2] Source: ....

....

[3] State the main idea/argument of your article. Summarize the points that support the main idea.

a. ....

....

....

....

....

....

b. ....

....

....

....

....

....

c. ....

....

....

....

....

....

APPROVED BY	

16 | It Adds Up and Up

GRADE LEVEL
6-8

| FIRST NAME | | | | | | | | | | | | | | | | | | | |
| LAST NAME | | | | | | | | | | | | | | | | | | | |

Write a story describing a simple lake food chain and the biomagnification of a fat-soluble toxin within that food chain from the perspective of one of the organisms. Include 2-3 action steps to correct the mercury problem.

APPROVED BY

16 | It Adds Up and Up

GRADE LEVEL
6-8

FIRST NAME																				
LAST NAME																				

Based on your article and the class discussion, answer the following questions as best as you can. Use extra paper if necessary.

[1] How is mercury released into the atmosphere? ....

....

[2] How does it get from the air into the lake? ....

....

[3] What is the effect of mercury in the lake? ....

....

[4] What effect does mercury have on humans? ....

....

[5] What would result if the amount of mercury released into the atmosphere were reduced?

....

....

[6] What is being done to reduce the amount of mercury released into the air and water?

....

[7] Who are the major players involved in mercury pollution? ....

....

[8] What are their points of view? ....

....

[9] Given the effects of mercury, why would some people resist efforts to control it? What might compel them to re-think their position?

....

....

[10] What steps can be taken to reduce the amount of mercury in the lake? ....

....

APPROVED BY	

INVESTIGATE: FINAL PROJECT

17 | Building a Web

GRADE LEVEL

K-8

varies

Developmental Modifications: Modify the assignment based on student age, ability and activities previously completed in this unit.

summary

As a class, students create a food web model that includes their research organism and additional details they have learned. Students may be assessed individually based on their ideas and contributions.

objectives

- Synthesize information and concepts learned during the unit.
- Coherently present what had been learned.

prerequisite

Several activities in the Lake Ecology Unit.

vocabulary

None

setting

INDOORS

subjects

Ecology, Art, Language Arts

standards

This Great Lakes in My World activity is aligned to the Common Core State Standards and to state learning standards in:

Illinois
Indiana
Michigan
Minnesota
New York
Ohio
Pennsylvania
Wisconsin

This alignment is available on your Great Lakes in My World CD in the "Standards" folder and on-line at http://www.greatlakes.org/ GLiMWstandards.

materials

- Journals
- Creature Cards
- Art supplies

background

There are many ways to model a food web. The important thing about this class model will be that it demonstrates the concepts learned during the unit. For example, the web must show that organisms are interconnected and must be set up in such a way that demonstrates the elasticity and complexity of the system. It is also important that information on organisms is accurate. Students may be creative with this project—it might be a two- or three-dimensional model. It could take the shape of a puzzle, a web, a mural or another idea.

procedure

1. As a class, discuss what type of models could represent the food web and then come to a consensus on one. Students should create a list of needed materials.
2. Students make a list of essential concepts that their food web should demonstrate. These should be concepts that were learned in the unit. Older students may challenge themselves by including invasive species and pollutants, and demonstrating the impacts of them.
3. Each student's journal should by now include a drawing of their organism, a list of research questions and answers to the questions. These answers may be in the form of writing, diagrams, charts, etc.
4. If making a class model, student should contribute a drawing (or 3-D model) of their organism. Students may be creative with this.
5. Students should also choose information to contribute that they have gathered about their organisms. This should be information that was gathered during research that is not inherent in the design of the food web model. For example, a list of predator/prey relationships would be redundant. Information should be presented in a way that is clear, concise and easy for other people to understand.
6. Students should refer back to their concept list to be sure the food web model incorporates central concepts from the unit. For example, organisms should be interconnected, the web should show that nutrients cycle through the ecosystem, etc. If the model covers all of the concepts on the students' list, as well as and individual research information, students will know they have done a good job.

wrap-up

1. Display the final food web model in the school or another local venue (library, shopping center, local events) to showcase students' work.
2. As a part of their final assessment, sixth through eighth grade students should write an essay explaining what they have learned in the unit.

extension

Have students use their models to teach students in other classes what they have learned.

assessment

Rubric on page 88

CONNECT   1 | Lake Connection

ELEMENTS	☆☆☆☆	☆☆☆	☆☆	☆
EMOTIONAL SKETCHES: Student draws an emotional sketch of how s/he was feeling at the moment and how s/he felt about the lake. Student includes a describing word for both sketches.	Addresses all of the components	Missing one component	Missing two components	Missing three or more components
FREE-WRITE: Student free-write and sharing explores his/her connection to the lake. The free-write addresses current perceptions of the lake and includes interactions with the lake. The free-write is appropriate in length with accurate spelling and grammar.	Addresses all of the components	Missing one component	Missing two components	Missing three or more components

CONNECT   2 | I Am a Camera

ELEMENTS	☆☆☆☆	☆☆☆	☆☆	☆
ARTWORK: Student selects an appropriate aspect of the lake to demonstrate his/her connection to the lake. Student's artwork reflects attention to detail and careful observation. Personal investment is obvious.	Addresses all of the components	Missing one component	Missing two components	Missing three or more components
DISCUSSION: Student is able to explain his/her selection. Student articulates concepts and questions that arise from artwork. Student uses active listening skills (eye-contact, confirming or referencing others' comments, affirmative gestures or comments).	Addresses all of the components	Missing one component	Missing two components	Missing three or more components

CONNECT   3 | Maps of Home

ELEMENTS	☆☆☆☆	☆☆☆	☆☆	☆
MAPPING: Student creates a place map indicating the school, his/her home and the lake. The map is detailed and specific. The map includes a key.	Addresses all of the components	Missing one component	Missing two components	Missing three or more components
DIRECTIONS: Student lists the correct directions from the school to the lake using the cardinal directions. Student accurately assesses the distance from the school to the lake. Student determines the best mode to travel from the school to the lake	Addresses all of the components	Missing one component	Missing two components	Missing three or more components
DISCUSSION: Student articulates concepts and questions that arose from mapping. Student articulates misconceptions about the proximity to the lake. Student uses active listening skills (eye-contact, confirming or referencing others' comments, affirmative gestures or comments).	Addresses all of the components	Missing one component	Missing two components	Missing three or more components

EXPLORE   4 | Watershed Orientation

ELEMENTS	☆☆☆☆	☆☆☆	☆☆	☆
WATERSHED DIAGRAM: Student draws an accurate diagram of his/her local watershed or "tablecloth" watershed. The drawing includes appropriate boundaries, names and directions of the major tributaries flowing into the Great Lakes, and any major natural areas and/or landforms. Student included a key.	Addresses all of the components	Missing one component	Missing two components	Missing three or more components
WATERSHED ESSAY: Student's essay explains what a watershed is and how watersheds are determined. Student includes a description of the location of his/her watershed in relation to the Great Lakes and the world. The essay has accurate spelling and grammar.	Addresses all of the components	Missing one component	Missing two components	Missing three or more components

EXPLORE   5 | Satisfy Your Curiosity

ELEMENTS	☆☆☆☆	☆☆☆	☆☆	☆
KNOWLEDGE GAINED	Student includes at least two new insights for each activity. The insights built upon the previous activity's experiences.	Student includes at least two new insights for 75% of the activities. Most of the insights builds upon the previous activity's experiences.	Student poses different questions for 50% of the activities. Less than half of the questions pertain to the species role in the food web.	Student poses different questions for less than 25% of the activities. None of the questions pertain to the species role in the food web.
QUESTIONS	Student poses different questions for each activity. More than half of the questions pertain to the species role in the food web.	Student poses different questions for 75% of the activities. Half of the questions pertain to the species role in the food web.	Student answered half of the questions.	Student answeres less than 25% of the questions.
LEARNINGS	Student answers all of the questions.	Student answers 75% of the questions.	Student correctly identifiesthe sources used for half of the journal pages.	Student correctly identifies the sources used for less than 25% of the journal pages.
SOURCES	Student correctly identifies the sources used for all research.	Student correctly identifies the sources Student includes at least two new insights for 75% of the activities. Only some of the insights address the knowledge gained in the previous activity.	Student correctly identifies the sources Student includes at least two new insights for 50% of the activities. Only some of the insights address the knowledge gained in the previous activity.	Student includes at least two new insights for less than 25% of the activities. The insights are not coherent and/or did not relate to the knowledge gained in previous activities.

EXPLORE   6 | Eco-Language

ELEMENTS	☆☆☆☆	☆☆☆	☆☆	☆
EXAMPLES AND DEFINITIONS: Student writes definitions and draws an example for each term.	Correct for all terms	Correct for 8-10 terms	Correct for 5-7 terms	Correct drawings for four or less terms
STORY: Story contains illustrations and definitions of "eco-language" words. Storyline is coherent and has a plot.	Addresses all of the components	Missing one component	Missing two components	Missing three or more components
READING AND FEEDBACK: Student actively participates in class discussions and read his/her story. Student gives and accepts feedback. Student uses active listening skills (eye-contact, confirming or referencing others' comments, affirmative gestures or comments).	Addresses all of the components	Missing one component	Missing two components	Missing three or more components

EXPLORE **7 | A Closer Look**

ELEMENTS	☆☆☆☆	☆☆☆	☆☆	☆
SPECIES SKETCH: Student replicates the drawing of the organism from the Creature Card. Student provides the organism's name and relevant characteristics that enables the student to identify live organisms.	Addresses all of the components	Missing one component	Missing two components	Missing three or more components
QUESTIONS: Student poses three questions about microscopic creatures using the 5 W's (who, what, where, when and how).	Includes three W questions	Missing one W question	Missing two W questions	Missing three or more components
MICROSCOPIC SKETCH: Student sketches a detailed drawing of his/her slide. Student includes the level of magnification and observation field. Student uses color to enhance the sketch.	Addresses all of the components	Missing one component	Missing two components	Missing three or more components
ANSWERS: Student answers all three W questions using personal observations and/or research materials. If research materials are used, sources are credited correctly.	Addresses all of the components	Missing one component	Missing two components	Missing three or more components

EXPLORE **8 | Fish Observation**

ELEMENTS	☆☆☆☆	☆☆☆	☆☆	☆
QUESTIONS: Student poses three questions about fish using the 5 W's (who, what, where, when and how).	Includes three W questions	Missing one W question	Missing two W questions	Missing three W questions
FISH SKETCH: Student sketches a detailed drawing of the fish. Student includes the length and height using the metric system. Student uses color to enhance the sketch.	Addresses all of the components	Missing one component	Missing two components	Missing three or more components
ANSWERS: Student answers all three W questions using personal observations and/or research materials. If research materials are used, sources are correctly identifies where necessary.	Addresses all of the components	Missing one component	Missing two components	Missing three or more components
FISH COMPARISON: Student correctly identifies both fishes' roles in the food web. Student supports his/her conclusion through observations and knowledge gained through the questions. Student is able to compare and contrast both fishes as well as define these fishes' relationship to each other and the food web.	Addresses all of the components	Missing one component	Missing two components	Missing three or more components

EXPLORE **9 | Web of Life**

ELEMENTS	☆☆☆☆	☆☆☆	☆☆	☆
PARTICIPATION: Student actively participates in both the food web activity and class discussion. Student references knowledge gained from the activity and made connections to his/her organism. Student uses active listening skills (eye-contact, confirming or referencing others' comments, affirmative gestures or comments).	Addresses all of the components	Missing one component	Missing two components	Missing three or more components
FOOD WEB DIAGRAM: The student makes logical connections between organisms in his/her food web.	Addresses all of the components	Missing one component	Missing two components	Missing three or more components

EXPLORE   **10 | Tangled Web**

ELEMENTS	☆☆☆☆	☆☆☆	☆☆	☆
PARTICIPATION: Student actively participates in both the food web activity and class discussion. Student references knowledge gained from the activity and makes connections to his/her organism. Student uses active listening skills (eye-contact, confirming or referencing others' comments, affirmative gestures or comments).	Addresses all of the components	Missing one component	Missing two components	Missing three or more components
FOOD WEB DIAGRAM: Student includes at least eight organisms in his/her food web. The food web includes several food chains, used arrows to indicate who eats whom, and includes all levels (decomposers, producers, herbivores, omnivores, carnivores, scavengers).	Addresses all of the components	Missing one component	Missing two components	Missing three or more components
ESSAY: Student was able to articulate how his/her organism fits into the food web. Student is able to explain the impact changes have in the food web. The student is able to draw conclusions about what happens to a food web when organisms are eliminated.	Addresses all of the components	Missing one component	Missing two components	Missing three or more components

EXPLORE   **11 | What's New?**

ELEMENTS	☆☆☆☆	☆☆☆	☆☆	☆
GAME WRAP-UP: Student compares and contrasts the game being played before and after a new player arrives. Specific examples are noted in the description.	Addresses all of the components	Missing one component	Missing two components	Missing three or more components
NATIVE AND NON-NATIVE ORGANISMS: Student determines two specific ways a non-native organism impacts a food web. Student notes any impact the non-native may have on his/her organism and/or food sources. Answers are thorough and specific.	Includes three W questions	Missing one W question	Missing two W questions	Missing three or more components
FOOD WEB DIAGRAM: Student draws a food web that includes at least two non-native organisms. The student includes a brief description of the non-native organisms' impact on the food web with special consideration given to any role overlap with native organisms. The food web uses arrows to depict who eats whom.	Addresses all of the components	Missing one component	Missing two components	Missing three or more components

EXPLORE   **12 | Great Lakes Relay**

ELEMENTS	☆☆☆☆	☆☆☆	☆☆	☆
NUTRIENT CYCLING AND ENERGY FLOW DIAGRAMS: Student accurately depicts the nutrient and energy level in both diagrams. Student explains how these two diagrams are similar and how they are different.	Addresses all of the components	Missing one component	Missing two components	Missing three or more components
FOOD WEB: Student creates a food web with 3 species not found in the previous diagrams. Student correctly depicts how nutrient cycles and energy flows through this food web. Student correctly explains how nutrient cycles and energy flows through this food web.	Addresses all of the components	Missing one component	Missing two components	Missing three or more components

INVESTIGATE   13 | Invasive Issues

ELEMENTS	☆☆☆☆	☆☆☆	☆☆	☆
PARTICIPATION: Student actively participates in creating the class table. Student uses appropriate cooperative learning skills (participation in group discussion, affirmation of teammates' ideas, equal distribution of tasks). Student works with his/her group to create a new food web depicting the invasive species' impact on native species.	Addresses all of the components	Missing one component	Missing two components	Missing three or more components
SOLUTIONS: Student brainstorms eight possible solutions to minimize non-native organism's impact on the lake food web. Student selects one solution to articulate in the essay. All sources are credited correctly.	Addresses all of the components	Missing one component	Missing two components	Missing three or more components
ESSAY: Student identifies a specific non-native organism and at least three ways it impacts the lake food web. Student presented one possible solution to minimizing the non-native organism's impact. The essay is well developed and thorough. All ideas presented are supported with evidence from research. Spelling and grammar are accurate.	Addresses all of the components	Missing one component	Missing two components	Missing three or more components

INVESTIGATE   14 | Moving Mercury

ELEMENTS	☆☆☆☆	☆☆☆	☆☆	☆
DIAGRAM 1: Student creates a diagram that shows how mercury enters the Great Lakes. It includes the appropriate components and is labeled.	Addresses all of the components	Missing one component	Missing two components	Missing three or more components
DIAGRAM 2: Student creates a diagram that shows mercury being passed through the Great Lakes food web. It includes the appropriate components and is labeled.	Addresses all of the components	Missing one component	Missing two components	Missing three or more components
DEMONSTRATION: Student defines bioaccumulation and plan to illustrate the concept, using the materials provided.	Addresses all of the components	Missing one component	Missing two components	Missing three or more components
CONCEPT MAP: Student uses the vocabulary provided to make a concept map that shows an understanding of bioaccumulation and biomagnification of mercury in the Great Lakes. Map is labeled and has arrows and additional words that explain and portray an accurate understanding. There are minimal spelling and grammatical errors.	Addresses all of the components	Missing one component	Missing two components	Missing three or more components
SOLUTIONS: Student brainstorms five possible solutions for minimizing mercury pollution.	Addresses all of the components	Missing one component	Missing two components	Missing three or more components

INVESTIGATE 15 | Solubility

ELEMENTS	☆☆☆☆	☆☆☆	☆☆	☆
PARTICIPATION: Student forms a hypothesis and helps establish an experiment to test the solubility of three different substances in water. Student records results of the experiment.	Addresses all of the components	Missing one component	Missing two components	Missing three or more components
DISCUSSION: Student participates in discussion following the experiment, decides what mercury is soluble in and writes about problems that mercury poses for animals.	Addresses all of the components	Missing one component	Missing two components	Missing three or more components

INVESTIGATE 16 | It Adds Up and Up

ELEMENTS	☆☆☆☆	☆☆☆	☆☆	☆
PARTICIPATION: Student participates in sand grain activity to understand "parts per million" by measuring, searching and asking questions in the discussion that follows.	Addresses all of the components	Missing one component	Missing two components	Missing three or more components
CALCULATIONS and QUESTIONS: Student works with others to establish equation components. Student calculates the mercury in their species and completes the total equation. Student answers journal page questions.	Addresses all of the components	Missing one component	Missing two components	Missing three or more components
WRAP-UP: Student reads a news article, summarizes it in writing, teaches others about it and answers journal questions. Student writes a story describing the lake food chain and the biomagnification of a toxin within the chain. Understanding of the concepts is evident.	Addresses all of the components	Missing one component	Missing two components	Missing three or more components

INVESTIGATE 17 | Building a Web

ELEMENTS	☆☆☆☆	☆☆☆	☆☆	☆
PARTICIPATION: Student participates in discussion of food web models, creates a list of needed materials and essential concepts to be demonstrated by the food web.	Addresses all of the components	Missing one component	Missing two components	Missing three or more components
RESEARCH AND DESIGN: Student contributes past work and additional research to the food web model. Concepts include predator-prey relationships, nutrient cycling, energy flow and (as appropriate) impact of invasive species and pollution. Student makes a detailed illustration of 3-dimensional model for the food web.	Addresses all of the components	Missing one component	Missing two components	Missing three or more components
WRAP-UP: Students verifies that all necessary information is included and answers questions if presenting to others. Student (6-8) writes an essay that explains knowledge gained from this unit.	Addresses all of the components	Missing one component	Missing two components	Missing three or more components

Unit 2
Sand Dunes

The Pitcher's thistle (Cirsium pitcheri) has special adaptations, including a 6 foot tap root, that enable it to live in the sand dunes. It is threatened by loss of habitat due to increased human activity.

? essential questions

- **What is unique about the sand dune ecosystem?**
- **How are organisms and their surroundings interrelated?**
- **What species live at the sand dunes and how do they survive?**

unit overview

Students begin the unit by getting to know sand dunes through poetry, a sand dune "journey", and discussion of experiences with sand. They look closely at sand and design an experiment to understand how sand dunes are formed. A field trip (or in-class "field trip") to the dunes allows students to make observations of the species in the dunes, and begin to explore the idea of succession. Students investigate the ways personal decisions affect the dunes, and debate the sides of the issue of sand dune mining. During the unit, students formulate questions about dune organisms and their habitats to create an educational book for a final project that demonstrates an understanding of the changing dune habitats and species' adaptations.

concepts

⬤ Ecosystems change over time, sometimes gradually, and sometimes suddenly. Given time, species evolve in response to change in the environment, developing adaptations for survival. The organisms living at sand dunes are adapted to the conditions of this habitat.

⬤ Sand dunes are made up of connected, yet diverse, micro-ecosystems formed by sunlight, wind and waves, and change over time with the colonization of organisms.

⬤ Sand dunes are impacted by human actions and decisions, which can have both positive and negative implications for the ecosystem.

unit activities

CONNECT

1 | Dune Inspiration

GRADE LEVEL
K-8

30 minutes

Developmental Modifications: Use K-3 Journal pages. With younger students, use the group poem option in this activity. Try to use each of the student's words when creating the poem.

summary

Learn about sand dunes, share dune experiences and create haiku poetry about dunes.

objectives

• Share sand dune experiences.
• Describe personal connections to the sand dune ecosystem through poetry.

prerequisite

None

vocabulary

Haiku: an unrhymed verse form of Japanese origin having three lines containing usually 5, 7, and 5 syllables respectively
Habitat: a place where a plant or animal naturally lives or grows

setting

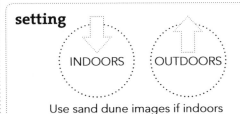

INDOORS   OUTDOORS

Use sand dune images if indoors

subjects

Earth Science, Geology, Social Studies

standards

This Great Lakes in My World activity is aligned to the Common Core State Standards and to state learning standards in:

Illinois
Indiana
Michigan
Minnesota
New York
Ohio
Pennsylvania
Wisconsin

This alignment is available on your Great Lakes in My World CD in the "Standards" folder and on-line at http://www.greatlakes.org/GLiMWstandards.

materials

• Pencil and journals
• Dune Images (on compact disc)
• Haiku guidelines on poster board or blackboard
• Note cards (if group option is used)
• Visual aids such as pictures (if indoors)
• Clipboards (if outdoors)

background

Haiku: "short Japanese poem: a form of Japanese poetry with 17 syllables in three unrhymed lines of five, seven, and five syllables, often describing nature or a season"

"Haiku," Microsoft® Encarta® Online Encyclopedia 2002 http://encarta.msn.com © 1997-2002 Microsoft Corporation. All Rights Reserved.

procedure

1. Ask students if anyone in the class has been to a sand dune. Have students share their experiences and memories. Ask if anyone has seen a sand dune in a movie or on TV. Have students share what they saw.
2. Use the following questions to introduce the unit and find out what students would like to know about sand dunes. Where would you go to find a dune? How is a sand dune like a beach? How is it different? How is a dune created? Can dunes change? Show photos from the compact disc.
3. Explain that dunes are made of sand and created by wind. Tell students that some are found in areas along the Great Lakes shoreline. Emphasize that a dune is a rare and changing habitat and supports unique plants and animals
4. As a class, practice brainstorming words that describe sand dunes and words that describe feelings about the dunes.
5. Students spend two minutes creating a list of words in their journals that describe sand dunes. Then, students spend two minutes creating a list of words in their journals that describe their feelings about the dunes.
6. Explain the format of a haiku poem and write guidelines on a poster board to bring to the beach. Poetry can still be considered "haiku," even if it does not adhere exactly to the 5-7-5 syllable format, but creates a feeling, mood, or image with words. Read examples of haiku poetry provided.

Individual Option

7. Have students spend 15 minutes creating a poem. In pairs, students share their poems, reading them aloud and comparing what is similar and what is different in the poems.

Group Option

7. Students each choose one word from their list to contribute to a class haiku and write this word on a note card. Students place their cards in a group on the ground or blackboard, where everyone can see. You will need approximately 8-16 words, depending on the number of syllables.
8. As a class, arrange the words into three lines. Allow for suggestions to move individual words. Record the class poem on paper or in journals and return note cards to students.

Poetry Examples

Temple bells die out.
The fragrant blossoms remain.
A perfect evening!
Matsuo Basho (1644-1694)

A giant firefly:
that way, this way, that way, this-
and it passes by.
Yoshi Mikami Issa (1762 - 1826)

You rice field maidens!
The only things not muddy
Are the songs you sing.
Raizan

No sky
no earth - but still
snowflakes fall
Hashin

Bugs
Beautiful, fat
Noisy, scary, crawling
Little, big, short, long.
Rachel Peterson, Grade 4
Central Elementary School, Muskegon

Michigan
Michigan is great
If you see the sparkling gate
Of deep, deep water.
Jacob Uetricht, Grade 4
Central Elementary School, Muskegon

Dunes
Rolling on the ground
The dune calls to all the plants
To join it today.
Samantha Peterson, Grade 4
Central Elementary School, Muskegon

wrap-up

1. Discuss with the class: Do students' poems capture their feelings about sand dunes?
2. How did this activity help students understand or talk about their personal connection to sand dunes and the lake?

assessment

Rubric on page 161

1 | Dune Inspiration

FIRST NAME

LAST NAME

[1] Words that describe the sand dunes:

[2] Words that describe your feelings about the dunes:

[3] Space for haiKu poem

APPROVED BY

1 | Dune Inspiration

FIRST NAME																					
LAST NAME																					

[1] Sand dune words

[2] Copy the poem:

APPROVED BY

CONNECT

2 | Making a Mark

GRADE LEVEL

4-8

30 minutes

Developmental Modifications: For younger students, skip procedure step #5 (journal questions #3 and #4).

summary

Students make marks in the sand and discuss how sand has made a mark on them.

objectives

- Recognize connections to the sand through reflection and sharing.
- Discuss sand dune experiences.
- Record responses to an experience.

prerequisite

None

vocabulary

Tread: to walk on or over; to walk along

setting

OUTDOORS

Beach

subjects

Art, Social Studies

standards

This Great Lakes in My World activity is aligned to the Common Core State Standards and to state learning standards in:

Illinois
Indiana
Michigan
Minnesota
New York
Ohio
Pennsylvania
Wisconsin

This alignment is available on your Great Lakes in My World CD in the "Standards" folder and on-line at http://www.greatlakes.org/ GLiMWstandards.

materials

- Pencils
- Journals
- Clipboards

background

Experiences, sights, sounds, feelings and relationships can all make lasting impressions on us. In this activity, students "play" in the sand to reflect on the importance of the sand dune ecosystem and discuss human impact on the Earth.

procedure

1. Ask students what it means to "make a mark."
   Explain that it has a physical meaning, such as writing your name on a piece of paper, but also means to make an impression or have an impact.

2. Demonstrate how easy it is to make a mark in moist sand. Tell students that they will be making their own marks in the sand while they think about how sand has made a mark on them. Explain that this mark can be a memory of sand, an experience in sand that was memorable, a story, a book, a movie, etc.

3. Have students spread out and spend 15 minutes on their own making a mark in the sand by digging, making footprints, building a sand castle or something else.

If there are two educators, split the class in half.

4. Have the students sit in a circle and describe the marks they made and how sand has marked, or made an impression on, them.

wrap-up

1. Consider the footprints the students have made in the sand. How do people make footprints, or leave marks, in other ways? Introduce the term "tread lightly" and explain that it is a phrase commonly used to remind people to reduce their impact on the environment. Explain that another frequently used phrase is, "Take only pictures and leave only footprints." Why is it important to tread lightly in natural areas? What marks can the beach erase and what marks cause permanent damage? What personal experiences do they have relating to damaged areas and how did it make them feel? What personal behavior can they adopt to tread lightly?

assessment

Rubric on page 161

 We value your thoughts and feedback on Great Lakes in My World. Please let us know about any oversights, errors or omissions you find, or if there are things you or your students particularly like.

Send your comments to: education@greatlakes.org

2 | Making a Mark

GRADE LEVEL
4-8

journal pages

FIRST NAME

LAST NAME

[1] What Kind of marK did you maKe in the sand?

[2] What Kind of memory, story, or experience does sand maKe you thinK of?

[3] Why is it important to tread lightly in natural areas?

[4] What personal behavior can you adopt to tread lightly?

APPROVED BY

CONNECT

3 | Dune Journey

GRADE LEVEL

3-6

Developmental Modifications: For younger students, do only the first two journal questions.

summary

Explore sand dunes through imagery and create a picture or diagram of the "journey."

objectives

- Visualize the sand dune ecosystem.
- Represent sand dunes through a picture or diagram.

prerequisite

None

vocabulary

Foredune: in a series of coastal dunes, the dune closest to the front
Backdune: dune at the end of a series of sand dunes
Trough: a long shallow depression between hills; also known as a swale; called an interdunal pond when filled with water

setting

↓

INDOORS

subjects

Earth Science, Geology, Social Studies

standards

This Great Lakes in My World activity is aligned to the Common Core State Standards and to state learning standards in:

Illinois
Indiana
Michigan
Minnesota
New York
Ohio
Pennsylvania
Wisconsin

This alignment is available on your Great Lakes in My World CD in the "Standards" folder and on-line at http://www.greatlakes.org/ GLiMWstandards.

materials

- Story (on next page)
- Recorded sound of waves (on compact disc)
- Art supplies
- Journals
- Pencils
- Clipboards if outdoors,
- Map of the Great Lakes (p. 17)

background

Coastal sand dunes are a biologically diverse and beautiful ecosystem. The glaciers, which covered the Great Lakes basin for over a million years, provided the major source of sand for the area's sand dunes. Lake Michigan's rare, internationally distinctive dunes were created over 10,000 years ago as the glaciers receded and the wind blew sand along the shore. The dunes took years to form, and the circumstances that created them are extremely unusual. The eastern shoreline of Lake

Michigan contains the largest concentration of freshwater dunes in the world. Dunes are also found in other Great Lakes locations such as Whitefish Dune State Park in Wisconsin, along the northern shore of Lake Michigan, and Grand Sable Dunes at Picture Rocks National Lakeshore. *Refer to resource list references for more detail on dune areas in the Great Lakes.*

procedure

1. Ask students what they know about sand. They may have many associations with sand. Create a list of their thoughts. Guide the process with the following questions: Where does sand come from? Where are areas made entirely of sand? What makes sand interesting?

2. Have students close their eyes and listen to the following description of sand dunes. If you have a recording of waves, play this as background.

Dune Hike
Imagine you are at the beach. Even if you have never been to the beach, think about what it would be like. Your bare feet push into the cool, wet sand. It feels soft under your toes. You hear the waves crashing into the shore. As you walk away from the water, you see hills of sand, called sand dunes. They are beautiful and mysterious. They look fun. There are long, green and brown grasses growing on them. You wonder why there seems to be so much grass growing in sand.

There is a path leading up the side of one of these hills. You decide to take it. The sand is very warm and dry on your feet. The sound of the waves grows dim. It is very quiet. You feel the wind in your hair. You notice that your hair is not the only thing affected by the wind. The sand is, too. You watch some sand grains skipping along, playing leapfrog with other sand grains, until they are all captured by the tall dune grass on the hill. This first dune is called the foredune.

As you walk along the path, you see the dunes create a series of hills that lead away from the beach. You wonder where all

this sand came from. As you continue to walk, the sun shines warmly on your skin. The only sound you hear is of a gull in the far distance. You notice that the dune now dips down into a low area, called a trough (rhymes with cough), which has water in it. You cool your feet in the water and wonder what sort of animals might live in the dunes or might be living in this pond in the trough.

Your heart begins to pound as you climb the second hill of sand, and when you reach the top you turn and look toward the lake. The spot on the beach where you once stood seems so small and you can see far over the lake. You feel as if you have the vision of a bird high in the sky. You turn to continue your journey across the dunes. You hike up and down the hills until you enter a shady forest. You sit down under a tree in the backdune forest and take a rest from your hike. You notice that even here, in the woods, it is sandy.

3. Have students draw part of, or the whole, journey they made in their imaginations. Have them write one or two words that describe how the journey made them feel.

4. After students finish drawing, draw a side view of the "journey" on the board (lake, beach, foredune, trough and backdune), or make the diagram from this activity into an overhead. Explain to students that some areas around the Great Lakes have the same type of sand dune ecosystem that they just "hiked" through. Ask students to identify which area they illustrated (according to the diagram) and label it on their drawing.

wrap-up

1. Students should share their drawings with a partner. If time permits, several students can share their drawings with the class.
2. For 4-6 graders, either have the students fill out the journal page, or use the questions on it to lead a discussion. Ask students how beautiful places like this can make our lives better.

3. Most of the sand dunes in the Great Lakes basin occur along the east side of Lake Michigan. Show students a map that includes this area. Have them locate Michigan and the area where the dunes are found. Additional dunes are found in Indiana, Wisconsin and on the northern portion of the Illinois shoreline. Locate these spots as well.

assessment

Rubric on page 161

3 | Dune Journey

GRADE LEVEL
3-6

journal | pages

FIRST NAME																			
LAST NAME																			

[1] Draw a picture of sand dunes.

[2] Describe your feelings about sand dunes:

....

....

....

....

....

....

....

....

APPROVED BY	

3 | Dune Journey

GRADE LEVEL
3-6

journal ≡ pages

FIRST NAME																						
LAST NAME																						

[3] Which part of the dunes did you draw?

....

....

....

[4] How did it feel to be on this journey?

....

....

....

[5] If you have never been to some dunes, was it difficult to imagine them?

....

....

....

....

[6] If you have been to dunes, did the description match what you remember?

....

....

....

[7] Based on what you Know so far, what is special or unique about dunes?

....

....

....

....

....

....

....

APPROVED BY	

EXPLORE

4 | Satisfy Your Curiosity

GRADE LEVEL

K-8

ongoing

Developmental Modifications: Included in the activity

summary

During the unit, students conduct an in-depth study on a sand dune species. The teacher arranges for this research to take place, e.g., dune field trip, library time, museum visit, guest speaker. The resulting information can be used in the students' final projects.

objectives

- Formulate research questions.
- Conduct research using varied sources.
- Describe the natural history of a dune species in detail.

prerequisite

Dune Inspiration or Sand Dune Journey

vocabulary

Ecology: a branch of science concerned with relationships between living things and their environment

Species: related organisms or populations potentially capable of reproducing fertile offspring

Adaptation: change in an organism or its parts that fits it better for the conditions of its environment; a structure resulting from this change

setting

INDOORS   OUTDOORS

subjects

Ecology, Environmental Science, Biology

standards

This Great Lakes in My World activity is aligned to the Common Core State Standards and to state learning standards in:

Illinois
Indiana
Michigan
Minnesota
New York
Ohio
Pennsylvania
Wisconsin

This alignment is available on your Great Lakes in My World CD in the "Standards" folder and on-line at http://www.greatlakes.org/ GLiMWstandards.

materials

- Creature Cards
- Journal pages
  (several copies per student)
- Research materials
- Resource people
- Sand dune diagram, page 122

background

Each coastal dune species has a unique natural history and set of adaptations. Life cycles may be short and simple, or long and complex. Adaptations may range from the sublime to the bizarre. Each animal species eats something and, in return, is eaten by something. And each species has the role of producer, consumer, or decomposer. Species geographical range, population status and evolutionary and ecological relationships with other species also offer fascinating insights into the complexity and richness of the dune ecosystem. For this activity, select information on each organism can be found on the Creature Cards. Research can be done through observation, the internet, community speakers, books, journals, and field trips. Local nature centers and museums may be willing to work with students on their research. They may also have observable specimens. See the resource list for specific titles.

procedure

1. Educators should read through the final project: Living Dune (4-8) or Life in the Dunes (K-3) to understand where this project is headed. Students' work from this activity can be used for the final project. Schedule several different sessions and methods for the species research. Using the Creature Cards and dune diagram provided (page 122), choose as many cards as there are children, making sure that the four dune areas are represented.

2. Tell the students they are going to have the opportunity to become experts on the ecology of one kind of plant or animal that lives in a coastal dune ecosystem. Introduce and explain the term "species," and give examples to help the students understand what it means. Explain that many ecologists (scientists who study the natural world) study one species, becoming respected authorities on that subject.

   For younger students (K-3), tell them they will have the chance to become experts on one type of plant or animal that lives in the dunes.

3. Using the cards provided, assign one species to each student, being sure to represent the four dune regions. Explain that students will have several opportunities during their dune studies to learn more about their species, and they should always be on the lookout for information about it. Explain that one thing they should become familiar with is their species' adaptations. Explain this word and give some examples (e.g. the camouflage color of a toad, the fins of a fish, the poisonous body of a monarch butterfly).

   For younger students (K-3), consider dividing the class into groups and assign one species to each group. Describe an adaptation as anything special that helps a plant or animal survive, such as a woodpecker's sharp beak, or a deer's camouflage fur. Ask if they can guess an adaptation for specific plants and animals.

4. Using journal pages, challenge each of the students to write two good scientific questions about their species, that require more than a "yes or no" response. These questions should require research in order to answer them. One of the questions should be about its adaptations. Other questions could focus on the species' life cycle, position in the food web, geographical distribution, population status, ecological role, evolutionary relationships and method for surviving the winter.

   For younger students (K-3), write "Where does my species live?" on the blackboard and have them copy it in their journals. Have students think of another question they could ask and help them write it in their journals. Consider these: What does my species have that makes it look special? How does my species survive in the winter? How does my species avoid getting eaten? How does my species get food?

5. Offer a variety of sessions and methods for research. Use the other activities in this unit as opportunities for students to gather additional information on the species.

   For younger students (K-3), include some good picture books. See resource list for recommendations.

6. Every time students complete a dune activity, reserve time so that they can use the knowledge gained to fill out another Satisfy Your Curiosity journal page on their species and create additional questions to research. For older students (4-8), at least half of the questions should pertain to the species' adaptations. Students should keep in mind that their species may use more than one ecosystem. For example, herring gulls nest in dunes, but travel to the lake and other areas to find food. Allow this movement to add another dimension to the students' research.

wrap-up

1. Save information and research from this activity for students' final projects.

assessment

Rubric on page 162

4 | Satisfy Your Curiosity

GRADE LEVEL
K-8

journal ≣ pages

FIRST NAME																			
LAST NAME																			

[1] I Know:

a.

b.

[2] I want to Know:

a.

b.

[3] I learned:

a.

b.

Sources:

APPROVED BY	

EXPLORE

5 | Sand Study

GRADE LEVEL
3-6

45 minutes

Developmental Modifications: For younger students, use the K-2 journal pages. The focus on designing an experiment can be toned down.

summary

Students learn how sand is formed by making some from rocks. They then examine and sketch the sand.

objectives

- Form a hypothesis.
- Explain how sand is formed.

prerequisite

Dune Inspiration, Making a Mark or Sand Dune Journey

vocabulary

Erosion: the breaking down of materials through wind and water action
Hypothesis: something not proved, but assumed to be true for purposes of further study or investigation
Scientific method: methods for the pursuit of knowledge involving the finding and stating of a problem, the collection of facts through observation and experiment, and the making and testing of ideas that need to be proven right or wrong
Sediment: material, such as sand or stones deposited by water, wind, or glaciers
Weathering: to expose to the weather; to change by exposure

setting

INDOORS   OUTDOORS

subjects

Earth Science, Geology

standards

This Great Lakes in My World activity is aligned to the Common Core State Standards and to state learning standards in:

Illinois
Indiana
Michigan
Minnesota
New York
Ohio
Pennsylvania
Wisconsin

This alignment is available on your Great Lakes in My World CD in the "Standards" folder and on-line at http://www.greatlakes.org/ GLiMWstandards.

materials

- Coffee can with lid
- Rocks
- Journals
- Pencils
- Magnifying glasses and/or microscopes
- Clipboards (if outdoors)
- Sandstone
- Sheet
- Tarp or large pieces of butcher paper

background

Great Lakes sand comes from different kinds of rocks and minerals.
In a handful of Great Lakes sand, the breakdown is approximately:

87%	10%	2-3%	Less than 1%
Quartz (many colors: white, clear, yellow, purple, green, brown)	Feldspar (cream, white, gray)	Magnetite (gray, black, brown)	Garnet (red) Calcite (white) Ilmenite (brown, black) Hornblende (green, brown, black) Epidote (yellow, green, brown, black)

procedure

1. Note: Because of the short amount of time given to create sand, this activity is most successful if a piece of sandstone is added to the container.

2. Take students outside and ask them to each collect one rock, or have the rocks ready for the students in the classroom. Tell students that all of their rocks will go into a coffee can. Show them that the container is empty.

3. Students should sit in a circle on the floor. Have the students make one observation (hard, rough, smooth, gray, small) about their rock as they put it in the coffee container. When all the rocks are in the container, tell students they will each be shaking the container 3-5 times, with the lid on.

4. Ask them to tell the person next to them what they predict will happen to the rocks. Will anything change inside the coffee can? This is a hypothesis.

5. When the shaking is finished, pour the rocks out onto a large piece of butcher paper or a sheet. After all the rocks pour out, a small amount of sand should come out as well.

6. Ask the students to work with a partner to explain: Where did the sand in the can come from? If students have trouble, explain that all sand comes from larger rocks. Explain that the process that happened inside the can is called erosion. When rocks are rubbed by wind, water, or other rocks, they wear down and sediment is formed. Ask students to work with their partner to figure out how they think sand at the beach and dunes got there.

7. As a class discussion, respond to the journal questions so that students see that rocks can be broken down into sand through hitting other rocks, which is caused by wind and water action. Have the students summarize the information in their journal pages.

wrap-up

1. Have students look at a few grains of sand through a magnifying glass and/or under a microscope. Have students draw three grains of magnified sand in their journals.

2. Ask them to list several words that describe each grain. Ask students to think about how the grains are different from each other. Why are they different from each other? How are they similar to the rocks in the can?

3. Complete the journal page questions.

(!) We value your thoughts and feedback on Great Lakes in My World. Please let us know about any oversights, errors or omissions you find, or if there are things you or your students particularly like.

Send your comments to: education@greatlakes.org

assessment

Rubric on page 162

5 | Sand Study

GRADE LEVEL
K-2

journal pages

FIRST NAME																				
LAST NAME																				

[1] Draw your rock.

[2] Draw the sand grains.

[3] Write 2 words that describe the sand grains.

[4] DRAW OR WRITE: How is sand formed from rocks?

APPROVED BY

5 | Sand Study

FIRST NAME																				
LAST NAME																				

[1] Form a hypothesis: What do you predict will happen on the inside of the container?

....

....

....

....

[2] Method: How did you test your hypothesis?

....

....

....

....

[3] Results: What happened inside the container?

....

....

....

....

[4] Analysis: Why did this happen?

....

....

....

....

[5] Define Erosion:

....

....

....

....

....

APPROVED BY	

5 | Sand Study

FIRST NAME																							
LAST NAME																							

[1] How do you think that the sand in sand dunes is formed?

[2] Draw the grains of sand that you observed:

[3] Describe the sand grains. How are they different from each other?

[4] How are they similar to and different from the larger rocks?

[5] How do you think that the sand in sand dunes is formed?

APPROVED BY

EXPLORE

6 | Moving Sand

4-8

45 minutes

Developmental Modifications: For younger students (K-3), this should be done as a demonstration. Journal Pages are included for this age.

summary

Students are introduced to the scientific method, and use it to design and conduct experiments on dune-plant relationships.

objectives

- Form and test a hypothesis.
- Design an experiment.
- Explain the effect of wind on sand.
- Describe the role that marram grass plays in stabilizing sand dunes.

prerequisite

Dune Inspiration or Sand Dune Journey and Sand Study

vocabulary

Control experiment: an experiment in which all factors are treated in the same way, except the agent being tested, and which is used as a standard to compare with the results of another experiment

Data: facts that can be used in calculating, reasoning, or planning

Hypothesis: something not proved, but assumed to be true for purposes of further study or investigation

Scientific method: methods for the pursuit of knowledge involving the finding and stating of a problem, the collection of facts through observation and experiment, and the making and testing of ideas that need to be proven right or wrong scientific method

Stabilize: hold steady; make firm

Substrate: the base on which an organism lives

setting

This activity is messy and is best done outside or on a tarp indoors. An electrical source is necessary.

INDOORS   OUTDOORS

subjects

Earth Science, Ecology

standards

This Great Lakes in My World activity is aligned to the Common Core State Standards and to state learning standards in:

Illinois
Indiana
Michigan
Minnesota
New York
Ohio
Pennsylvania
Wisconsin

This alignment is available on your Great Lakes in My World CD in the "Standards" folder and on-line at http://www.greatlakes.org/ GLiMWstandards.

materials

- Aluminum pans
- Hair dryers
- Safety glasses
- Stop watches
- Sand
- Clumps of grass (with roots)
- Pieces of graph paper taped onto cardboard
- Pencils
- Large tarp (if indoors)
- Straws or hair dryers
- Extension cord for hair dryers

background

It has taken thousands of years for the dunes along the Great Lakes to form through a unique combination of wind, water and vegetation that moves, sorts, and traps sand particles. Marram grass (*Ammophila breviligulata*) requires burial by sand for optimal growth, making it one of the primary plants for dune stabilization and formation.

Advance preparation: Please note that there are two ways to do this activity, a low-tech and a high-tech version. In the low-tech version, use straws instead of hair dryers. With straws, the activity can be done on a smaller scale, so smaller pans and a smaller grass species than marram grass can be used. In either case, students should wear goggles or safety glasses and keep their straws or hair dryers pointed low.

procedure

1. Ask students how they think sand dunes are formed. How long do they think it takes? Why would it be important to understand how dunes are formed? *Explain that dunes are formed through wind and water moving the sand. This happens over long periods of time.*

2. Divide students into groups of four. Show students the pans, sand and straws or hair dryers. Ask students how they could create a demonstration of how a sand dune is formed. Record responses on the board. *They could put sand in the pan, then blow on it with the straw or hair dryer until a mound is formed.* Ask students what they think would happen if they kept blowing after the mound was formed. *The sand would blow away.* Ask students why sand dunes are able to exist without just blowing away.

3. If the class has not visited sand dunes yet, show them some photos. Ask students what they see on the dunes. *Marram grass.* Ask students if they think the grass has any impact on the stability of the dune. *Marram grass is able to grow in the sand, and its roots stabilize the dune by trapping blown sand, and then other plants are able to grow.*

4. Ask students, in their small groups, to design an experiment that shows how sand dunes maintain stability, without blowing away. Introduce the concept of the scientific method and its essential components.

5. Have groups share their ideas and record responses on the board. They should come to a consensus as a class as to the best possible experiment design. Once the class has

agreed on a procedure, have students outline the following information in their journal pages and write in any responses they know so far (up to results and conclusion):

Our experiment suggestion:
* In each group of four, there should be the following roles:
  – Hair Dryer or Straw Operator   – Timer
  – Recorder   – Direction Giver

a. Each group should set up two aluminum pans with sand, one with grass (experimental set-up) and one without (control set-up). The sand should start out in minimal dune-like piles. Place the grass roots into the sand in the pan. Stand the graph paper up along the side of the pan.

b. The direction giver reads out the steps of the student-written procedure and assists when necessary.

c. The hair dryer or straw operator blows at a low intensity on each pan for 6 intervals of 10 seconds, which the timer should measure. The "wind" applied to each "dune" must be the exact same intensity and duration.

* After each interval, the recorder should carefully trace the outline of the "dune" on the graph paper, being careful not to disturb the dune, and label each outline. The recorder should also make any other relevant notes.

* Once this is completed, the group should review the data and write up a conclusion.

wrap-up

1. Have the class discuss their results. What was the difference between the sand with and without the grass? Did the grass have an impact on the stability of the sand or not? What would happen if some of the marram grass disappeared under the sand? All of the marram grass? What is the relationship between the wind, sand and grass? *The wind moves the sand into dunes, which provide a substrate for the grass, which in turn holds the dunes in place. Together, they create the beginning of a habitat for many life forms.*

2. Now that the beginning of a habitat has been created, what else is needed for more organisms to colonize the dune? *Some responses might include: water (an interdunal pond), soil (this is created as the grass and other plants decompose, mixing organic material with the sand), food, shelter (these will come in the form of other plants and animals coming to the area).*

3. Ask students: if they visited the sand dunes, what types of living things might they find there? See Creature Cards for ideas.

assessment

Rubric on page 163

Contributing Author: Joyce Tuharsky

6 | Moving Sand

GRADE LEVEL
K-3

journal pages

FIRST NAME																				
LAST NAME																				

[1] DRAW a picture of a sand dune. Include: SAND and GRASS.

[2] DRAW other plants and animals you might find at the sand dunes.

[3] Why is marram grass important for the sand dune?

....

....

....

....

APPROVED BY	

6 | Moving Sand

GRADE LEVEL
4-8

journal pages

FIRST NAME																					
LAST NAME																					

[1] Objective: What is the reason you are doing this experiment?

....

....

....

[2] Hypothesis: What do you think will happen in this experiment and why?

....

....

....

[3] Materials: What will you need in order to conduct the experiment?

....

....

....

....

[4] Procedure: How will your experiment be done?

....

....

....

....

....

....

[5] Results: What happened?

....

....

....

....

....

[6] Draw a conclusion: What is the meaning of the results? Does the data support your
    hypothesis or not?

....

....

....

....

APPROVED BY	

EXPLORE

GRADE LEVEL
4-8

90 minutes

7 | Adaptations and Observations

Developmental Modification: Use K-3 Journal Pages. Younger students should be closely chaperoned and should focus only on adaptations, not the concept of succession.

summary

Students observe organisms in sand dune ecosystems and determine the adaptations that help them live there.

objectives

- Describe some of the specialized adaptations of sand dune organisms.
- Recognize the four regions of a sand dune ecosystem.
- List traits of the four regions in a sand dune ecosystem.

prerequisite

Sand Dune Journey

vocabulary

Abiotic: non-living
Organism: an individual living thing that carries on the activities of life by means of organs which have separate functions but are dependent on each other; a living person, plant, or animal
Mutation: an inherited change in genetic material
Ecosystem: communities of interacting organisms and abiotic (nonliving) components; an ecosystem can be as small as a rotting log or as large as an ocean; ecosystems are nested inside one another
Micro-ecosystem: A smaller ecosystem within a larger ecosystem
Succession: A series of natural changes in an ecological community; these changes occur because the living organisms and abiotic factors of the community bring about new conditions which are better suited for other organisms

setting

OUTDOORS

Sand dunes

subjects

Ecology, Biology, Environmental Science

standards

This Great Lakes in My World activity is aligned to the Common Core State Standards and to state learning standards in:

Illinois
Indiana
Michigan
Minnesota
New York
Ohio
Pennsylvania
Wisconsin

This alignment is available on your Great Lakes in My World CD in the "Standards" folder and on-line at http://www.greatlakes.org/GLiMWstandards.

materials

- Pencils
- Notebooks
- Sand Dune Creature Cards (do not have asterisk*)
- Sand Dune Diagram (page 122)
- Clipboards

background

The sand dune ecosystem has several different micro-ecosystems: beach, foredune, trough or interdunal pond, and backdune or forested dune. Many of the species that live in sand dune ecosystems are specialized and well-adapted to it. Before starting this activity, use the diagram (p. 122) to select the sand dune Creature Cards and divide them into groups by micro-ecosystem.

procedure

1. Take students on a walk through a sand dune ecosystem. Ask students to make silent observations as they walk. As the group enters each region of the sand dune ecosystem, the guide should announce it and make a few general remarks about its characteristics.

2. Students can refer to the drawings they made in their journals during Sand Dune Journey to see where they are in the dunes.

3. Explain that the changing ecosystems in the sand dunes are an example of succession, and define the term. Each ecosystem is made up of interacting organisms and abiotic (non-living) components that are specially adapted for that area.

4. Once the group has walked through the whole area, show the class four sand dune Creature Cards (one from each region). Have them guess which micro-ecosystem each organism lives in, based on their observations. Ask for reasons for the answers to assess the students' current knowledge and ideas. It will also guide them to begin to make critical observations.

5. In pairs, students choose a region for a more detailed visit. Have students answer questions on the first journal page for this part of the activity.

6. Proceed to the second journal page, again working in pairs.

   NOTE: Students observing the beach may become frustrated at the lack of organisms. They should understand that it may be challenging to find organisms, as it is difficult for any organisms to live in the beach habitat. They may focus on why this is the case. *It is an area of extreme change and little protection.*

7. Proceed to the third journal page.

8. Each pair joins join up with another pair who has been working in a different region. Each group is given eight Creature Cards to study: two from each of the micro-ecosystems. As a group of four, students figure out which organisms live in each of the sand dune areas. The group should use the knowledge that each student acquired in the different regions. As a group, for each organism, list two traits or characteristics that enable that species to live in the particular habitat.

wrap-up

1. Discuss the special characteristics that organisms have for living in the dunes. Do you think it is coincidental that these organisms are each perfectly suited for the environment in which they live? *Yes and no: while mutations in organisms are random, organisms selectively co-evolve with their environment.*

2. How do you think this happens and why? *If an organism is born with a genetic mutation that aids in its survival and ability to reproduce, it's likely to pass on the mutation to its offspring.*

3. Ask students to think of an example of a species from another habitat that is not suited to life in the dunes. What challenges would it face?

Discussion Questions for grades 6-8

4. How long do you think it might take for a species introduced to a new ecosystem to adapt? *Many generations. Introduced species generally do not do well or negatively impact other organisms by competing for resources. Would this have any impact on other organisms that are already established? How have humans adapted to their environments?*

> ## *Satisfy Your Curiosity* QUESTION IDEAS
>
> - *What special adaptations does my organism have?*
> - *What habitat is it best suited for and why?*
> - *Does my organism have specific interactions with other organisms for which it has developed special adaptations? What are they?*

assessment

Rubric on page 163

7 | Adaptations and Observations

GRADE LEVEL
K-3

journal pages

| FIRST NAME | | | | | | | | | | | | | | | | | | | | |
| LAST NAME | | | | | | | | | | | | | | | | | | | | |

[1] DRAW one animal and one plant.
[2] CIRCLE 2 adaptations in each picture.

Animal

Plant

[3] MaKe an X where you found the plant, maKe an O where you found the animal.

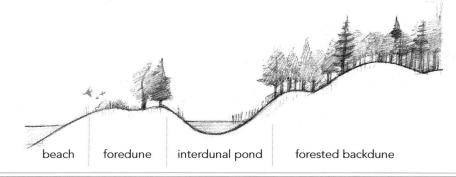

beach   foredune   interdunal pond   forested backdune

| APPROVED BY | |

7 | Adaptations and Observations

GRADE LEVEL
4-8

journal pages

FIRST NAME																			
LAST NAME																			

[1] Which region of the sand dunes are you observing? (Circle one)

beach   foredune   interdunal pond   forested backdune

[2] Do a two-minute sketch of the region you are in. Make a mark to indicate where you are in the dunes.

[3] What are three things that make this region different from other regions in the sand dunes?

a.
....

....

b.
....

....

c.
....

....

APPROVED BY	

7 | Adaptations and Observations

GRADE LEVEL
4-8

journal pages

FIRST NAME																						
LAST NAME																						

[1] For each pair of students, choose two organisms to observe: one plant and one animal. If no animals are visible within the first minute of observation, choose another plant to sketch instead. Sketch the chosen organisms.

[2] What makes these organisms well-suited for living in this ecosystem? For example, the gills of a fish make it well-suited for living underwater, and the spreading roots of marram grass make it well-suited for living in the sand.

....

....

[3] What makes this ecosystem a good place for plants and animals to live?

....

....

[4] What makes this ecosystem a difficult place for plants and animals to live?

....

....

[5] How are dune species better equipped than others to live in this ecosystem?

....

....

....

APPROVED BY	

7 | Adaptations and Observations

GRADE LEVEL
4-8

FIRST NAME																				
LAST NAME																				

Find another pair who has been working in a different sand dune region. Each group will be given Creature Cards to study from the different micro-ecosystems.

As a group of four, figure out which organisms live in each of the sand dune areas.

For each organism, groups list two characteristics that enable it to live in the particular micro-ecosystem (Micro-ecosystem choices: beach, foredune, interdunal pond or trough and backdune).

ORGANISM NAME	MICRO-ECOSYSTEM	CHARACTERISTIC 1	CHARACTERISTIC 2

APPROVED BY	

EXPLORE

GRADE LEVEL

8 | Indoor Dunes

4-8

60 minutes

Developmental Modification: For younger students in grades 4-5, keep the focus on adaptations, and less on the concept of succession.

summary

Students study Creature Cards at sand dune ecosystem stations and determine what adaptations help the organisms to live in their environments.

objectives

- List organisms that live in the dunes.
- Describe the specialized adaptations of sand dune organisms.
- Explain the different habitats in sand dunes.

prerequisite

Sand Dune Journey

vocabulary

Ecosystem: communities of interacting organisms and nonliving (abiotic) components; an ecosystem can be as small as a rotting log or as large as an ocean; ecosystems are nested inside of one another

Habitat: the place or environment where a plant or animal naturally or normally lives and grows, can describe a smaller ecosystem within a larger ecosystem

Succession: a series of changes in the ecological community that inhabits a region

Adaptation: change in an organism or its parts that fits it better for the conditions of its environment

setting

INDOORS

subjects

Ecology, Biology

standards

This Great Lakes in My World activity is aligned to the Common Core State Standards and to state learning standards in:

Illinois
Indiana
Michigan
Minnesota
New York
Ohio
Pennsylvania
Wisconsin

This alignment is available on your Great Lakes in My World CD in the "Standards" folder and on-line at http://www.greatlakes.org/ GLiMWstandards.

materials

- Creature Cards
- Journals
- Pencils
- Sand Dune Diagram (copy for each station, page 122)
- Sign (for each station)
- Stations around the room

background

Sand dunes start as bare sand, then become dunes with grass helping to hold them in place. Over time, shrubs and trees are able to take root. As more time passes, a full forest, also called a climax forest, is able to grow at the back edge of a dune system. This change in ecosystems that takes place over time is called succession.

During succession, a series of changes occurs in the ecological community that inhabits a region. Succession happens because the activities of living organisms and abiotic factors change the conditions of a region so that it becomes more inhabitable by a different group of organisms.

In sand dunes, an example of the changing communities is beach, foredune, interdunal pond, forested backdune. If marram grass takes root on a beach, its roots will begin to trap sand, causing small dunes to form. This then sets the stage for additional plant and animal life to inhabit the dunes. In sand dunes, an example of the changing communities is beach, foredune, interdunal pond, forested backdune. Each of these habitats is an ecosystem that transitions into the next.

Note: If classes cannot take a field trip to the sand dunes, this can be used as an in-class alternative activity. This activity can also be done prior to a field trip to the sand dunes to give students background information.

procedure

1. Stations need to be set up around the room, as students will circulate through stations to study the habitats that make up sand dunes. At each station there should be the diagram of the beach, foredune, interdunal pond (also called a trough) and backdune. An arrow should point to the one section at each different station. At each station, there should also be the name of the habitat (region) and three to five sand dune Creature Cards. See Journal Pages for stations and accompanying questions. Depending on the number of students, you may want to set up each station twice for smaller groups.

2. Have students look in their journals at the drawing of sand dune regions they did in *Dune Journey*. Explain that the sand dune ecosystem is an example of "succession" and define this word. Ask students to explain how they think succession is exemplified in the sand dune ecosystem. Take a few responses.

3. Tell students they will be taking an in-class field trip to the dunes today. They will be going to different stations to learn about the different areas of a sand dune ecosystem and the organisms that live there. They will work in small groups and rotate between the different stations, spending 10 minutes at each. At each station, they will answer questions in their journals.

4. Explain that each of the four sand dune regions is made up of plants and animals specially adapted to live in that environment. For example, the fins of a fish make it well-suited for swimming in water; the long beak of a heron helps it to fish.

5. Tell students that as they go through the stations, they should be thinking about the order in which succession happens in a sand dune ecosystem.

> ### *Satisfy Your Curiosity* QUESTION IDEAS
>
> - *What special adaptations does my organism have?*
> - *What habitat is it best suited for and why?*
> - *Does my organism have specific interactions with other organisms for which it has developed special adaptations? What are they?*

wrap-up

Station questions and wrap-up questions can be discussed after the activity or on the following day.

1. Answer in journals and discuss as a class: What is an adaptation? Give an example that you learned from the stations. What is succession? How do the sand dunes demonstrate succession?

2. Do you think that any one of these habitats is more important than another? Why or why not?

3 Have students give a show of hands to see which area was their favorite. If there is an even dispersal of hands, students can be grouped by area of interest for the final project. If not, the teacher should assign students to groups for the project.

assessment

Rubric on page 163

Sand Dune Diagram

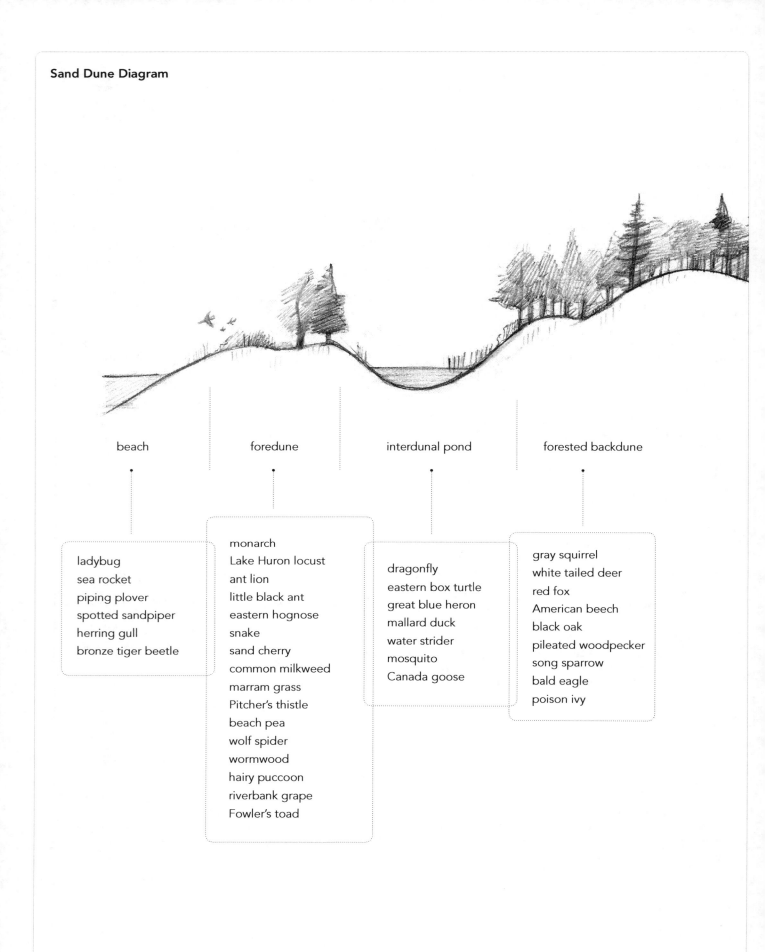

beach

ladybug
sea rocket
piping plover
spotted sandpiper
herring gull
bronze tiger beetle

foredune

monarch
Lake Huron locust
ant lion
little black ant
eastern hognose
snake
sand cherry
common milkweed
marram grass
Pitcher's thistle
beach pea
wolf spider
wormwood
hairy puccoon
riverbank grape
Fowler's toad

interdunal pond

dragonfly
eastern box turtle
great blue heron
mallard duck
water strider
mosquito
Canada goose

forested backdune

gray squirrel
white tailed deer
red fox
American beech
black oak
pileated woodpecker
song sparrow
bald eagle
poison ivy

*This diagram shows where some sand dune plants and animals live. These species are part of the Great Lakes Creature Cards.

8 | Indoor Dunes

GRADE LEVEL
4-8

journal pages

FIRST NAME																		
LAST NAME																		

Beach Station

Description: In the sand dune ecosystem, the beach is the area that changes most. The temperature, wind and waves cause big changes for this area every day. Sea rocket (a plant) and the tiger beetle (an insect) live here. Dead insects and fish often wash up here along the shoreline.

[1] Predict: Do you think that many or few animals would be able to live on the beach?
    Hint: Do many sudden changes make life harder or easier?
....

....

[2] Look at the Creature Cards. Sketch and label one beach organism.

[3] What adaptations enable it to live in (or visit) this habitat?
....
....
....
....

[4] Why do you think birds such as, gulls and sandpipers visit the beach?
....
....
....
....

APPROVED BY	

8 | Indoor Dunes

GRADE LEVEL
4-8

FIRST NAME																			
LAST NAME																			

Foredune Station

Description: The foredune is where marram grass causes sand to begin building up into a dune. Temperatures get very hot in this area, reaching between 120°F (48.8°C) and 180°F (82.2°C). The organisms here must adapt to the temperatures in order to survive. Some burrow underground to reach cooler temperatures.

[1] What time of day do you think animals in this area would be would be most active? Why?

....

....

....

[2] Marram grass is adapted for sand burial. As it gets buried by blowing sand, its leaves grow longer. It has fine, dense roots, which trap sand particles. Explain: Why are these fine, dense roots important for survival in the foredune area?

....

....

....

....

[3] Sketch and label one plant or animal from the Creature Cards.

[4] What adaptations enable it to live in this habitat?

....

....

....

....

APPROVED BY	

8 | Indoor Dunes

GRADE LEVEL
4-8

journal   pages

FIRST NAME																				
LAST NAME																				

Interdunal Pond

Description: Small ponds often form between the foredune and the backdune. This is called a trough or interdunal pond. The Great Lakes control the water level in these ponds. When the lake level is low, so is the pond. Dune systems do not always have interdunal ponds.

[1] If interdunal ponds have low water levels one year and high water levels the next year, do you think the same kinds of organisms are able to live there each year? Why or why not?

....

....

....

[2] What adaptations will some of the organisms that live here have? Give two examples.

....

....

....

[3] Sketch and label at least one organism from the interdunal pond area.

[4] What adaptations enable it to live in this habitat?

....

....

....

....

APPROVED BY	

8 | Indoor Dunes

GRADE LEVEL
4-8

FIRST NAME																		
LAST NAME																		

BacKdune

Description: The area behind the foredune (and interdunal pond, if there is one) is the bacKdune. It is protected from the force of the wind and has a layer of topsoil. This enables taller shrubs and trees to grow here, creating a cool, shady forest.

[1] What is different about the bacKdune forest from the beach and the foredune areas? (Hint: read the descriptions of the other two areas.)

....

....

....

....

....

[2] There are more animals able to live in the bacKdune forest than other dune areas. Why?

....

....

....

....

....

[3] SKetch and label one organism that lives in the bacKdune area.

[4] What adaptation enables it to live in this habitat?

....

....

....

....

....

APPROVED BY	

8 | Indoor Dunes

GRADE LEVEL
4-8

journal 	 pages

FIRST NAME																			
LAST NAME																			

[1] What is a good definition of an adaptation? Give an example from the stations.

[2] What is succession? How do the sand dunes demonstrate succession?

[3] Do you think any one of these habitats is more important than another?
Why or why not?

APPROVED BY	

EXPLORE

9 | Adaptation Stories

GRADE LEVEL

3-6

90 minutes

Developmental Modifications: Younger students can illustrate an organism and show how it uses its adaptation.

summary

Students listen to a story about an organism's adaptations, then conduct research on an adaptation of a certain species, and write stories about it.

objectives

- Formulate and research questions.
- Summarize research information in a short story.
- Explain how adaptations make organisms well suited for their environment.

prerequisite

Indoor Dunes or Adaptation and Observations

vocabulary

Organism: an individual living thing that carries on the activities of life by means of organs which have separate functions but are dependent on each other; a living person, plant, or animal

Species: a class of things of the same kind and with the same name; made up of related individuals able to produce fertile offspring

setting

INDOORS

subjects

Ecology, Language Arts, Art

standards

This Great Lakes in My World activity is aligned to the Common Core State Standards and to state learning standards in:

Illinois
Indiana
Michigan
Minnesota
New York
Ohio
Pennsylvania
Wisconsin

This alignment is available on your Great Lakes in My World CD in the "Standards" folder and on-line at http://www.greatlakes.org/ GLiMWstandards.

materials

- Research materials (Creature Cards, internet, books)
- Journals
- Pencils
- Art supplies (optional)
- 2 copies of sand dune animal Creature Cards (black and white is fine)

background

In this activity, students combine language arts and science to create a story that can be shared with younger students or classmates. This activity asks students to investigate how organisms use actual adaptations. A variation of this activity explores Native American myths that attempt to explain how certain organisms came to have certain characteristics. Students could then write from a more mythological and creative perspective.

procedure

1. Make 2 copies of the dune animal Creature Cards and hand out one per student. Collect cards. Students role play the animals and without speaking, find the other student mimicking the same animal. What adaptations did they use in the charade?

2. Read the following adaptation poem to the class.

   Eastern Hognose Snake
   There's a sand dune snake
   With an upturned nose.
   His snout is in the air
   Everywhere he goes.

   In and out of sand dunes,
   From the forest to the pond,
   He lifts up his hognose
   All day long!

   It's not for sniffing flowers,
   It's not to keep it off the land.
   He uses his hognose
   For digging in the sand.

   When the hognose gets hungry,
   He can dig up a toad.
   He digs a burrow in winter
   To keep out of the cold.

   If the tip of a hognose
   Was not turned up, but down,
   He wouldn't find his dinner
   Hiding underground.

   And if his nose wasn't shaped
   To be one of a kind,
   He'd have to find a burrow
   That someone else had left behind.

   Author: Anne Richardson

3. Discuss what is learned from this poem. Use the following examples of questions answered by this poem:
   - Why is the eastern hognose snake's snout upturned?
   - What does the snake use this snout for?
   - Does it have more than one purpose?
   - What would this snake's life be like without this adaptation?
   - Discuss what adaptations students used in their charade.

4. Explain that students create their own stories or poems about organism adaptations they study. If students have not been studying an organism from Satisfy Your Curiosity, then have students choose an organism from the Creature Cards. The stories do not have to rhyme. It is not important for students to be accurate about how their species evolved. Students should use the information to determine why this species has its particular adaptations. Their stories should reflect scientific thinking: making observations, asking good questions, and attempting to formulate answers to these questions.

5. Students should begin by describing the organism's habitat. They should choose one adaptation of the organism that they find interesting. Students should formulate questions about the organisms' adaptations: e.g. How does this adaptation make the organism well-suited for its environment?

6. Students should do research (Creature Cards, internet, books) to find out what the adaptation is used for. For example, a lake trout has a larger mouth than a chub so that it can eat organisms as large as fish. With a small mouth, it wouldn't be able to eat fish. Instead, a chub eats plankton.

7. Students write a story using the researched information about how their organism uses its adaptation. The stories should be interesting and scientific, showing how the adaptation is used by the organism to aid in its survival.

8. If desired, students could read Native American myths that investigate how certain organisms came to have certain characteristics. They could then write a creative, mythological story and illustrate it.

wrap-up

1. Students share their stories with the class or younger students.

2. Students may re-write and bind their stories in a book format with illustrations.

assessment

Rubric on page 164

9 | Adaptation Stories

GRADE LEVEL
3-6

| FIRST NAME | | | | | | | | | | | | | | | | | | | | | |
| LAST NAME | | | | | | | | | | | | | | | | | | | | | |

[1] Organism's name

....

....

....

....

[2] Organism's adaptation and interesting features

....

....

....

....

....

....

....

....

....

....

[3] Describe the organism's habitat.

....

....

....

....

....

....

....

....

....

....

....

| APPROVED BY | |

9 | Adaptation Stories

GRADE LEVEL
3-6

journal pages

FIRST NAME

LAST NAME

[4] What questions do you have about this adaptation?

a.

b.

c.

[5] What answers did you find in your research?

a.

b.

c.

APPROVED BY

9 | Adaptation Stories

GRADE LEVEL
3-6

journal pages

| FIRST NAME | | | | | | | | | | | | | | | | | | | | | | |
| LAST NAME | | | | | | | | | | | | | | | | | | | | | | |

[6] Write your story here.

APPROVED BY

EXPLORE

10 | Succession Circles

GRADE LEVEL
6-8

 60 minutes

summary

Students record sand dune ecosystem observations in a Venn diagram to show overlapping biotic and abiotic factors in the succession of sand dunes.

objectives

- Use a Venn diagram to explain how sand dune ecosystems change over time.

prerequisite

Indoor Dunes or Adaptations and Observations

vocabulary

Abiotic: non-living (such as sand, water, sunlight)
Biotic: living (such as insects, birds, plants)
Succession: a series of changes in the ecological community that inhabits a region
Venn diagram: circles that overlap to show factors that exist in common
    between two or more elements

setting

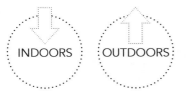

INDOORS   OUTDOORS

subjects

Ecology

standards

This Great Lakes in My World activity is aligned to the Common Core State Standards and to state learning standards in:

Illinois
Indiana
Michigan
Minnesota
New York
Ohio
Pennsylvania
Wisconsin

This alignment is available on your Great Lakes in My World CD in the "Standards" folder and on-line at http://www.greatlakes.org/ GLiMWstandards.

materials

- Pencil
- Journal pages
- Creature Cards
- Dune diagram
- Dune information resources

background

Sand dunes clearly demonstrate a change from beach, to foredune, to trough/interdunal pond, to forested backdune. Each new ecosystem has a different set of abiotic factors and organisms that characterize it. However, because there is not a clear delineation between the ecosystems, there are areas with an overlap of the biotic and abiotic factors between the ecosystems.

procedure

1. As a class, brainstorm a list of the abiotic factors that make up an ecosystem. *A possible list includes: wind, temperature, sunlight, soil and water.* Brainstorm a list of the biotic factors that make up an ecosystem. *A possible list includes: animals, plants, humans, bacteria and fungus.*

2. In pairs, have students label one set of Venn diagram circles. Students may get their information from observations made in previous activities. Based on the characteristics of each ecosystem, students fill in the abiotic factors as they apply to each ecosystem. *For example, the beach has sandy soil, extreme high and low temperatures, bright sunlight, high wind.*

3. In the second set of circles, students choose organisms that live in each ecosystem. Use the dune diagram and list provided with this curriculum.

4. For both sets of diagrams, in the spaces where the circles overlap, students list the factors and organisms that overlap between the two ecosystems.

5. Students answer journal questions when finished with the diagram.

wrap-up

1. Discuss students' answers on the journal pages. What biotic and abiotic components of the dune regions appeared in the overlapping spaces between regions? *Think about similarities and differences in soil, wind, temperature, sunlight, and water and organisms that use multiple dune regions for food and shelter. Based on these components, what is happening that allows for the sand dune ecosystems to change? Write at least one sentence for each transition.*

Suggestions for sentence examples:

Beach – wind action and erosion to form sand.
Foredune – marram grass must take root to stabilize sand, continued wind action.
Interdunal Pond/ Trough – water collects in the space between dunes, allowing specialized wetland plants to grow.
Forested Backdune – trees take root in the damp, most soil created by the pond water and organisms. Debris breaks down to create a soil that is less sandy and allows other plants to take root.

2. Which area has the harshest conditions? Why? *Beach, no shelter.*

3. Which area has the mildest conditions? Why? *Forest, greatest amount of shelter.*

4. Consider which species use more than one ecosystem within the sand dunes and discuss what organism adaptations make this possible.

 We value your thoughts and feedback on Great Lakes in My World. Please let us know about any oversights, errors or omissions you find, or if there are things you or your students particularly like.

Send your comments to: education@greatlakes.org

assessment

Rubric on page 164

10 | Succession Circles

FIRST NAME

LAST NAME

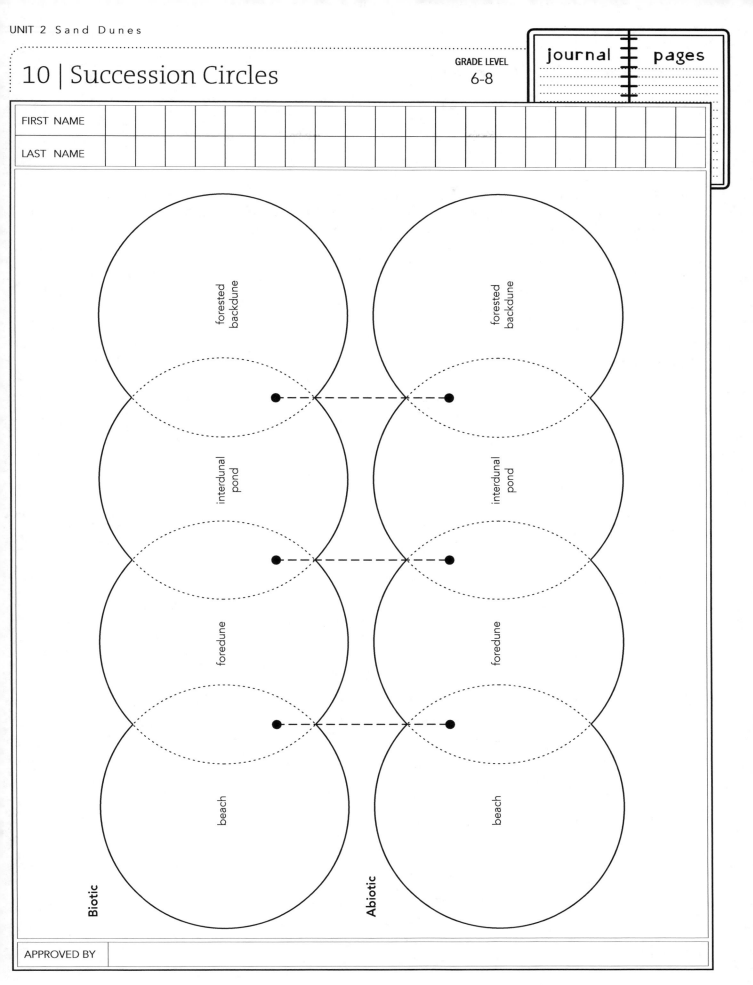

Biotic

forested backdune

interdunal pond

foredune

beach

Abiotic

forested backdune

interdunal pond

foredune

beach

APPROVED BY

10 | Succession Circles

GRADE LEVEL
6-8

FIRST NAME																				
LAST NAME																				

What biotic and abiotic components of the dune regions appeared in the overlapping spaces between regions? Based on these components, what is happening that allows for the sand dune ecosystems to change? Write at least one sentence for each transition.

[1] Beach

....

....

....

[2] Foredune

....

....

....

[3] Interdunal Pond

....

....

....

....

[4] Forested Backdune

....

....

....

....

[5] Which area has the harshest conditions? Why?

....

....

....

....

[6] Which area has the mildest conditions? Why?

....

....

....

....

APPROVED BY	

INVESTIGATE

11 | Dune Decisions

GRADE LEVEL

4-8

45 minutes

Developmental Modifications: For younger students, read the examples and have a class discussion about possible ways to respond to the dilemmas.

summary

Students work in small groups to discuss dune dilemma cards and their personal decisions.

objectives

- List reasons sand dunes are valuable.
- Discuss humans actions that help and hurt sand dune ecosystems.
- Decide on actions that help sand dunes have a healthy future.

prerequisite

Dune Inspiration, Dune Journey or Making a Mark and Adaptations and Observations, Indoor Dunes

vocabulary

Students will use vocabulary from previous activities

setting

INDOORS

subjects

Environmental Science, Social Studies

standards

This Great Lakes in My World activity is aligned to the Common Core State Standards and to state learning standards in:

Illinois
Indiana
Michigan
Minnesota
New York
Ohio
Pennsylvania
Wisconsin

This alignment is available on your Great Lakes in My World CD in the "Standards" folder and on-line at http://www.greatlakes.org/GLiMWstandards.

materials

- Pencil
- Paper or journals
- Dune dilemma cards

background

Great Lakes sand dunes are a beautiful and rare ecosystem. They host a wide diversity of plants and animals and are a tremendous tourist draw. Sand dunes form as the roots of marram grass trap sand and in this way, a mound of sand gradually grows. It is thought that sand dunes form over thousands of years, which means that they would not be easily replaceable if destroyed.

Threats to Dunes
In spite of their value, there are many threats to sand dunes. Great Lakes sand dunes continue lost every day to sand dune mining. Sand is mined from dunes for use as molds for machinery parts in industry and for making glass. Sand can be sold for as little as $5-$10/ton.

Non-native invasive plant species such as baby's breath (Gypsophila paniculata) and garlic mustard (Alliaria petiolata) have spread rapidly and outcompete native species for space and resources. Habitat destruction from sand mining and development also pose great threat. Recreational use by off-road vehicles and pedestrians damages vegetation and causes significant erosion. In our lives we all make decisions that can help or hurt an outdoor area. Making a decision that helps an ecosystem, and the plants and animals that live there, requires knowledge, thought and practice. Discussing real-life dilemmas can help students to be thoughtful in the actions they take.

procedure

1. Have students describe sand dune experiences to each other. If many students have been to the dunes, this can be done in pairs. If few students have been, one or two students can describe their experiences to the class.

2. As a class, brainstorm a list of the reasons that sand dunes are important. *The list might include: support animal and plant life, beautiful, a place for people to visit.* Add any other ideas that students have. Their ideas may not necessarily be healthy for the sand dunes (such as climbing on dunes), but should be added as part of the initial list.

3. Divide students into groups and distribute dilemma cards to each group. Students read cards and discuss possible solutions. Within the group, students may have different answers for their personal reactions. Ask students to come up with an answer that they can share with the class. Students record their dilemma and answers in their journals.

4. Have each group describe a different dilemma, and then their response. Engage the class in a discussion about the dilemmas.

5. As a class, create a list of individual actions that the students feel they can take in order to help protect sand dunes.

Dilemmas

#1. Dune Climbers
You are at the beach with friends. Someone suggests climbing on the sand dunes and running down them for fun. What do you do?

Choices:
a. Say that it sounds like fun and race your friends to the top of the dune.

b. Point out the "No walking on the dunes" sign and suggest other ideas such as walking or running along the beach, looking for interesting rocks, or building sand castles.

c. Tell your friends that many plants and animals live in the dunes. Walking on the dune can destroy the marram grass roots that hold the dune in place, which means that eventually the dune will be destroyed. Suggest other ideas for fun to your friends.

d. Other?

#2. Developing the Dunes
You find out that your community is allowing sand dunes to be removed so that houses can be developed that have easy beach access and views of the Great Lakes. What do you do?

Choices:
a. Write a letter to the local paper explaining the value of the sand dune ecosystem. For example, sand dunes draw tourists to communities. When tourists spend money in a community, this can help boost the local economy. In addition, sand dunes are home to many plants and animals that will no longer have a place to live if sand dunes are removed.

b. Ask your family to buy a house that will be built where the dunes once were because you would like to live near the beach.

c. Encourage your family to get involved in this issue by attending town meetings where decisions are made regarding developing the Great Lakes shoreline.

d. Other?

procedure continued

#3. Picnic Problem

Your family is having a picnic at the beach. You have brought delicious food and have had a wonderful day at the beach. When you leave, your family does not want to bring the extra food home. They want to leave it at the beach, figuring that birds or other animals will eat the leftovers. What do you do?

Choices:

a. Explain that leaving food at the beach is not a good idea as it attracts animals to the beach. Animals live at the beach, but food can attract more than usual. When animals come to the beach and eat, they often leave their droppings behind. The bacteria from animal (and human!) waste can get into the water and make it unhealthy for people to swim in the lake.

b. Offer to help carry some of the food back, so that one or two people don't have to do all the work. Explain the idea of "carrying out what you carried in" so that you leave no trace of your visit. We share the beach with other people who do not want to see signs of previous visitors.

c. Encourage your family to leave the food behind on the beach.

d. Other?

#4. Litter Leavers

You are at the beach with friends. When you pick up your towels and flip-flops to head home, you notice garbage that you all have left behind in the sand. What do you do?

Choices:

a. Ignore it. It will soon blow away or be buried by the sand.

b. Wait until your friends leave, then pick up the garbage. You know it's not right to litter, but are embarrassed to ask your friends to help you pick up the garbage.

c. Ask your friends to help you pick up garbage, telling them that wildlife on the beach and dunes sometimes mistakes garbage for food, and can get sick or die by eating it.

d. Pick up the litter and throw it away without saying anything about it.

e. Explain that leaving garbage at the beach is not a good idea as it attracts more animals than usual to the beach. When animals come to the beach, they often leave their droppings behind. The bacteria from animal (and human!) waste can get into the water and make it unhealthy for people to swim in the lake.

d. Other?

wrap-up

1. Discuss the following: Which of these dilemmas has happened to you? What other moral dilemmas do you encounter at the beach? How easy would it be to actually respond in the way that you know is best for the dunes and the beach? Why are many people reluctant to discourage friends and family from doing things that are easy and fun, but cause damage?

   Additional questions include:
   - Why are people reluctant to get involved with public actions such as letter writing, or attending town hall or city council meetings?
   - What kinds of benefit and strength might come to those who take a stand on an issue? What kind of approach with people is likely to be well-received? Poorly received?

2. Bring out the benefit and value of:
   - Understanding the issue
   - Having personal conviction to take action
   - Using good "people skills"
   - Little steps and compromise
   - For quiet types: bring out the importance of actions speaking louder than words
   - Discuss the backfire effect of "preaching"

3. Create a class list of actions individuals can take to help protect the dunes and have students initial next to the actions they can personally do.

assessment

Rubric on page 164

11 | Dune Decisions

GRADE LEVEL
4-8

journal ≡ pages

FIRST NAME																					
LAST NAME																					

[1] Why are sand dunes important?

[2] In your own words, describe the dilemma your group is discussing.

[3] What decision will you choose? Why?

[4] What actions can you take to help sand dunes stay healthy?

APPROVED BY

INVESTIGATE

12 | Dune Mining Debate

GRADE LEVEL
6-8

90 minutes

summary

Students role-play in debates to learn the pros and cons of sand dune mining as an environmental issue. As an extension, students may take action in their own community.

objectives

- Discuss varying sides of the sand dune mining issue.
- Engage in an effective debate.
- Summarize current events in their community relating to dune mining.
- Articulate a position on the sand dune mining issue.

prerequisite

Dune Inspiration or Making a Mark, and Adaptations and Observations or Indoor Dunes. A visit to sand dunes is highly recommended.

vocabulary

Debate: a regulated discussion of a problem between two matched sides
Bias: an attitude that always favors one way of feeling or acting over any other

setting

INDOORS

subjects

Environmental Science, Ecology

standards

This Great Lakes in My World activity is aligned to the Common Core State Standards and to state learning standards in:

Illinois
Indiana
Michigan
Minnesota
New York
Ohio
Pennsylvania
Wisconsin

This alignment is available on your Great Lakes in My World CD in the "Standards" folder and on-line at http://www.greatlakes.org/ GLiMWstandards.

materials

- Sand dune mining articles (on compact disc)
- Pencils
- Journals

background

Sand Dune Mining: Lake Michigan houses the largest concentration of freshwater sand dunes in the world. Sand dune formation takes place over thousands of years and begins when unusually fine sand blows inland and builds up in small mountains up to 300 feet in height. The dunes support plant and animal life that can't be found elsewhere and were the birthplace for the field of ecology. Once they are gone, it would be difficult for them to be replaced.

Michigan, with the highest number of sand dunes in the Great Lakes region, continues to lose dunes every day to sand dune mining. Sand is mined from dunes for use as molds for machinery parts in industry and for making glass. Sand can be sold for as little as $5-$10/ton. Mining takes place at a number of sites in Michigan in the dunes.

For additional information on sand dunes see:
http://www.greatlakes.org/dunes

Fishbowl Debate: The style of debate the students will be using is called a fishbowl. Half of the class will debate while the other half, in a circle around the debaters, observes. The students switch between debaters and observers halfway through the time period. The observers may not speak during the debate. Their job is to take notes on the behavior of the debaters. Before students trade roles, the observers will report on their observations. The class may discuss ways to make the next round of debate more successful.

....

procedure

Setting up the Debate

1. Have students reflect on what it feels like to press a hand or foot into moist sand. Ask them what would happen if you poured plaster into the impressions that their hands make. Tell students that sand packs very tightly, so it is used in industry to create molds for machinery parts, including parts for cars and planes. Large quantities of sand are used this way. Sand is also used for glass making. When sand is taken from sand dunes for this use it is called sand dune mining.

2. Tell students they will work in small groups to learn about sand dune mining. Each group will be given a role and will take part in class debate to defend it. Explain how the next day's debate will be conducted (see next page). What makes a good debate? Have students brainstorm a list of ways to make the debate successful.

The list might include:

- *Listening to each other*
- *Talking loudly enough for others to hear*
- *Being polite and choosing a moderator to facilitate.*

3. Students review the information about sand dune mining. They should read one of the provided articles (on CD), then break into small groups to teach other students about the article they read. Students should summarize their article into three sentences to share with other students.

4. As a class, brainstorm a list of relevant characters involved in sand dune mining.

The list might include:

- *Tourist coming to visit the Great Lakes*
- *Sand dune miner (private land owner looking for a permit)*
- *Purchasing agent for car parts manufacturer*
- *Resident who loves the dunes*
- *Owner of a sand dune mining company that has been in the family for several generations and has employed hundreds of people*
- *Resident who never visits the dunes, and owns a local restaurant/hotel*
- *Jobless person looking for work*
- *Geologist with dune formation information*
- *Consumer shopping for a new car*
- *Resident who believes that natural resources are primarily for human use*

5. As a class, decide on the roles needed for the debate. Students might work in pairs or small groups. For example, there could be a group of miners, a group of residents, and a group of geologists. These groups would work together on preparing their role for the debate.

6. Once roles have been chosen, students should review their own roles, as well as the roles of others for best preparation. Students write a summary of the statements they would like to contribute to the debate. In addition, students write a three to five sentence summary of their personal beliefs on the sand dune mining issue.

procedure continued

The Debate

1. Divide the class into observers and debaters.

2. Review the elements of a successful debate and the guidelines for the fishbowl method. Students are looking for the qualities of debate that have been previously decided. Are people listening to each other? Are they interrupting one another? Are they speaking clearly?

3. Each group of debaters will have one to two minutes (depending on class timing) per group to make an initial statement. A spokesperson can be elected for this. Once this is complete, each group will have one to two minutes to make counter-arguments. Then, each group will have one to two minutes to defend their positions.

4. Observers should report on their observations. Discuss as a class: What was positive about the debate? How could the debate have been more effective?

5. Trade fishbowl positions and repeat for the second group.

wrap-up

1. Have students use their observations of the debate and their written summaries to answer the questions in their journals.

2. As a class, discuss the importance of researching all sides of an issue. Refer back to the debate for reference on this point. What is bias? It is easier to take a stand after learning about only one side of an issue. This may have become apparent during the debate if all parties argued articulately. It is important to base conclusions on facts rather than bias.

extension

- To more fully explore this issue, follow the current events in sand dune mining in your area and discuss taking action locally as a class. Journal pages are provided for this.

- Research the issue: look for newspaper articles and web sites, call companies and organizations who own local sand dunes. Don't forget to research all sides of the issue!

- In small groups, brainstorm a list of facts that students have learned in their research. Then, brainstorm a list of issues or problems.

- As a class, decide if there is a problem with the current, local sand dune mining situation. If so, try to summarize it in one or two sentences.

- Discuss: how do the students feel about this problem? What experiences or stories do they have that contribute to their feelings on the issue?

- Is there more information the class needs in order to take an educated stance on the issue? If so, this is a good time to follow up on or conduct more research. The sand dunes section of the Alliance for the Great Lakes' web site is a great place to start: http://www.greatlakes.org/dunes.

- Decide as a class: What position does the class take on the issue? Does the class find that change needs to take place? The class may not agree on the issue. In this case, it may be helpful to go back into the debate format again until either a consensus is reached or the class decides to disagree.

- What steps can the class take to become involved in this issue in their community and make change? Break into small groups to brainstorm action methods and opportunities. In these small groups, decide on the strengths of the class in this particular situation—given the circumstances and the opportunities available, what approach would be the most effective for this class?

- Share the small group work with the class and work toward a class consensus.

- Establish a timeline and take steps that the class decides on as a group.

- At a pre-decided point, evaluate the steps the class has taken. Have these steps been effective in moving toward the class objective? Do they need to be modified or changed?

- Celebrate any action or accomplishment.

assessment

Rubric on page 165

12 | Dune Mining Debate

GRADE LEVEL
6-8

FIRST NAME

LAST NAME

[1] List the elements of a good debate.

[2] Write three sentences summarizing your article.

a.

b.

c.

[3] List possible characters that would be involved in a debate on sand dune mining. Circle the characters the class chooses for the classroom debate.

APPROVED BY

12 | Dune Mining Debate

GRADE LEVEL
6-8

journal pages

FIRST NAME

LAST NAME

[1] My character in the sand dune mining debate:

[2] Why is the sand dune mining issue important to your character?

[3] Write a three to five sentence summary of the statements you/your group would like to contribute to the debate on behalf of your character.

[4] Write a three to five sentence summary of your personal beliefs on the sand dune mining issue. How are they different or similar to the beliefs of your character?

APPROVED BY

12 | Dune Mining Debate

GRADE LEVEL
6-8

journal pages

FIRST NAME

LAST NAME

[1] Write your opening statement here. You will have one to two minutes to present this statement.

[2] Make notes here during the debate for your counter-argument. (One to two minutes)

[3] Make notes here for your final defense. (one to two minutes)

APPROVED BY

12 | Dune Mining Debate

GRADE LEVEL
6-8

journal ≡ pages

FIRST NAME																					
LAST NAME																					

[1] How has your initial stance on the issue changed or not changed as a result of the debate?

....

....

....

....

....

[2] What makes this a difficult issue to debate?

....

....

....

....

....

[3] Which group do you believe had the strongest argument? Explain why you feel it was strong.

....

....

....

....

....

[4] What made this debate work well?

....

....

....

....

....

[5] What aspects of the debate could be improved?

....

....

....

....

....

APPROVED BY	

12 | Dune Mining Debate

GRADE LEVEL
6-8

journal   pages

| FIRST NAME | | | | | | | | | | | | | | | | | | | |
| LAST NAME | | | | | | | | | | | | | | | | | | | |

[1] If your class would like to take action on the sand dune mining issue, brainstorm a list of actions that could help to solve the problem.

[2] Write down the action the class has chosen to take.

[3] Write down the class timeline for action steps, including a dates to evaluate the process and decide how successful the you are.

|--------|--------|--------|--------|--------|--------|--------|--------|---------|

[4] Once you have completed your project, use additional paper to reflect on challenges you faced and what you achieved.

| APPROVED BY | |

INVESTIGATE: FINAL PROJECT

13 | Life in the Dunes

GRADE LEVEL

K-3

180 minutes

summary

Students create a booklet that summarizes their understanding of the sand dune ecosystem.

objectives

- Synthesize what has been learned about sand dunes.
- Determine evaluation criteria.
- Review work with peers.

prerequisite

Basic understanding of adaptations, succession, dune ecosystem and dune organisms. Students should have completed most of the activities in this unit.

vocabulary

Students will use vocabulary from previous activities

setting

INDOORS

subjects

Ecology, Biology, Art

standards

This Great Lakes in My World activity is aligned to the Common Core State Standards and to state learning standards in:

Illinois
Indiana
Michigan
Minnesota
New York
Ohio
Pennsylvania
Wisconsin

This alignment is available on your Great Lakes in My World CD in the "Standards" folder and on-line at http://www.greatlakes.org/ GLiMWstandards.

materials

- Creature Cards
- Journals
- Research materials
- Book-making materials
- Art supplies

background

Students can show that they fully understand information by transforming it into a format that can be used to teach other people. The creation of a communication piece allows students to synthesize and give meaning to the activities that make up this unit.

procedure

1. Tell students they will be making storybooks about sand dunes. Their books will tell the story of what they learned during the unit. Their books may take a variety of forms. For example, accordion, pop-up, binder, varying sizes, etc. You may wish to have the class choose one style to make it easier to assist students with their book-making.

2. Once a format has been chosen, the next step is for students to determine what information needs to be included in the booklet. Students should take some time to review their journals, then brainstorm a list of essential elements. Use the following questions to guide the class: What are the most important things you learned during the unit? This list may include things such as: species adaptations, descriptions of the sand dune regions, and how the sand dunes change over time. What would you like to remember about sand dunes? What do you think other people should know about sand dunes? This list may include things such as specific plants and animals, what sand dunes look like, and why they are a special place.

3. Write the list on the board and have students copy it into their journals.

4. The stories may be made entirely of pictures, or may include writing as well. Stories may be simply a re-telling of what students have learned, or they may include characters and fictional events (for example, a child on a journey in the sand dunes).

5. Students should find information and ideas for their stories in their journals, and include Satisfy Your Curiosity organisms.

6. Stories should include a drawing of the dune regions and descriptions of each of the four dune regions, including the landscape and organisms that live there.

extension

Students may share their finished product with the community. Possibilities include:
- read booklets to other children in the school
- display them in the school, or
- display them in the local library, community center or nature center.

Resources
Discovering Great Lakes Dunes, Elizabeth Brockwell-Tillman and Earl Wolf, 1998
Borne of the Wind: An Introduction to the Ecology of Michigan Sand Dunes, Dennis A. Albert, 2000

wrap-up

1. Allow students to share their stories with the class by reading and explaining the pictures.

2. Students can talk about what they like about each other's work and how they would improve their own work next time.

assessment

Rubric on page 150. Or, use this rubric as a model to create your own for your class with student input. The competency areas should come from the list of essential elements for the final project, determined by you and the class.

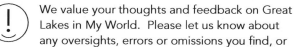

We value your thoughts and feedback on Great Lakes in My World. Please let us know about any oversights, errors or omissions you find, or if there are things you or your students particularly like.

Send your comments to: education@greatlakes.org

13 | Life in the Dunes

GRADE LEVEL
K-3

journal pages

FIRST NAME

LAST NAME

[1] What have you learned about sand dunes?

[2] What do you want people to Know about sand dunes?

APPROVED BY

13 | Life in the Dunes

FIRST NAME																		
LAST NAME																		

Make a storybook with words and pictures

[3] What Kind of book will you make?

....
....
....
....
....
....

[4] What will the story be about?

....
....
....
....
....
....
....
....
....
....
....
....
....
....
....
....
....
....

APPROVED BY	

INVESTIGATE: FINAL PROJECT

14 | Living Dune

GRADE LEVEL

4-8

180 minutes

summary

Students create a booklet or other communication piece that summarizes their understanding of the sand dune ecosystem.

objectives

- Synthesize what has been learned about sand dunes into a communication piece.
- Determine evaluation criteria.
- Review projects with peers.

prerequisite

Activities from Sand Dune Unit, to include an understanding of adaptations, succession, dune ecosystem and dune organisms.

vocabulary

Students will use vocabulary from previous activities

setting

INDOORS

subjects

Ecology

standards

This Great Lakes in My World activity is aligned to the Common Core State Standards and to state learning standards in:

Illinois
Indiana
Michigan
Minnesota
New York
Ohio
Pennsylvania
Wisconsin

This alignment is available on your Great Lakes in My World CD in the "Standards" folder and on-line at http://www.greatlakes.org/ GLiMWstandards.

materials

- Sand Dune Creature Cards
- Journals
- Research materials
- Book-making materials
- Art supplies

background

Students can show that they understand information by transforming it into a format that can teach others. The creation of a communication piece allows students to synthesize and give meaning to the dune activities that they took part in throughout the unit. This activity format can be used to wrap up other units.

procedure

1. Explain to the students that it's time to put together all of the information they've learned about sand dunes, and they will do that by making team booklets. The groups may choose other formats for conveying information, such as PowerPoint or a web site.

2. Using the first journal page for this activity, divide the students into groups of 4 based on their Satisfy Your Curiosity species. Each group should have a student representing a species from each of the four dune region: beach, foredune, trough, and backdune. If desired, let the group choose the format of their book: binder, pop-up, accordion, various sizes, etc.

3. Using the accompanying journal pages, have the class decide what these books should include. Students should review their journals and brainstorm a list of essential elements. Ask them: What are the most important things you learned about sand dunes during this unit?

4. Using Journal Page 2, also discuss the important aspects of a communication piece in terms of evaluation. Be sure to mention clarity, accuracy, creativity, and consistency. Include these and other appropriate criteria the students think of for student evaluation of the projects. We recommend using the journal pages and including the following components:

- Species adaptations
- An overview of the entire sand dune ecosystem
- A diagram of the four dune regions along with an explanation of how they are connected
- Other diagrams and illustrations as appropriate

A section devoted to each dune region that includes the following:
- Biotic and abiotic components
- Three things that make it different from other regions
- Three things that make it similar to the other regions
- Detailed information on the Satisfy Your Curiosity organisms (adaptations, use of other regions or ecosystems, etc.)
- Information on two additional species (one plant, one animal)

5. Students should divide the work, but all parts should be uniform in look and consistent in format in order to match. The dune booklets should include illustrations and diagrams where appropriate. Students may divide up the work so that each student completes one section of the booklet.

6. Students may follow the journal questions as outlined, crossing out and adding to them according to the list of essential elements decided upon by the class.

wrap-up

1. In their small groups, have students review and evaluate a booklet made by another group. Each group should present their own booklet to the class.

2. While listening to the presentation, students can check it against the list of essential elements to make sure that all of the pieces are there.

3. Presenters should explain to the class what new things they learned from this booklet and what new ideas it gave them about how to put together a communication piece.

4. All groups should have a turn to present.

extension

Students may share their finished product with the community. Possibilities include: read booklets to younger children in the school or at a nearby school, display them in the school, or display them in the local library, community center or nature center.

Resources
Discovering Great Lakes Dunes, Elizabeth Brockwell-Tillman and Earl Wolf, 1998
Borne of the Wind: An Introduction to the Ecology of Michigan Sand Dunes, Dennis A. Albert, 2000

assessment

Rubric on page 166. Or, use this rubric as a model to create your own for your class with student input. The competency areas should come from the list of essential elements for the final project, determined by you and the class.

14 | Living Dune

GRADE LEVEL
4-8

FIRST NAME

LAST NAME

[1] My group members:

....

....

....

[2] My booklet section: CIRCLE ONE

BEACH   FOREDUNE   TROUGH/POND   BACKDUNE/FOREST

[3] Describe what information will be in the communication piece and how it will be designed and laid out. Use the space below for diagrams and sketches that show what the communication piece will look like.

....

....

....

....

....

....

....

....

....

Diagram your communication piece here:

APPROVED BY

14 | Living Dune

FIRST NAME																				
LAST NAME																				

[4] List essential elements to be included in final project. This list will be used to evaluate the project.

....

....

....

....

....

....

....

....

[5] What are the most important things learned in this unit?

....

....

....

....

....

....

....

....

[6] What are the most important aspects of a communication piece?

....

....

....

....

....

....

....

....

....

APPROVED BY	

14 | Living Dune

GRADE LEVEL
4-8

journal ≡ pages

FIRST NAME																				
LAST NAME																				

[7] Overview of the sand dune ecosystem: Write a brief description and/or a diagram
of the sand dune ecosystem. Hint: Look at your Dune Journey journal pages

....
....
....
....
....
....
....
....
....
....
....
....
....

For each of the four sand dune regions, answer the following questions. Include written
explanations, illustrations and diagrams as needed to make the answers clear and
complete. Use these pages for notes before creating the final version of the project.

[8] Describe the biotic and abiotic components of the region.

....
....
....
....
....

[9] What 3 things make this region unique and different from other sand dune regions?

....
....
....
....

APPROVED BY	

14 | Living Dune

FIRST NAME																				
LAST NAME																				

[10] What 3 things make this region similar to other sand dune regions?

....

....

....

[11] Describe the **Satisfy Your Curiosity** species for this region. What special
adaptations does it have to help it survive in this environment? What other regions
of the sand dunes or other ecosystem does this species inhabit or visit? What
other questions did you formulate and answer about this species?

....

....

....

....

....

....

[12] Describe 2 more species (1 plant and 1 animal) that live in this region and explain
what physical and behavioral adaptations make these organisms well suited for their
environment.

....

....

....

....

....

[13] How are the four dune regions interconnected?

....

....

....

....

....

....

APPROVED BY	

INVESTIGATE: FINAL WRAP-UP

15 | Dune Reflection

GRADE LEVEL

K-8

30-60
minutes

summary

Students reflect on their connection to the dunes, what they have learned in the unit and what steps they can take to keep the dunes healthy.

subjects

Environmental Science, Ecology

standards

This Great Lakes in My World activity is aligned to the Common Core State Standards and to state learning standards in:

Illinois
Indiana
Michigan
Minnesota
New York
Ohio
Pennsylvania
Wisconsin

This alignment is available on your Great Lakes in My World CD in the "Standards" folder and on-line at http://www.greatlakes.org/ GLiMWstandards.

objectives

• Reflect on knowledge gained in the Sand Dune unit.

prerequisite

Students should have completed Living Dune or Life in the Dunes

vocabulary

Students will use vocabulary from previous activities

materials

• Journals
• Large flip chart (if outdoors) marker board, or chalkboard (if indoors)
• Markers or chalk

setting

OUTDOORS

Sand dunes preferable

background

In order to complete their learning, students will benefit from taking the time to reflect on what they have learned and why they have been studying the dunes. This activity format can be used to wrap-up other units.

....

procedure

1. If possible, take students back to the dunes. If students do not go back, show pictures of the dunes in the classroom. At the dunes, allow time for exploration and personal reflection. Students may walk around, play in the sand, write or draw. The amount of time spent on this is optional, depending on the time available. Consider asking students to plan activities that combine learning and fun.

2. Gather students together in a comfortable, shady location. Ask students to share some of the ways they are connected to dunes. Allow students to share stories, ideas or feelings. Write (or have a student write) these on your large paper or chalkboard.

3. Ask students to share some of the things they have learned about dunes. Write these as well. Once students have shared, have them try to group ideas into broad categories.

4. Ask students to brainstorm a list of solutions they can propose to solve problems related to dunes. Write these down for students.

5. Ask students why they have come up with these solutions. Why do they want to help the dunes? What makes the dunes important to them? Write these things down as well.

....

wrap-up

1. Have students take time to write or draw about their most important learning or accomplishment during the unit. Students should include why this is significant.

2. If students have proposed additional actions they would like to take to help the dunes, keep these notes to follow-up with in class.

3. Take the rest of the time available to celebrate the learning and accomplishments of the class during the unit.

extension

The model of this activity can be used in all other units as a method for reflection and further involvement.

....

assessment

Rubric on page 166

CONNECT 1| Dune Inspiration

ELEMENTS	☆☆☆☆	☆☆☆	☆☆	☆
HAIKU: Student brainstorms a list of sand dune-related words and creates a haiku poem that follows the format and demonstrates feeling and interest in the dunes. Students creates an accompanying illustration, as required.	Addresses all of the components	Missing one component	Missing two components	Missing three or more components
SHARING: Student shares their haiku poem and discusses similarities and differences with another poem.	Addresses all of the components	Missing one component	Missing two components	Missing three or more components

CONNECT 2 | Making a Mark

ELEMENTS	☆☆☆☆	☆☆☆	☆☆	☆
MARK MAKING: Student makes a mark in the sand that has apparent significance to her/him.	Addresses all of the components	Missing one component	Missing two components	Missing three or more components
DISCUSSION: Student actively contributes to the discussion and reflects on her/his connection to sand dunes by discussing personal experiences and ideas. Student uses active listening skills (eye-contact, confirming or referencing others' comments, affirmative gestures or comments).	Addresses all of the components	Missing one component	Missing two components	Missing three or more components

CONNECT 3 | Dune Journey

ELEMENTS	☆☆☆☆	☆☆☆	☆☆	☆
DISCUSSION: Student contributes any prior knowledge of sand dunes to the discussion. Student uses active listening skills (eye-contact, confirming or referencing others' comments, affirmative gestures or comments).	Addresses all of the components	Missing one component	Missing two components	Missing three or more components
LISTENING: Student attentively listens to the description of the dune journey without distracting others. Personal investment is obvious.	Addresses all of the components	Missing one component	Missing two components	Missing three or more components
DRAWING: Student draws a representation of her/his imagined dune journey and reflects on which part of the dunes s/he drew. Students share drawing with a partner.	Addresses all of the components	Missing one component	Missing two components	Missing three or more components
JOURNAL (4-6): Student responds thoughtfully to the 4 journal prompts.	Addresses all of the components	Missing one component	Missing two components	Missing three or more components

EXPLORE   **4 | Satisfy Your Curiosity**

ELEMENTS	☆ ☆ ☆ ☆	☆ ☆ ☆	☆ ☆	☆
KNOWLEDGE GAINED	Student includes at least two new insights for each activity. The insights build upon the previous activity's experiences.	Student includes at least two new insights for 75% of the activities. Most of the insights build upon the previous activity's experiences.	Student includes at least two new insights for 50% of the activities. Only some of the insights address the knowledge gained in the previous activity.	Student includes at least two new insights for less than 25% of the activities. The insights are not coherent and/or do not relate to the knowledge gained in previous activities.
QUESTIONS	Student poses different questions for each activity. More than half of the questions pertain to the species role in the food web.	Student poses different questions for 75% of the activities. Half of the questions pertain to the species role in the food web.	Student poses different questions for 50% of the activities. Less than half of the questions pertain to the species role in the food web.	Student poses different questions for less than 25% of the activities. None of the questions pertain to the species role in the food web.
LEARNINGS	Student answers all of the questions.	Student answers 75% of the questions.	Student answers half of the questions.	Student answers less than 25% of the questions.
SOURCES	Student correctly identifies the sources used for all of the journal pages	Student correctly identifies the sources used for 75% of the journal pages.	Student correctly identifies the sources used for half of the journal pages.	Student correctly identifies the sources used for less than 25% of the journal pages.

EXPLORE   **5 | Sand Study**

ELEMENTS	☆ ☆ ☆ ☆	☆ ☆ ☆	☆ ☆	☆
SAND STUDY: Student contributes a rock, develops a hypothesis and helps to shake the rocks.	Addresses all of the components	Missing one component	Missing two components	Missing three or more components
PARTNER: Student works with a partner to discuss where sand comes from and the significance of erosion.	Addresses all of the components	Missing one component	Missing two components	Missing three or more components
OBSERVATION: Student closely observes and sketches 3 particles of sand under a hand lens or microscope and uses appropriate descriptive words.	Addresses all of the components	Missing one component	Missing two components	Missing three or more components
JOURNAL: Students answers journal questions thoroughly, accurately and reflectively.	Addresses all of the components	Missing one component	Missing two components	Missing three or more components

EXPLORE   **6 | Moving Sand**

ELEMENTS	☆☆☆☆	☆☆☆	☆☆	☆
DISCUSSION: Student participates in the initial discussion and exhibits active listening skills (eye-contact, confirming or referencing others' comments, affirmative gestures or comments).	Addresses all of the components	Missing one component	Missing two components	Missing three or more components
EXPERIMENT DESIGN: Student contributes to an experiment design that addresses the question, answers journal questions, shares design ideas, and helps decide on class experiment.	Addresses all of the components	Missing one component	Missing two components	Missing three or more components
EXPERIMENT: Student follows directions and works well with others to accurately conduct the experiment with group (4-8), or helps set-up and observes demonstration. (K-3).	Addresses all of the components	Missing one component	Missing two components	Missing three or more components
CONCLUSIONS: Student discusses experiment and draws accurate conclusions. Student contributes to discussion about sand dune habitat.	Addresses all of the components	Missing one component	Missing two components	Missing three or more components

EXPLORE   **7 | Adaptations and Observations**

ELEMENTS	☆☆☆☆	☆☆☆	☆☆	☆
DUNE WALK: Student walks quietly in the dunes, making observations and listening to the educator's explanations. Student makes initial guesses about where organisms would live.	Addresses all of the components	Missing one component	Missing two components	Missing three or more components
OBSERVATION: Student makes observations and responds to journal questions, sketching 1 plant and 1 animal. Responses are accurate and show attention to detail.	Addresses all of the components	Missing one component	Missing two components	Missing three or more components
COMPARISON: As part of a group, student shares research with another group and uses it to hypothesize where each organism would live. Student records responses in her/his journal.	Addresses all of the components	Missing one component	Missing two components	Missing three or more components
DISCUSSION: Student participates in large group discussion and exhibits active listening skills (eye-contact, confirming or referencing others' comments, affirmative gestures or comments). Student is able to explain adaptations and articulate examples.	Addresses all of the components	Missing one component	Missing two components	Missing three or more components

EXPLORE   **8 | Indoor Dunes**

ELEMENTS	☆☆☆☆	☆☆☆	☆☆	☆
DISCUSSION: Student participates in initial discussion on sand dune habitat and exhibits active listening skills (eye-contact, confirming or referencing others' comments, affirmative gestures or comments).	Addresses all of the components	Missing one component	Missing two components	Missing three or more components
STATIONS: Student works with group to thoughtfully answer questions in their journals at each of the 4 stations. Student makes careful and accurate sketches with labels. Student differentiates between the micro habitats, and identifies adaptations needed to live in each one.	Addresses all of the components	Missing one component	Missing two components	Missing three or more components
DISCUSSION: Student defines and gives examples of organism adaptations. Student is able to discuss and explain the different micro habitats.	Addresses all of the components	Missing one component	Missing two components	Missing three or more components

EXPLORE **9 | Adaptation Stories**

ELEMENTS	★★★★	★★★	★★	★
PARTICIPATION: Student listens to the poem and responds to questions about the organism and its adaptations.	Addresses all of the components	Missing one component	Missing two components	Missing three or more components
RESEARCH: Student chooses an organism, poses questions about it that refer to adaptations, and finds answers to questions using multiple sources.	Addresses all of the components	Missing one component	Missing two components	Missing three or more components
STORY: Student creates a story (K-3: brief story and drawing with adaptation circled) that explains the adaptation, uses creativity, and contains an illustration. Student shares her/his story (drawing) with a partner, the class, or a younger student.	Addresses all of the components	Missing one component	Missing two components	Missing three or more components

EXPLORE **10 | Succession Circles**

ELEMENTS	★★★★	★★★	★★	★
BRAINSTORM: Student participates in initial brainstorm and contributes to list of biotic and abiotic elements in a sand dune ecosystem.	Addresses all of the components	Missing one component	Missing two components	Missing three or more components
VENN DIAGRAM: Student fills in each Venn diagram circle with 2 living and 3 nonliving components. Student lists the overlapping factors in each micro habitat.	Addresses all of the components	Missing one component	Missing two components	Missing three or more components
WRAP-UP: Student discusses the components of her/his Venn diagram and writes sentences describing the factors that contribute to the transitions between the micro habitats. Student responds to journal prompts and is able to articulate the meaning of succession as it applies to ecosystems.	Addresses all of the components	Missing one component	Missing two components	Missing three or more components

INVESTIGATE **11 | Dune Decisions**

ELEMENTS	★★★★	★★★	★★	★
BRAINSTORM: Student shares dune experiences and contributes reasons to appreciate sand dunes to the class brainstorm list.	Addresses all of the components	Missing one component	Missing two components	Missing three or more components
DILEMMAS: Student reads and responds to dilemma cards. Student records her/his own and group responses, noting how they are alike or different.	Addresses all of the components	Missing one component	Missing two components	Missing three or more components
DISCUSSION: Student helps report the dilemma and response to the class, takes part in the class discussion, and decides how this activity might change her/his real-life responses. Student contributes to the list of positive actions that can be taken for the health of sand dunes.	Addresses all of the components	Missing one component	Missing two components	Missing three or more components

INVESTIGATE 12 | Dune Mining Debate

ELEMENTS	☆☆☆☆	☆☆☆	☆☆	☆
PARTICIPATION: Student lists components of a good debate and people who might play key roles in a sand dune mining debate. Student uses active listening skills.	Addresses all of the components	Missing one component	Missing two components	Missing three or more components
RESEARCH: Student reads and summarizes an article, and shares the information with others. Students notes and discusses the point of view in the article and any bias that might be inherent to it.	Addresses all of the components	Missing one component	Missing two components	Missing three or more components
PREPARATION: Student writes a (3-5 sentence) clear statement of her/his personal beliefs about sand dune mining. Student works with others to create a statement for their character in the debate, making sure that the statement is based in fact.	Addresses all of the components	Missing one component	Missing two components	Missing three or more components
PARTICIPATION: Student fully participates in her/his role as debater and observer, adhering to time limits, taking notes, and maintaining composure as necessary. Student evaluates the debate and reflects on whether or not her/his personal position has changed as a result of the activity.	Addresses all of the components	Missing one component	Missing two components	Missing three or more components

INVESTIGATE 13 | Life in the Dunes

ELEMENTS	☆☆☆☆	☆☆☆	☆☆	☆
PREPARATION: Student aids in determining class criteria for the projects. Student works with other students and uses the guiding questions to determine format of final project, the audience it will serve, the information that it will include, and the roles that each student will take to complete the project.	Addresses all of the components	Missing one component	Missing two components	Missing three or more components
PROJECT: Student's project contains information about the sand dune micro habitats organisms adaptations, what makes the dunes unique, and (older students) biotic and abiotic factors, and succession.	Addresses all of the components	Missing one component	Missing two components	Missing three or more components
COMPONENTS: Student's project is clear, accurate, consistent in quality, creative, and contains a visual component.	Addresses all of the components	Missing one component	Missing two components	Missing three or more components
PRESENTATION: (4-8) Student evaluates another group's work and aids in presenting her/his project or the evaluated group's project to the class. Student ensures all aspects are presented and contributes her/his knowledge gain as a result of the project. Student displays and/or presents the project to another class or to the larger community	Addresses all of the components	Missing one component	Missing two components	Missing three or more components

INVESTIGATE 14 | Living Dune

ELEMENTS	☆ ☆ ☆ ☆	☆ ☆ ☆	☆ ☆	☆
PREPARATION: Student aids in determining class criteria for the projects. Student works with other students and uses the guiding questions to determine format of final project, the audience it will serve, the information that it will include, and the roles that each student will take to complete the project.	Addresses all of the components	Missing one component	Missing two components	Missing three or more components
PROJECT: Student's project contains information about the sand dune micro habitats organisms adaptations, what makes the dunes unique, and (older students) biotic and abiotic factors, and succession.	Addresses all of the components	Missing one component	Missing two components	Missing three or more components
COMPONENTS: Student's project is clear, accurate, consistent in quality, creative, and contains a visual component.	Addresses all of the components	Missing one component	Missing two components	Missing three or more components
PRESENTATION: (4-8) Student evaluates another group's work and aids in presenting her/his project or the evaluated group's project to the class. Student ensures all aspects are presented and contributes her/his knowledge gain as a result of the project. Student displays and/or presents the project to another class or to the larger community	Addresses all of the components	Missing one component	Missing two components	Missing three or more components

INVESTIGATE 15 | Dune Reflection

ELEMENTS	☆ ☆ ☆ ☆	☆ ☆ ☆	☆ ☆	☆
REFLECTION: Student reflects on what s/he has learned, problems dunes face, possible solutions and how to convey knowledge to others. Student writes goals based on these reflections.	Addresses all of the components	Missing one component	Missing two components	Missing three or more components
GOALS: Student designs a do-able project with achievable goals, while working productively with a team and using past and new knowledge.	Addresses all of the components	Missing one component	Missing two components	Missing three or more components
IMPLEMENTATION: Student works with others to implement and present a project that serves to preserve, educate about, and/or celebrate sand dunes.	Addresses all of the components	Missing one component	Missing two components	Missing three or more components

Unit 3
Wetlands

The great blue heron (Ardea herodias) is the largest heron in the Great Lakes and plays an important role in the wetland ecosystem.

essential questions

- **What are wetlands?**
- **How do wetlands work?**
- **What is the importance of wetlands in the Great Lakes watershed?**

unit overview

Concepts are explored first through the understanding of a watershed, and how coastal wetlands are connected to the Great Lakes. This is followed by activities that focus on how wetlands hold and filter water, and why this is important to the Great Lakes. A field trip to a wetland allows students to explore the biodiversity and the abiotic components that interconnect to create a complex system that filters water. Focused observations of plants and animals in the wetland give students the background they will need for the final project, which is to create a constructed wetland in the classroom. An issue-related activity explores taking action for wetland preservation within the community.

concepts

⦿ Complex systems are nested, one inside another, so that each system impacts or interacts with the next. The watersheds of coastal wetlands are nested within the larger watersheds of each of the Great Lakes. A wetland is an area in which the soil is saturated long enough during the year to support wetland plants and animals.

⦿ Living and nonliving factors work together in a wetland to create a biologically diverse system that can hold and filter water. This is significant because wetlands act as a physical barrier by holding water and releasing it slowly, protecting the Great Lakes from damage due to flooding and erosion. In addition, water that leaves the wetland is cleaner than it was when it entered, protecting the Great Lakes from polluted runoff water.

⦿ Wetlands contain tremendous biodiversity and are essential for the healthy functioning of the Great Lakes ecosystem and organisms.

unit activities

CONNECT

1 | Wetland Alphabet

GRADE LEVEL

K-4

90-135 minutes

Developmental Modifications: For K-2, discuss and show how words begin with different letters. Students can each work on one word to create a class alphabet book or each create their own.

summary

Students create an alphabet book of wetland words. They become familiar with wetlands while practicing letters, writing and drawing.

objectives

- List some parts of a wetland.
- Define wetland words.
- Make a class or individual alphabet book.

prerequisite

None

vocabulary

Wetland: an area in which the soil is saturated long enough during the year to support wetland plants and animals

setting

INDOORS

subjects

Language Arts, Art, Ecology

standards

This Great Lakes in My World activity is aligned to the Common Core State Standards and to state learning standards in:

Illinois
Indiana
Michigan
Minnesota
New York
Ohio
Pennsylvania
Wisconsin

This alignment is available on your Great Lakes in My World CD in the "Standards" folder and on-line at http://www.greatlakes.org/ GLiMWstandards.

materials

- Journals
- Pencils
- Art supplies
- Image of wetland (on cd)

background

Wetlands include marshes, swamps, bogs, wet meadows, and transitional edges of streams, rivers and lakes. Wetlands provide habitat for a wide variety of organisms; more growth and nutrient cycling takes place in wetlands than in any other ecosystem. Wetlands play an important role in improving water quality and reducing floods: they slow surface runoff, protect shorelines from erosion, retain nutrients, trap sediment and process organic waste, and then slowly release filtered water. When using Creature Cards for this activity, species that live in an interdunal pond would also live in a wetland.

This project can be adapted for use with any of the Great Lakes in My World units. Use Great Lakes Creature Cards for images for some of the words below.

Alphabetic examples of wetland words:

Algae: *aquatic plants that contain chlorophyll and can make food from sunlight, but lack roots, stems, or leaves; range from microscopic single cells to large structures.*

Bird, Butterfly, Beaver, Bullrush, Bog

Catfish, Cattail, Caterpillar, Crayfish

Dragonfly, Duck

Eggs, Estuary: *The mouth of a river valley, or a bay or lagoon receiving fresh water, protected from open water but still influenced by it.*

Fish, Frog, Fen

Gull, Grass

Heron

Insect, Ice

Joe-pye Weed: *Tall, perennial herb 60-200 cm. high with one to several stems and orange flowers.*

Kids

Loon, Lotus, Lagoon: *An area of shallow water separated from the lake by dunes.*

Muskrat, Mink, Marsh, Mud, Milkweed: *Plant that produces a milky juice, has flowers. Found in wet soil.*

Nest, Nutrients

Otter

Pond, Purple Loosestrife, Pitcher Plant

Quaking Aspen

Rock, Reflection, River, Rain

Snail, Snake, Salamander, Soil, Swamp

Tadpole, Turtle, Toad, Tributary: *A stream that flows to another stream or body of water.*

Underwater

Vegetation, Vapor: *Water in its gaseous state;* Vascular Plant: *A plant with tissue—xylem and phloem—to carry water and sugars through the plant.*

Water Strider, Wet, Willow, Water

Xylem: *Vascular tissue that carries water through the stems, roots, and leaves.*

Yellow Perch, Yellow-headed blackbird

Zooplankton: *Microscopic organisms that float freely in water. Cannot produce food from sunlight.*

EXAMPLE

D is for *dragonfly*

A dragonfly spends part of its life in the water, and part of its life on land.

procedure

1. As a class, ask students to describe a wetland. Show images (from compact disc). Brainstorm a list of words about wetlands, including objects and organisms that are important to a wetland. If the class has difficulty with any letters, use the list in the background section for more ideas.
2. Assign each student a letter and a word. More than one student may have the same letter, and use different words.
3. In their journals, students should write the letter and word as neatly as possible.
4. Have students write a sentence about their object or organism and draw a picture. For grades 3-4, have students write one to three research questions about it.
5. Students can find information about select organisms on the Creature Cards and can do additional research through books or the internet.
6. Collect the students' work to assemble one collective alphabet book, or to copy sets so that each student can construct their own A-Z book.

....

wrap-up

1. Share the wetland alphabet book with another class. Display them in the library or during a parent visit night. Students in grades 3-4 could share their books with students in K-2.

....

extension

As an ongoing research project, students could spend time each day making a new word, until they complete the alphabet. This project idea can extend to other art projects, such as: clay tiles or quilt blocks. As a way for older and younger students to work together, students in grades 3-4 can write out the word and younger students can copy it. The older students can later help the younger students to assemble their class alphabet book.

....

assessment

Rubric on page 246

1 | Wetland Alphabet

GRADE LEVEL
K-4

journal pages

FIRST NAME																			
LAST NAME																			

[1] Write the letter and word below.

.... is for..

.... is for..

[2] Draw a picture of the word.

[3] Write a sentence about your word here.

....

....

....

[4] Write questions and answers here.

....

....

....

....

....

APPROVED BY	

2 | Wetland Song

45 minutes

Developmental Modifications: For kindergarten, write the song lyrics beforehand and teach them to the students.

summary

Students create and sing a wetland song to the tune of Row, Row, Row Your Boat using words from their alphabet books.

objectives

- List some parts of a wetland.
- Create a song based on wetlands.

prerequisite

Wetland Alphabet

vocabulary

Wetland: an area in which the soil is saturated long enough during the year to support wetland plants and animals

setting

INDOORS   OUTDOORS

subjects

Music, Language Arts, Ecology

standards

This Great Lakes in My World activity is aligned to the Common Core State Standards and to state learning standards in:

Illinois
Indiana
Michigan
Minnesota
New York
Ohio
Pennsylvania
Wisconsin

This alignment is available on your Great Lakes in My World CD in the "Standards" folder and on-line at http://www.greatlakes.org/ GLiMWstandards.

materials

- Chalkboard
- Piano or guitar (optional)

background

Wetlands include marshes, swamps, bogs, wet meadows, and transitional edges of streams, rivers and lakes.

This activity can be adapted for use in any of the Great Lakes in My World units.

The melody to Row, Row, Row Your Boat is made up of the notes C, E, and G. It has only one chord, which is C major.

procedure

1. Choose several words from Alphabet Wetland to include in the song.

2. For each word, as a class, brainstorm a list of describing words and a list of action or feeling words. Write the lists on the board. Include additional facts that the students know about these chosen organisms.

3. From the list of describing words, choose three words. From the list of action or feeling words, create a short sentence. Ask for volunteers to help create the sentences.

4. Using the above, create a verse of the song for each word.

   For example
   C is for cattail.
   Tall, brown, and fuzzy.
   The wind will blow their seeds away.
   C is for cattail.

   D is for dragonfly.
   Bright, shiny, and fast.
   They catch mosquitoes for lunch.
   D is for dragonfly.

5. Write the verses on the board so that the students can see them.

6. Play the C chord on the piano or guitar and have the students hum the tune to Row, Row, Row Your Boat. Continue to play the C chord and have the class sing the verses to their song to the tune they just hummed.

wrap-up

Students can perform their wetland song for another class or parents.

extension

This activity could be used again and again—either by creating new verses or by singing it as a part of each day during the wetland unit.

assessment

Rubric on page 246

3 | Mud Painting

45 minutes

Developmental Modifications: Younger students can do this activity with close supervision and at a site with well-defined trails that they stay on.

summary

Students create resist paintings on fabric using wetland objects and wetland mud, while reflecting on life in a wetland.

objectives

- Discuss the ethics of collecting natural objects.
- Create a piece of artwork using the technique of resist painting with natural objects.
- Reflect on a wetland as a habitat for plants and animals.
- Describe what one type of a wetland looks and feels like.

prerequisite

None

vocabulary

Resist painting: a piece of artwork that uses one substance that resists another in order to create an image; in this activity, the natural objects "resist" the mud by covering areas of the cloth

Habitat: a place or type of place where a plant or animal naturally or normally lives or grows

setting

Wetland, preferably one with open water, mud, and easy access

OUTDOORS

subjects

Art, Science

standards

This Great Lakes in My World activity is aligned to the Common Core State Standards and to state learning standards in:

Illinois
Indiana
Michigan
Minnesota
New York
Ohio
Pennsylvania
Wisconsin

This alignment is available on your Great Lakes in My World CD in the "Standards" folder and on-line at http://www.greatlakes.org/ GLiMWstandards.

materials

- Piece of light-colored fabric for each student: cotton duck canvas works well and can be purchased in bulk at art supply stores
- Mud from the wetland
- Natural objects
- Waders
- Bucket of water to clean hands

background

Resist painting is done by using a paint/dye-resistant material such as wax to create a picture on paper or fabric, then coloring the fabric with paint or dye. When the resist is removed, the areas that were covered will have no dye.

procedure

1. Advance Preparation: Visit the site you'll be using to check conditions. Share obstacles or off-limit areas with chaperones (e.g. sections of deep water or sawgrass). Check on restrictions at the site for collecting natural objects. Send permission slips and notes home with students regarding proper dress - old shoes or boots, old clothes, sturdy jeans, no shorts.

2. Discuss with the class the ethics of collecting natural materials. Ask students what they think is appropriate to collect, in what way, and in what quantity. Let them know that laws prohibit collection of feathers from migratory birds, all nests, and those plants on the Threatened and Endangered Species List. Many natural areas do not always allow the collection of leaves, mushrooms and berries. (Check on what is allowed at the site you will be visiting). Botanists do not generally collect a plant unless there are at least 10 others of the same species nearby. Discuss the difference between renewable and nonrenewable materials.

3. Establish rules: no throwing mud, no pushing people in the water, must stay within boundaries. Give each student a piece of fabric and have him or her dip it into the wetland to get it wet. If this is not possible, or if it is dangerous, an adult should do this or have buckets of water for the students to use. For younger children, it is recommended that parents or chaperones get the fabric wet.

4. Have students collect natural objects such as leaves, rocks and grasses (in moderation) and arrange them on their fabric.

5. Allow students to collect some mud from the wetland. The stain from the mud is what will dye their fabric. They should pile the wet mud onto their fabric being very careful not to disturb the arranged objects. If the mud is allowed to seep under the edges of the objects, their images will not show up. The objects that work best are flush against the fabric.

6. Allow the mud to dry in the sun. While the mud is drying, clean mud off hands, do the wrap-up and guide the students through a different wetland activity from this unit, time allowing.

7. When the fabric is dry, peel the mud and objects off of the fabric to reveal the pictures.

wrap-up

1. As a class, discuss what objects each student chose to include in their mud paintings and why. How did it feel to dip their hands into the mud? What did students observe about the wetland while working? What makes this a good place for organisms to live? What might life be like for plants and animals living in the wetland?

2. Have students choose from the above discussion questions and free-write about the experience and their reflections on the wetland.

assessment

Rubric on page 246

We value your thoughts and feedback on Great Lakes in My World. Please let us know about any oversights, errors or omissions you find, or if there are things you or your students particularly like.

Send your comments to: education@greatlakes.org

3 | Mud Painting

GRADE LEVEL
4-8

FIRST NAME																				
LAST NAME																				

Choose one or more questions and respond during the given amount of time.

[1] What did you observe about the wetland?

....
....
....
....
....
....
....

[2] What makes this a good place for organisms to live?

....
....
....
....
....
....
....

[3] What might life be like for plants and animals living in the wetland?

....
....
....
....
....
....
....
....

APPROVED BY

EXPLORE

4 | Groundwater Exploration

GRADE LEVEL
4-8

60-90 minutes

Developmental Modification: Younger students can forego the internet research and focus on a general map and an illustrated version of the water journey story.

summary

Students make a model to learn how groundwater moves. They locate wetlands on a map of the local watershed and write about the movement of water through their watershed.

objectives

- Locate local wetland(s) in relation to the school and the nearest Great Lake.
- Gain a greater understanding of the watershed concept.
- Observe groundwater flow in a model wetland.
- Describe and diagram the path of water in their local watershed.

prerequisite

Mud Painting, Wetland Alphabet, Watershed Orientation (Lake Unit)

vocabulary

Groundwater: water within the earth that supplies wells and springs
Permeable: having pores or openings that permit liquids or gases to pass through
Water table: the upper limit of the portion of the ground completely soaked with water
Aquifer: the geologic material that stores, transports and yields groundwater

setting

INDOORS

subjects

Geography, Geology

standards

This Great Lakes in My World activity is aligned to the Common Core State Standards and to state learning standards in:

Illinois
Indiana
Michigan
Minnesota
New York
Ohio
Pennsylvania
Wisconsin

This alignment is available on your Great Lakes in My World CD in the "Standards" folder and on-line at http://www.greatlakes.org/ GLiMWstandards.

materials

- Clear, big plastic container (large plastic bin)
- Pitcher of water
- Soil
- Sand
- Rocks
- Clay
- Journals
- Pencils
- Highlighter
- Internet access
- Map(s)
- Topographic map of the area

background

A watershed is an area of land that is drained by a body of water. Wherever you are, you are in a watershed. The boundary between two watersheds occurs where water that falls on one side of the line flows toward one body of water, while water falling on the other side of the line flows toward another body of water. Watersheds do not follow political boundaries.

Two thirds of the world's freshwater is found underground and called groundwater. This water is found in aquifers and appears at the surface as springs. Very often groundwater is interconnected with the lakes and rivers. Groundwater is all the water below the water table stored in empty spaces below the surface. Water flows through permeable surfaces into the top layer of soil. From there, it either flows into a body of water, is taken up by plant roots, or flows below the water table into the saturated zone. Groundwater flows through air pockets between soil and rock particles, following the path of least resistance. Larger soil or rock particles (such

as sand or gravel) have larger air pockets, while smaller particles (such as silt or clay) have smaller air pockets for groundwater.

Groundwater is important to the Great Lakes ecosystem. It may discharge directly to the lakes or indirectly as water that feeds the tributaries. It is also a source of drinking water for many communities in the Great Lakes basin. In addition, shallow groundwater can provide moisture to plants.

Surface runoff is water that flows over the surface of the land into bodies of water. When precipitation (rain, snow) exceeds the rate of infiltration into the soil, the ground is saturated and surface runoff begins. When a surface is non-permeable, e.g., parking lot, surface runoff begins as soon as precipitation becomes steady. Runoff may include pollutants such as; sediment, excess nutrients, trace metals, organic pollutants, grease, oil and salt from roads.

....

procedure

Part One

1. Briefly review the concept of a watershed, and have students look again at the watershed maps (from Watershed Orientation on page 17. Ask students to look at the map and find wetlands near their school. Point out any they will be visiting.

2. Look at a local map. Once you have located your wetland and watershed, outline them on a road map of your region that shows rivers and the lake. Use pencil first, then marker. If you can obtain more than one map, try this activity in small groups.

3. Show the students the map and point out a nearby wetland. Have the students locate the school and the local Great Lake on the map. In what watershed are your school and the wetland? What does that mean? *A watershed is an area of land that is drained by a particular body of water. Everything is located in a watershed. If your school and the wetland are a part of the same watershed, then the rain that falls on the playground ends up in the same place as the water that seeps through the soil in the wetland. You are in the larger watershed of your Great Lake, and a smaller watershed of a river or stream.*

4. You are located in a watershed within a watershed, like a set of Russian dolls. Examine this set of "Russian dolls" to find all of your watersheds. What is the largest watershed in which your school is located? *If you are located in the Midwest, then you are in the watershed of the Atlantic Ocean. Look on the map to find the St. Lawrence River, which flows from the Great Lakes to the Atlantic Ocean.* What is the next largest watershed in which your school is located? *The Great Lakes watershed. All of the water within the Great Lakes basin (or watershed) flows into one of the Great Lakes.* What is the next largest watershed in which your school is located? *You are within the watershed of one of the Great Lakes. Look on the Great Lakes Watershed map from Watershed Orientation on page 17 to find out which one.* What is the next largest watershed in which your school is located? *This is the smaller watershed that you found on the internet. It may be the watershed of a river, stream, or wetland.*

procedure continued

Part Two

1. Now that students can map their watershed, let them discover what it means for water to flow through one. Explain the concept of groundwater and tell students is one of the ways that water makes it way back into the Great Lakes. It is an especially important source because the Great Lakes were formed by glaciers and have relatively few surface tributaries.

2. Fill 2-3 clear plastic containers with the soil, clay, sand and rocks. Allow students to decide where each material will go in the bins. Having several bins will allow students to see better and to compare different bin set-ups.

3. Pour some water into the bins, and from the side of the container, watch it move through the materials. Explain to students that they are watching what it would look like if they could see water moving underground. The bottom of the bin represents impermeable bedrock. Tilt the bin to show water moving as it would downhill. Ask students to imagine this happening on a larger scale. Ask students why the water moves differently through/around the different materials in the bin. *Water takes the path of least resistance, so it will move around objects or substrates that are more difficult to move through. Water moves through different substrates at different rates (quickly through sand, slowly through clay).*

4. Have the students take a close look at the map. Is their wetland a coastal or inland wetland? Can they tell how the water from the wetland eventually finds its way to the lake ? Do they think it moves underground or above ground? Is the wetland located near a river or tributary? Does it have direct contact with the lake, or does the water travel primarily through the soil? *It will help to look at a topographic map of the area to determine the directions of water flow.*

5. Ask a volunteer to highlight the possible path that water takes from the wetland to the Great Lake.

6. Ask students to begin thinking about why it is significant that the wetland is (or is not) connected (hydrologically) to the Great Lake.

7. Have a volunteer highlight the roads on the map that go from the school to the wetland site.

8. Ask students what would be the best way to get to the wetland: is it within walking distance; is there a bus or train that goes there?

wrap-up

1. Take students outside, or even just to the window. Pour a glass of water onto the ground. Explain that if there was a lot of rain, this water will make its way into the body of water that drains your watershed. Explain that if conditions are fairly dry, it will evaporate instead, become absorbed by the soil or be taken up by plant roots. Ask the students to imagine the path that the water might take from school on its way to the wetland, the river or stream, and eventually the lake. What might it have to go through and what are some things it could encounter on its way? *Sewer pipes, large rocks, groundhog tunnels, deep roots. It may help students to imagine that it is raining in order to visualize the water moving through the watershed.*

2. Have students spend 10 minutes writing on this in their journals. They may want to illustrate their writing with a diagram. *The water could be used by plants or animals, travel underground through the soil, evaporate and rain down again in a new place, etc.*

extension

Have students research problems related to groundwater depletion and pollution for Great Lakes communities dependent on this groundwater.

(!) We value your thoughts and feedback on Great Lakes in My World. Please let us know about any oversights, errors or omissions you find, or if there are things you or your students particularly like.

Send your comments to: education@greatlakes.org

assessment

Rubric on page 246

4 | Groundwater Exploration

GRADE LEVEL
4-8

FIRST NAME																			
LAST NAME																			

[1] Define: watershed

....

....

....

[2] What is groundwater?

....

....

....

[3] Why is groundwater important to people and to watersheds?

....

....

....

[4] Sketch a map of your local watershed. Include your school, a wetland, any rivers or streams, and the Great Lake nearest you. Draw arrows from the wetland to the lake, following the path you think the water might take.

APPROVED BY

4 | Groundwater Exploration

GRADE LEVEL
4-8

journal ≡ pages

| FIRST NAME | | | | | | | | | | | | | | | | | | | | | |
| LAST NAME | | | | | | | | | | | | | | | | | | | | | |

[5] Water Journey: Write about the path water might take from where you're sitting to the lake. What might it encounter along the way?

APPROVED BY

5 | Value of Wetlands

Developmental Modification: (K-3) Do the model as a demonstration and read the poem Value of a Wetland for class discussion and illustration. Use K-3 Journal Pages.

summary

Students participate in a demonstration of the values of a wetland and use poetry to discuss the significance of a wetland ecosystem.

objectives

- Create a simple model of a wetland.
- Describe several values of a wetland.
- Discuss the importance of a wetland to the Great Lakes ecosystem.

prerequisite

Mud Painting, Alphabet Book, or Wetland Song

vocabulary

Habitat: a place or type of place where a plant or animal naturally or normally lives or grows

Filter: a substance with pores through which a gas or liquid is passed to separate out floating matter

Runoff: water from rain or snow that flows over the surface of the ground and finally into lakes and streams

setting

OUTDOORS

subjects

Ecology

standards

This Great Lakes in My World activity is aligned to the Common Core State Standards and to state learning standards in:

Illinois
Indiana
Michigan
Minnesota
New York
Ohio
Pennsylvania
Wisconsin

This alignment is available on your Great Lakes in My World CD in the "Standards" folder and on-line at http://www.greatlakes.org/ GLiMWstandards.

materials

- Handful of soil
- Aluminum foil baking dish with a hole punched in one corner
- Pitcher of water
- Sponges (1 or 2- large enough to fill the baking pan)
- Tub to catch spilled water, if done indoors

background

Wetlands hold runoff water and release it slowly into the soil, which prevents destruction from floods and saves water for future use. Wetlands function as a natural water filter. Sediment in the water settles to the bottom of a wetland, and the plants absorb pollutants in the water. In these ways, coastal wetlands act as a natural buffer for the Great Lakes. Wetlands provide habitat for many Great Lakes organisms as well as species that cannot live in the Great Lakes and prefer wetlands only, allowing for a high level of biodiversity in the Great Lakes and its watershed. Many Great Lakes fish swim into coastal wetlands to spawn; many insects spend the first part of their lives in wetlands; some species feed in both the wetlands and the Great Lakes.

Threats to Wetlands

Two-thirds of original Great Lakes coastal wetlands have been destroyed or degraded by filling and drainage for development, such as urban expansion and farmland and by dredging for commercial and recreational water traffic. Wetlands may be polluted by industrial and commercial operations, agricultural runoff, stormwater and other sources. Pollutants can include sediment, excess nutrients, trace metals, organic pollutants and grease, oil and salt from roads.

Wetlands on the Great Lakes are also susceptible to invasive species such as zebra mussels, purple loosestrife and phragmites. Shoreline wetlands are susceptible to introduced species because they are located in the shallow areas at the end of the creeks and rivers that flow into the Great Lakes and St. Lawrence River.

procedure

This activity may be done: 1) as a demonstration with volunteers, 2) in small groups with teacher direction, 3) as a student-directed experiment in which students are given some background and asked to design a model of wetland functions using the materials provided. This is written as a demonstration.

1. Show students the aluminum pan with the sponges in it and tell them that it represents a wetland. Ask for a volunteer to hold the "wetland". Pour some water into the wetland and explain that it is raining. Watch how much water comes out of the hole in the pan *(not much)*.
2. Ask the students why the water didn't all come out of the pan. *The sponges, or wetland soil and plants, absorbed the water. Press gently on the sponges so that more water comes out of the pan. Explain that the wetland slowly releases water into the soil.*
3. Take the sponges out of the pan. The wetland has been removed, and the pan now represents a parking lot, or another paved surface. Pour water into the pan again and watch as it all comes out of the hole. Ask students why this happened. *There was nothing to absorb the water. Ask students where this water will go. Into the lakes, streets, sewers, neighborhoods, etc. At this point, the water is no longer usable, as it is dirty from the streets.*
4. Discuss the role of wetlands in holding water. What would happen if the runoff water all went into the city streets and the lakes? What impacts would this have on the lake? What impacts would this have on your neighborhoods? *Without wetlands to hold excess water, the lake and surrounding areas would flood.*

5. Ask for a new volunteer to hold the wetland and one to add soil to the pitcher of water. Explain that this represents dirty water (which it is). After wringing out the sponges and returning them to the pan, pour the dirty water into the wetland. Watch the water that flows out of the pan and gently squeeze the sponges to release more water.
6. Ask students what they observe. *The water leaving the pan is cleaner than the water in the pitcher. The soil is trapped in the wetland. Explain that the sponge catching the dirt represents sediment that settles to the bottom of a wetland and pollutants that are absorbed by plant roots.*
7. How does a wetland's filtration ability impact water that re-enters the lakes from the wetlands? What would happen if the wetlands weren't there to filter water before it entered the lake? *Wetlands filter pollutants and excess nutrients from water. Without the wetlands, the lake would have a higher pollutant level.*
   Consider using other objects (coffee filter, strainer) as metaphors for the ways a wetland functions.
8. Ask students what other values a wetland might have. What plants and animals might live in a wetland? *Answers might include: algae, lily pads, frogs, fish, birds. Why do these organisms need a wetland instead of another habitat? Wetlands provide a water source for at least part of the year, which is essential for organisms that spend all or part of their lives in the water. The water in wetlands creates special soil that allows wetland plants to grow.*

wrap-up

1. Have a class discussion about the value of holding and filtering water, and wetland habitat. Are these things important? Why? Who uses this water? *Wetlands are valuable in that they prevent flooding of the lake and surrounding areas and they keep the lake water clean. The water that moves through wetlands is used by many plants and animals, and may also be used for human drinking water, depending on your local area.*

Wetlands are necessary for a healthy Great Lakes fishery as many fish live in wetlands for part of their lives.
2. Read "Value of Wetlands" poem and discuss the main points with students.
3. Have students draw pictures in their journals to illustrate the points that were demonstrated. They should draw an example of a wetland, not a pan and sponges.

assessment

Rubric on page 246

5 | Value of Wetlands

GRADE LEVEL
4-8

journal pages

| FIRST NAME | | | | | | | | | | | | | | | | | | | |
| LAST NAME | | | | | | | | | | | | | | | | | | | |

[1] Think about the activity with the sponge and the pan of water. Draw a diagram of a wetland that shows that it holds water like a sponge. Include plants and soil in your picture.

[2] Think about the activity with the dirty water. Draw a diagram of a wetland that shows how it filters water. Include sediment that falls to the bottom of a wetland and the roots of plants that absorb other pollutants.

APPROVED BY

5 | Value of Wetlands

FIRST NAME

LAST NAME

Value of Wetlands

I go down to the wetland
For my favorite thing
The chorus of peepers
That sing in the spring.

The slider turtles
Bask on a log
After the morning
Has lifted the fog.

Heavy clouds drop
Their rain on the ground;
It pools in the ponds
That keep the water around.

Cattails still cling
To their seeds for good luck
And their roots reach deep,
Down into the muck.

Invertebrates hide
At the bottoms of weeds,
While red-winged blackbirds
Bounce in the tops of the reeds.

Nymphs swim underwater
Until they become
Dazzling dragonflies
That shine in the sun.

The lake that is filled
With water so clean,
The fish that spawn,
And the birds that preen,

Owe much to the wetlands,
The ponds, and streams,
The special places
Where freshwater gleams.

The species that live
In the wetlands make
The water cleaner
Before it flows to the lake.

The wetlands are the
Great Lakes' key to survive;
The keepers of water,
The cradles of lives.

Author: Anne Richardson

[3] Draw a diagram of a wetland. Include plants and animals (see poem) that would live
in a wetland.

APPROVED BY

5 | Value of Wetlands

FIRST NAME																			
LAST NAME																			

[1] Fill in the blanks.

A wetland _____ _____ _____ _____ _____ water, preventing floods.

A wetland _____ _____ _____ _____ _____ _____ _____ water, making it clean.

A wetland provides _____ _____ _____ _____ _____ _____ _____ for plants and animals.

Word Bank: FILTERS   HABITAT
             SPACE   MUD
             EMPTIES   HOLDS

[2] Draw a picture of a wetland that shows it is a home for plants and animals.

APPROVED BY	

EXPLORE

6 | Wetland Observation

GRADE LEVEL

4-8

90-135 minutes

Developmental Modifications: For younger students, use K-3 journal pages and follow procedure modifications.

summary

Students work in small groups to record observations of the wetland and make connections between its plants, animals, soils, water and topography.

objectives

- Observe and record different aspects of a wetland, including the water, soil, plants, animals and changes in topography.
- List relationships that exist within the wetland.
- Discuss the significance of wetlands to the Great Lakes.

prerequisite

Wetland Song, Wetland Alphabet, or Value of Wetlands

vocabulary

Topography: features of a landscape, with special attention paid to changes in elevation

setting

OUTDOORS

Wetland

subjects

Geology, Biology, Ecology, Art, Language Arts

standards

This Great Lakes in My World activity is aligned to the Common Core State Standards and to state learning standards in:

Illinois
Indiana
Michigan
Minnesota
New York
Ohio
Pennsylvania
Wisconsin

This alignment is available on your Great Lakes in My World CD in the "Standards" folder and on-line at http://www.greatlakes.org/ GLiMWstandards.

materials

- Glass jars with lids
- Quart-sized sealable bags
- Journals
- Pencils
- Field guides
- Clipboards
- Pond nets
- Chaperones
- Hand lenses

background

Students will be observing aspects of the wetland, including soils, plants, animals, and other components of the physical environment. Observation is the basis of science. Students must learn to be keen observers of their natural surroundings in order to formulate questions and make connections.

Soil Types

Different types of soil develop under different types of conditions affected by:

"Parent" rock - weathering breaks down this rock into mineral particles. Physical weathering comes from ice, rain and wind. Chemical weathering occurs, for instance, when water dissolves certain minerals.

Climate and topography - warm, humid areas allow for more chemical weathering and biological activity. So, cool, dry climates have shallower and less developed soils. Slopes bring water erosion exposing more rock to weathering.

Plants and animals - these prevent erosion and help develop soil. Death and decay add organic matter that, in turn, supports more life.

Time - Over long periods of time, soils can become deep and well-developed unless they erode quickly or have been protected by weathering.

Soil is made up of organic and mineral particles. The mineral particles are recognized by size:

* clay (less than 0.002mm)
* silt (.002-.2mm)
* sand (.2-1mm)
* gravel (1-64mm)

Water and air fill the spaces between the particles. Water flows faster through large particles than small particles. Thus, sandy soils drain quickly, but clay soils do not.

Wetland Soils

Scientists call wetland soils "hydric." Since wetlands are not always wet, the presence of hydric soils often helps to determine whether or not a piece of land is actually a wetland. Hydric soils form when the land remains so saturated for an extended period of time that oxygen cannot fill any of the spaces between the soil particles. Only certain wetland plants can live in these conditions and they too, help to determine if a site is actually a wetland.

There are various kinds of hydric soils, but many have the following characteristics:

* excessive moisture
* "rotten egg" odor
* reddish or dark-colored streaks
* thick layer of decaying plants
* black, bluish gray or gray color below the surface

Plant Identification

Plant identification can begin by looking at the pattern of leaves along the stem. Some plants have leaves that emerge only at the base (basal) , e.g., dandelion. Some have leaves along the stem either alternate growth or opposite growth.

| Opposite | Alternate |

procedure

Part One: Observation Skills

This part of the activity can also be done at school before the field trip.

1. Ask students to take 5 minutes to walk around and look for a rock that fits into his/her hand to bring back to the group. If this part of the activity is done in the classroom, another object, such as pencils, could be used in place of rocks.

2. Have students sit in a circle on the ground. (This can be done in two groups) Give them time to make some observations about their rocks and for older students, record them in their journals.

3. Have students place their rocks into the center of the circle, then close their eyes. While their eyes are closed, mix up the pile of rocks.

4. Now, have students open their eyes. Ask for a volunteer to look through the pile and find his/her rock. The student should tell the class 2 defining features that make his/her rock different from all of the others. Allow for a few more volunteers.

5. Ask students what sorts of things about their rocks might be important to observe and record. How detailed do observations need to be? What about observations of the wetland? *The more detailed the students' observations and journal entries are, the more information they will have to refer to later. As time goes by, it will be more difficult to recall details unless they have been recorded.*

Part Two: Small Group Observation (at wetland)

1. Explain that students will be making focused observations about the wetland and recording them in their journals. Like the rock activity, it is important that their observations are detailed. They may make notes, ask questions, make sketches, charts to include the necessary content. They should follow the directions in the Journal Pages.

2. Divide students into four groups with chaperones for each group (two abiotic groups: physical environment and soil; two biotic groups: plants and animals) The Critical Critters or Bugs in the Mud activity may be condensed into one of these small groups, yielding five groups instead of four. You may have students rotate through each of these stations, or spend time at only one station, depending on the time available. If they are not rotating through all of the stations, they only need to answer journal questions for their own group, but should read through or discuss the questions for other groups.

3. If students do not rotate through all of the stations, form new groups made up of one student from each original group, a technique also known as "jigsaw." This works best with older students. Students should each spend three-five minutes sharing their journal responses with the new group members.

4. At some point during the day, all students should take some time to sketch the wetland.

Tips for this activity

Physical Environment

If the water from the wetland doesn't flow into a stream or river, there might be another way in which the wetland water finds its way to the Great Lake. The wetland water seeps into the soil, and likely becomes a part of the groundwater, which will ultimately make its way to the lake or an aquifer. Ask students to make a note in their drawings of where the local Great Lake is, even if it cannot be seen from the wetland.

Soil

See Background section and Journal Page directions. If comparing wetland and Great Lake soils, consider that wetlands have special soils; the soil from your wetland will probably be more rich in organic matter than the soil in the lake.

Animals

Discuss the differences and similarities between plants and animals and their basic needs: food, water, habitat. Regarding whether or not an animal could be found in the Great Lakes - some wetland animals do not ever live in lakes, or they may spend part of their lives in the wetland, and part on land or in the lake.

Plants

See Background notes.

If there is open water, have students observe plants that are surrounding it, in it (emergent), and under it (submergent).

- When choosing one plant on which to focus a journal entry, each student in the group should choose a different plant with help from the teacher. This information will be used again in Name that Plant.
- When discussing whether or not this plant could be found in the Great Lakes, consider that wetland plants require special soil and bacteria that lives in the soil. Some plants may be able to live in a large lake, and some may not.

Plant collection for Name that Plant activity: If plant collection is allowed, consider collecting one plant of each species studied. Press it between several layers of newspaper and cardboard, or use a plant press. Carefully dig up roots and spread out leaves and petals when pressing. These are called herbarium samples and should include a collection label with pertinent details such as date and location.

....

wrap-up

1. Ask students what they saw during the day. Allow time to share discoveries or interesting observations. Explain to the class that they were asked to observe a wide range of things in a short time period, so now they will synthesize the information. For 4-8, use the Synthesis Page to focus the discussion. For K-3, use each station's Journal Page.
2. After they have completed filling out the Journal Pages, have them share responses and discuss answers.

- Ask the students where they think the water in the wetland is coming from. *In some cases, water may be fed in through a stream or river, it may come from groundwater, it may be runoff water from another surface, or some combination.*
- Ask students what types of soils they found. Ask how they think the soil plays a role in holding the water in place. *Clay holds water and releases it slowly, due to the small grain size. Sand grains have more space between them, so water can easily slip through. In some cases, sand or gravel can act as an aquifer, holding water in the spaces between the grains, if there is bedrock to ultimately keep the water from seeping away.*
- How do plants play a role in holding the soil or water in place? *The roots of plants hold the soils in place and filter the water as it passes through. Plants also provide food and shelter for other organisms and help filter pollutants from the water by absorbing them through their roots.*
- How does the water leave the wetland? *It may drain through a river or stream, through groundwater, evaporation, or transpiration.*
- Ask students what animals they saw. Ask students what ideas they have about why these animals choose to live in or around a wetland.
- Have students conclude by talking about what they liked about the wetland.

3. For grades 4-8, tell students they will play a game in which their group must try to find connections between the parts of a wetland, and record them in the journal pages. They can work in their original observation groups For K-3, have students discuss the connections between aspects of the wetland in a large group.
4. They are looking for ways in which their biotic or abiotic components interact or depend on each other for survival. *For example, plants need soil to root in, and the roots in turn hold the soil in place; animals eat each other to gain nutrients and energy. The goal is to find as many connections as possible. A connection might be a predator-prey relationship, or other ways in which organisms depend on each other.*
5. At the end of 15 minutes, grade 4-8 groups should present the connections they found to the class. Students should also explain how these connections benefit the wetland. Ask students to think about how this is related to the Great Lakes. *The elements of a wetland work together to provide habitat for organisms, to hold and release water into the Great Lakes, and to filter water before it reaches the Great Lakes.*

Extension

If you know of another school doing a similar project, do some water quality testing and compare results with the wetland of the other class. To find other schools with whom to compare data, go to http://globe.gov/. Discuss how the health of your wetland impacts the Great Lakes.

....

assessment

Rubric on page 247

6 | Wetland Observation

GRADE LEVEL
K-8

FIRST NAME

LAST NAME

[1] Object Observations

[2] What are you looking forward to seeing and doing at the wetland?

APPROVED BY

6 | Wetland Observation

GRADE LEVEL
4-8

journal pages

FIRST NAME																			
LAST NAME																			

[1] SKetch the wetland here.

[2] What questions do you have about the wetland and its inhabitants?

....

....

....

....

....

....

....

APPROVED BY	

6 | Wetland Observation

GRADE LEVEL
4-8

journal pages

FIRST NAME																		
LAST NAME																		

Physical Environment Observations

Date:_____ Time:_____ Location:_____

[1] Weather (cloud cover, wind, approximate temperature, precipitation, humidity)

....

[2] What are the major landforms? For example, hills, valleys, ridges plains.

....

....

[3] What is the approximate size of the wetland? Estimate the length and width in meters.

....

[4] Is the wetland exposed to the sun? How much?

....

[5] How is the wetland connected to the local Great Lake?

....

....

[6] What is its source of water? Does it have an inlet?

....

[7] Do you think the water from the wetland seeps into the groundwater? How might
    you be able to tell? Does the wetland have an outlet?

....

....

[8] What surrounds the wetland?

....

....

....

[9] Other observations:

....

....

....

APPROVED BY	

6 | Wetland Observation

GRADE LEVEL
4-8

FIRST NAME																			
LAST NAME																			

Animal Observations

[1] What animals do you see?

....

....

....

....

....

....

....

[2] Choose one animal to sketch. Choose an insect so that you can observe it for
several minutes. If you cannot see an animal, look for signs of animals, such as:
tracks, feathers, fur, burrows, shells, chewed twigs or scat (animal droppings).

APPROVED BY	

6 | Wetland Observation

FIRST NAME																	
LAST NAME																	

Animal Observations

Focus on a small animal, such as an insect, so that you can observe it for several minutes.

[1] Where is the animal?

....

....

[2] What is it doing?

....

....

[3] Is it in the water or on land? Why?

....

....

[4] Can you tell or guess what it eats?

....

....

[5] Do you think it is a predator or a prey animal? Why?

....

....

[6] Is the animal interacting with another animal? If so, how?

....

....

[7] Is the animal interacting with any plants? If so, how?

....

....

[8] Do you think that this animal could be found in the Great Lakes? Why or why not?

....

....

....

APPROVED BY	

6 | Wetland Observation

GRADE LEVEL
4-8

journal ≣ pages

FIRST NAME																		
LAST NAME																		

Plant Observations

[1] Record the common plants and their locations. If a field guide is available, try to identify them. Describe several plants:

a. ....

b. ....

c. ....

[2] Choose one plant to study. Draw the plant and fill in the information. Label important characteristics on the drawing.

TYPE (circle one)
Woody/Herbaceous

BRANCHING
Opposite/Alternate

FLOWERS
Yes/No
Number of Petals _____
Color _____

SEEDS
Fruit/Nut/Parachute/
Hitchhiker/Other

LEAVES
Color _____
Shape _____
Height _____

OTHER INFORMATION _____
_____
_____
_____

SUNLIGHT
Sunny/Shady

SOIL
Wet/Medium/Dry
Clayey/Sandy/Mixed

LOCATION
Underwater/Emerging
from the water/At the edge
of the water/On land

ABUNDANCE
High Number/Medium/Very
Few

OTHER PLANTS NEARBY
_____
_____
_____
_____
_____
_____
_____

[3] Do you think this plant could be found in the Great Lakes? Why or why not?

....

....

....

APPROVED BY	

6 | Wetland Observation

FIRST NAME																	
LAST NAME																	

Soil Observations

Conduct some tests to learn about the soil. Test one sample from underwater and one from the edge of the wetland.

[1] Fill a jar three quarters with water. Add a handful of soil to the jar. Secure the lid and shake. Let the jar stand undisturbed for 15 minutes. The soil will separate into its parts: sand on the bottom, then silt, then clay; the organic material will float on top. Note: All of these parts may not necessarily be present. Repeat this with soil from the edge of the wetland.

[2] While waiting for the soil to separate, conduct another test to determine the soil type. Pick up some wet soil. Roll it between your palms into a worm shape. Try to bend the worm into a circle. If the circle cracks or falls apart, the soil contains more sand; if it stays smooth, it contains more clay.

[3] Draw the jars of soil and label the layers of sand, silt, clay, and organic material.

In the wetland   At the edge of the wetland

[4] How do the soil samples compare?

....

....

[5] What is the breakdown of soils in the jar (amounts of sand, silt, clay and organic material)?

....

....

[6] What makes up most of the soil in each of these areas?

....

[7] If you can, compare the soil from the bottom of your Great Lake with the soil of the wetland. How do the compare? Why do you think this is the case?

....

....

APPROVED BY	

6 | Wetland Observation

GRADE LEVEL
4-8

journal ⫿ pages

FIRST NAME																			
LAST NAME																			

Synthesis of Observations

[1] What is the significance of the following parts of this wetland?

Landforms ....

Location..

Sunlight/Shade ....

Soil Type ....

Animals...

Plants ....

[2] How did the water get into the wetland?

....
....
....
....

[3] How does the water leave the wetland and where does it go?

....
....
....
....
....

[4] Based on your observations, what makes a wetland an important place?

....
....
....
....
....

APPROVED BY	

6 | Wetland Observation

| FIRST NAME | | | | | | | | | | | | | | | | |
| LAST NAME | | | | | | | | | | | | | | | | |

[1] Making Connections

Here are examples of connections. How many more can your group find?

Thing A		Thing B		Relationship
Dragonfly	→	Mosquito	→	Predator-prey relationship
Cattail	→	Soil	→	Plants need soil to root in
Frog	→	Water	→	Animal needs water to drink and lay eggs
Milkweed	→	Sun	→	This plant needs lots of sunlight

| APPROVED BY | |

6 | Wetland Observation

GRADE LEVEL
K-3

FIRST NAME																				
LAST NAME																				

Environment Observations

[1] Draw the wetland

[2] Description of the wetland:

....
....
....
....
....
....
....
....
....
....

APPROVED BY	

6 | Wetland Observation

GRADE LEVEL
K-3

journal pages

FIRST NAME

LAST NAME

Environment Observations

[1] DATE: _____ _____ _____
(MONTH)   (DAY)   (YEAR)

[2] TIME: _____ : _____

[3] WEATHER (CIRCLE ONE):

SUNNY   CLOUDY   RAIN   SNOW

[4] TEMPERATURE (CIRCLE ONE):

HOT   COLD   TEMPERATURE_____

[5] What is around the wetland?..

....

....

....

....

[6] How is the wetland connected to your Great Lake?
....

....

....

....

....

....

....

....

APPROVED BY

6 | Wetland Observation

GRADE LEVEL
K-3

FIRST NAME																				
LAST NAME																				

Animal Observations

[1] DRAW AN ANIMAL
Choose one animal to draw. Look for animals on land, in the sky, in the mud, and in the water. If you do not see any animals, look for signs of animals. Draw the signs. Signs include tracks, scat, feathers, shells, chewed twigs, fur, or habitat.

[2] DESCRIPTION:
Write a description of the animal or signs of the animal.

....

....

....

....

....

....

....

....

APPROVED BY	

6 | Wetland Observation

FIRST NAME																				
LAST NAME																				

Plant Observations

[1] DRAW A PLANT
Choose one plant to draw. Think about choosing a plant from one of these parts
of the wetland: edge of the water, in the water (emergent) or under the water
(submergent).

[2] DESCRIPTION
Write a description of the plant. Include where the plant is located (emergent,
submergent, at the wetland's edge).

....

....

....

....

....

....

....

APPROVED BY	

6 | Wetland Observation

GRADE LEVEL
K-3

FIRST NAME																	
LAST NAME																	

Soil Observations

Do some tests to learn about the soil. Test one sample from underwater and one from the edge of the wetland.

1. Fill a jar three quarters with water. Add a handful of soil to the jar. Put on the lid and shake. Let the jar stand for 15 minutes. The soil will separate into parts: sand on the bottom, then silt, then clay. The organic material will float on top. Note: All of these parts may not be present. Repeat this with soil from the edge of the wetland.

2. While waiting for the soil to separate, pick up some wet soil. Roll it between your palms into a worm shape. Try to bend the worm into a circle. If the circle cracks or falls apart, the soil contains more sand; if it stays smooth, it contains more clay.

3. Draw the jars of soil and label the layers of sand, silt, clay, and organic material.

[1] DRAW THE JAR OF SOIL. Label the layers: SAND   SILT   CLAY   ORGANIC

[2] Describe the soil. What makes up most of this soil?

....

....

....

....

....

APPROVED BY	

EXPLORE

GRADE LEVEL

7 | Bugs in the Mud

K-3

60 minutes

summary

Students look for insects, snails, worms and other small wetland creatures and draw the most common ones in their journals.

objectives

- Observe invertebrates in a wetland.
- Draw an invertebrate found in the wetland.
- Discuss the importance of invertebrates in a wetland.

prerequisite

Wetland Alphabet, Value of Wetlands, Wetland Observation (or do in conjunction with this activity)

vocabulary

Invertebrate: an animal with no backbone; these are usually small, such as spiders, worms, insects and crayfish; some are so small the can only be seen with a microscope

setting

Wetland or bring samples from wetland into the classroom

OUTDOORS

subjects

Ecology, Biology

standards

This Great Lakes in My World activity is aligned to the Common Core State Standards and to state learning standards in:

Illinois
Indiana
Michigan
Minnesota
New York
Ohio
Pennsylvania
Wisconsin

This alignment is available on your Great Lakes in My World CD in the "Standards" folder and on-line at http://www.greatlakes.org/GLiMWstandards.

materials

- Buckets/ plastic tubs (one for every three students)
- Hand lenses
- Ice cube trays (one for every three students)
- Journals
- Small pond nets
- Pencils
- Plastic jar for each student
- Field guides
- Wetland Creature Sheet (page 206-207)
- Clipboards
- Chaperones

background

This activity may be done on its own or as part of Wetland Observation. Species each have a range of tolerance for the environmental conditions in which they live. Some species are good indicators of pollution, acidity, or nutrient levels. For example, a species might not be able to tolerate pollution, so if it is found, it indicates clean water. The types of invertebrates students are likely to find are: insects in their immature stages, adult insects, mites, snails and worms. Invertebrates play important roles in the wetland that range from helping with decay to serving as food for other organisms.

procedure

Advance Preparation: If possible, have an adult go to the wetland ahead of the class to collect water samples in buckets, making sure each bucket has a variety of critters.

Follow-up: The identification of the most common macroinvertebrates in the wetland will be used in Living Life cycles and in the completion of the final project, Mini-Wetland.

1. Explain to students that they will be looking at very small creatures that live in the wetland. Most of them cannot live long out of water, so they need to be kept wet at all times. Students will each have a jar—they should keep these filled part way with water so that when they find an animal to look at, they can place it into the jar right away. Once students have finished looking at the animal, they should place it into the ice cube tray—which should also be filled with water. Respect should be shown to all of the animals— even though they are small, they are important.

2. Ask students if they think that all wetlands are the same. Why not? Ask if they think a plant or animal could live in any wetland. *Some can only survive in certain wetlands where the conditions are just right. For example, some may prefer ponds, rivers or lakes. Different plants and animals prefer different types of wetlands, depending on the water quality and conditions. Plants and animals even prefer different areas of the same wetland.*

3. If you are at the wetland site, scoop some water into buckets. Make sure to have some of the samples include soil from the bottom. Fill each sample bucket with water from a different area, making sure there are critters in each bucket. Some areas to consider are: vegetated banks, unvegetated banks, silty substrate, gravel substrate, and wood debris.

4. In small groups, students should look in their buckets for tiny organisms. They may use small pond nets to scoop organisms into their jars for a closer look. Look carefully—some organisms are so small that they are easily overlooked even when in the net! Many of them could be in the soil, attached to dead leaves or camouflaged.

5. Each time a student finds an animal, they should place it into the ice cube tray (after examining it in their jar, if they choose). Encourage students to try and put all the beetle nymphs (or other like species) in one cube, for instance, and all mayflies in another, etc. This will allow students to see which type of organisms are the most common. Students may try to identify the organisms based on the pictures on the Wetland Creature Sheet or a field guide.

6. Once students are finished examining the animals in their sample, they should count the number of animals in each cube of the tray. Which had the highest number? The lowest number? Students should write the numbers in their journals. Students may use the information sheet to learn more about the organisms they find in the wetland. While this information is very general and simplified, it provides some context for study.

7. Students should each choose an organism to carefully draw in their journals. They should look at their organism through a hand lens to get the most accurate observation.

8. If time allows, students should return the organisms from the ice cube trays into the buckets and rotate. Once this is complete, empty the buckets back into the water from where they came.

wrap-up

1. Class discussion: What types of animals did the students find? What did they look like? How big were they? Which were the most common animals in each sample?

2. How can tiny animals be important in the wetland? *Each animal plays an important role in the wetland food web. These animals are food for other animals and contribute to the life of the wetland.*

3. What role do you think these organisms play in the wetland? *Some of these organisms eat decaying material, which helps to keep the wetland clean. Some are carnivores, meaning that they eat other animals.*

sources

Mandaville, S M., Bioassessment of Freshwaters Using Benthic Macroinvertebrates- A Primer. First Ed. Feb. 1999, Chapter II: Freshwater Benthic Ecology
http://lakes.chebucto.org/ZOOBENTH/BENTHOS/ii.html

assessment

Rubric on page 247

Wetland Creature Sheet

NAME		DESCRIPTION	POLLUTION TOLERANCE
Mayfly		Mayflies are only found in water during their juvenile stages. Many mayflies can live close together.	Intolerant. Found in good water quality only.
Stonefly		Stoneflies are found in water during their nymph stage. They prefer cool, clean streams with high dissolved oxygen. Some are found on the shores of large lakes.	Intolerant. Found in good water quality only.
Caddisfly		Caddisflies can be found in streams, lakes, marshes, vernal pools, and ponds.	Intolerant. Found in good water quality only.
Riffle Beetle		Riffle beetles are found in water during all stages of their life cycle.	Intolerant. Found in good water quality only.
Hellgrammite		Hellgrammites are aquatic in their larval stages and are the largest of all aquatic insects. Alderflies require mud, silt, or detritus.	Intolerant. Found in good water quality only.
Water Bug		Water bugs breathe air. They can tolerate acidic conditions.	Somewhat Tolerant. Found in good or fair water quality.

Wetland Creature Sheet

NAME	DESCRIPTION	POLLUTION TOLERANCE
True Water Mite	Water mites have eight legs, like spiders.	Somewhat tolerant. Found in good or fair water quality.
Scud or Side Swimmer	Scuds cannot live in acidic water.	Somewhat tolerant. Found in good or fair water quality.
Aquatic Sowbug	Sowbugs are sometimes confused with scuds, but are wider than they are high, and walk slowly along surfaces.	Somewhat tolerant. Found in good or fair water quality.
Crayfish	Crayfish can grow up to 6" long, and look like small lobsters. They can be found under loose rocks, feeding on detritus and other macroinvertebrates.	Somewhat tolerant. Found in good or fair water quality.
Damselfly, Dragonfly	These two insects live in water during their juvenile stages. They are .5"-1", have six legs, and large eyes. They are both predators with a hinged grasping 'jaw,' large eyes, and slender legs.	Somewhat tolerant. Found in good or fair water quality.
Aquatic worm	In polluted water, worms are much more common than other species.	Tolerant. Found in any water quality.

7 | Bugs in the Mud

GRADE LEVEL
K-3

journal pages

FIRST NAME																				
LAST NAME																				

[1] BUG NAME ....

[2] DRAW THE BUG

[3] HOW MANY IN EACH BOX? WRITE IN THE NUMBERS.

[4] CIRCLE THE HIGHEST NUMBER. UNDERLINE THE LOWEST NUMBER.

APPROVED BY	

8 | Critical Critters

60 -90 minutes

summary

Students look for macroinvertebrates in various water samples from a wetland. Students identify and record the organisms they find and discuss their ecological significance to the wetland.

objectives

- Observe macroinvertebrates in a wetland.
- Draw a wetland macroinvertebrate.
- Discuss the importance of macroinvertebrates in a wetland.
- Discuss macroinvertebrates as water quality indicators.
- Differentiate between microhabitats within a wetland.

prerequisite

Values of a Wetland, Wetland Observation (or do in conjunction with this activity)

vocabulary

Macroinvertebrate: organism lacking a backbone that is large enough to be seen by the naked eye, e.g. insects, crayfish, worms and snails
Benthic organism: organism living on the bottom of a body of water
Indicator: a species whose presence helps to identify the quality of a natural area; some insect nymphs, for instance, require clean, well-oxygenated water of a particular temperature range
Detritus: dead and decaying matter

setting

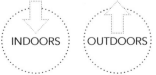

INDOORS   OUTDOORS

Wetland or bring samples from wetland into the classroom

subjects

Ecology, Biology

standards

This Great Lakes in My World activity is aligned to the Common Core State Standards and to state learning standards in:

Illinois
Indiana
Michigan
Minnesota
New York
Ohio
Pennsylvania
Wisconsin

This alignment is available on your Great Lakes in My World CD in the "Standards" folder and on-line at http://www.greatlakes.org/ GLiMWstandards.

materials

- Buckets/ plastic tubs (one for every three students)
- Ice cube trays (one for every three students)
- Small pond nets
- Hand lenses
- Pencils
- Plastic jar for each student
- Journals
- Field guides
- Wetland Creature Sheets (on page 206)
- Clipboards
- Chaperones
- 3 Copies of Journal Page 211

background

This activity may be done on its own or as part of Wetland Observation. Species each have a range of tolerance for environmental conditions. Some species are good indicators of pollution, acidity or nutrient levels. For example, a species might not be tolerant of pollution, so if it is found, it indicates clean water. Macroinvertebrates play important roles in the wetland, that range from breaking down detritus to serving as food for other organisms. The types of macroinvertebrates students are likely to find are: insects in their immature stages, adult insects, mites, snails and worms.

procedure

Advance Preparation: If possible, have one adult go to the wetland ahead of the class to collect water samples in buckets, making sure each bucket has a variety of critters. Students may need multiple copies of the accompanying journal page.

Follow-up: The identification of the most common macroinvertebrates in the wetland will be used in Living Life Cycles and in the completion of the final project, Mini-Wetland.

1. Divide students into groups of three. Explain to students that they will be looking at very small creatures that live in the wetland. Most of them cannot live long out of water, so they need to be kept wet at all times. Students will each have a jar—they should keep these filled part way with water so that when they find an animal to look at, they can place it into the jar right away. Once students have finished looking at the animal, they should place it into the ice cube tray, which should also be filled with water. Respect should be shown to all of the animals. Even though they are small, they are important.

2. Ask students if they think that all wetlands are the same. Why not? Ask if they think a plant or animal could live in any wetland. *Some can only survive in certain wetlands where the conditions are just right. For example, some may prefer ponds, rivers or lakes. Different plants and animals prefer different types of wetlands, depending on the water quality and conditions. Plants and animals even prefer different areas of the same wetland.*

3. Explain that the students will determine the water quality of their wetland based on the organisms they find. It is important to carefully identify each organism, and record each finding in the journals.

4. Before working with the organisms, have students generate several research questions about macroinvertebrates. They will research these onsite and back in the classroom.

5. If you are at the wetland site, scoop some water into buckets. Make sure to have some of the samples include soil from the bottom. Fill each sample bucket with water from a different area, making sure there are critters in each bucket.

Some areas to consider are: vegetated banks, unvegetated banks, silty substrate, gravel substrate, and wood debris.

6. In small groups, students should look in their buckets for tiny organisms. They may use small pond nets to scoop organisms into their jars for a closer look. Look carefully—some organisms are so small that they are easily overlooked even when in the net! Many of them could be in the soil, attached to dead leaves or camouflaged.

7. Each time a student finds an animal, they should place it into the ice cube tray (after examining it in their jar, if they choose). Encourage students to try and put all the beetle nymphs (or other like species) in one cube, for instance, and all mayflies in another, etc. This will allow students to see which type of organisms are the most common. Students may try to identify the organisms based on the pictures on the informational sheet or a field guide. Students observe and draw three organisms. Students should record the sample area: vegetated bank, gravel bottom, etc. and try to identify the organisms based on the pictures on the informational sheet or field guide. Students should use the information available to make notes in their journals about the type of conditions in which these organisms live. Students can also be making observations about the water clarity and soil type.

8. Have groups rotate through each of the water samples. Once this is complete, empty the buckets back into the wetland from where they came.

9. If students do not rotate through all sample buckets, have them re-arrange groups, one student from each original group in the new groups. Students should compare notes with the other students and fill in any new information into the journals.

10. In these groups, have students discuss possibilities for the condition of their wetland: is it acidic or basic? Polluted or clean? High or low in nutrients? *The information sheet provides very general information about the organisms. Although the actual wetland situation is more complex, the sheet is a good starting place for study. Students may conduct additional research.*

wrap-up

1. Each group should report their conclusions to the class, then engage in a class discussion. Discuss: What are the most common organisms found in this wetland? What have the macroinvertebrates revealed about the wetland? Is the evidence conclusive or not? Why? What is the use of doing this type of study? What roles do some of these organisms play in the wetland?

2. Information gathered in this activity can be used to complete Living Life Cycles and Mini Wetlands.

assessment

Rubric on page 247

8 | Critical Critters

GRADE LEVEL
4-8

journal ≡ pages

FIRST NAME

LAST NAME

[1] Three questions about macroinvertebrates:

a. ....

b. ....

c. ....

[2] Species ....

[3] Draw the organism here:

[4] Sample Area: ....

[5] Number Found: ....

[6] Pollution Tolerance Level: ....

[7] Other Notes: ....

....

....

....

APPROVED BY

EXPLORE

9 | Living Life Cycles

GRADE LEVEL

3-6

60-90 minutes

Developmental Modifications: Older students may focus on the different types of life cycles that organisms undergo and create skits that allow students to compare and contrast organisms.

summary

Students study the life cycles of aquatic insects, discuss the importance of wetlands as habitat and create a skit about life cycles.

objectives

- Become familiar with the life cycle of a wetland macroinvertebrate.
- Explain the role of the wetland in a species' life cycle.
- Present the life cycle of a macroinvertebrate.
- Demonstrate an understanding of the importance of macroinvertebrates in a wetland.

prerequisite

Wetland Observation, Bugs in the Mud or Critical Critters

vocabulary

Molt: to shed hair, feathers, outer skin, or horns with the cast-off parts being replaced by a new growth
Nymph: the immature stage of an insect that has incomplete metamorphosis
Metamorphosis: the process of basic and usually rather sudden change in the form and habits of some animals during transformation from an immature stage (as a tadpole or a caterpillar) to an adult stage (as a frog or a butterfly)
Larva: the wingless form of an insect that hatches from the egg and does not resemble the adult (larvae - plural)
Pupa: insect in the non-feeding stage of metamorphosis between nymph and adult, often characterized by enclosure in a cell or cocoon (pupae - plural)

setting

INDOORS   OUTDOORS

subjects

Life Science

standards

This Great Lakes in My World activity is aligned to the Common Core State Standards and to state learning standards in:

Illinois
Indiana
Michigan
Minnesota
New York
Ohio
Pennsylvania
Wisconsin

This alignment is available on your Great Lakes in My World CD in the "Standards" folder and on-line at http://www.greatlakes.org/GLiMWstandards.

materials

- Journals
- Poster board
- Pencils
- Markers
- Research materials: books, internet, experts

background

Wetlands provide rich habitat for a wide diversity of life. They are an essential breeding ground for many animals, providing critical food, shelter and water for young. Whether for laying eggs, or finding food, many organisms spend all or part of their lives in or near a wetland. Insects and amphibians are two groups that frequently use wetlands as a place for their offspring to spend part or all of their life cycles. Wetlands that are connected to a Great Lake provide breeding grounds for some lake species, increasing the diversity of life in and around the lake.

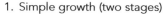

Insect Life Cycles
Once insects hatch, they follow one of three growth cycles, depending on their species.

1. Simple growth (two stages)

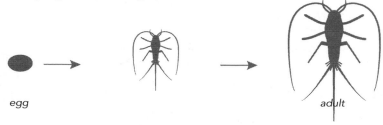

egg   adult

Examples: springtails and silverfish. The young look just like their parents, but are smaller. As they get older, they get larger. There are not many insects with simple growth.

2. Incomplete metamorphosis (three stages)

egg   nymph   adult

Examples: grasshoppers, dragonflies. The young, called nymphs, are wingless. They may or may not look like their parents, depending on the species. As they get older, they repeatedly molt. During their last molt, they emerge as winged adults.

3. Complete metamorphosis (four stages)

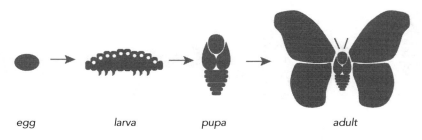

egg   larva   pupa   adult

Examples: butterflies, beetles, mosquitoes, caddisfly. The wormlike young, called larvae (singular - larva), look nothing like their parents. They have no wings or compound eyes. Their job is to simply eat. As they grow, they repeatedly molt. Once they stop, they become pupae (singular - pupa), and some spin a cocoon. As pupae, their bodies change greatly, and they emerge as adults. Most insects have complete metamorphosis.

Amphibian Life Cycles
Three stages

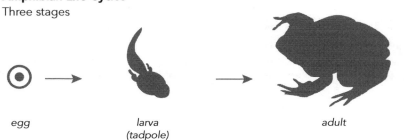

egg   larva   adult
                (tadpole)

Frogs, toads and salamanders also go through metamorphosis. All three of these amphibians lay their eggs in moist or wet spots. Each hatch into larvae - called tadpoles or polliwogs. These have gills and a tail but no limbs. As they grow, tadpoles gradually lose their tails and gills and gradually grow lungs and legs. Eventually they are adults, and may or may not stay in the wetland, depending on the species.

Suggested Resources
National Audubon Society Field Guide to North American Insects and Spiders, Audubon Society Nature Guides Wetlands, Peterson First Guide to Insects of North America, video: Bugs Don't Bug Us

procedure

1. Discuss the life stages that humans undergo: baby, child, adolescent, young adult, adult, elder. Make the connection to other species that have changes throughout their lives.

2. In pairs, choose one insect from Bugs in the Mud or Critical Critters journal entries to study. Students should focus on insects rather than other invertebrates (snails, mites, etc.) because all insects go through similar life stages.

3. Have students create research questions about the species and its life cycle, using the journal pages. Students should use books, field guides, and/or the internet to research the questions in their journals:

   Possible responses to #4 in Journal Pages. Some insects lay their eggs underwater. When the eggs hatch, the insects spend the first part of their lives underwater. Some insects remain aquatic as adults, while others move onto land. The eggs and bodies of aquatic insects are adapted for living underwater for all or part of their life cycles.

4. In their research, students should look for pictures of their insect's life cycle and draw it in their journals.

5. Break students into groups according to insect choice. Each group should design a skit to act out the life stages of their insect. All students should act out each stage, so students recognize it is one insect going through multiple stages. In each stage, one student should explain what is happening and how the insect depends on the wetland during this part of its life. Students in grades 5-6 should have detailed explanations of each life stage, including both internal and external changes to body structures and functions, feeding, and habitat requirements.

6. Students perform their skits for the class and present their research through diagrams and charts.

wrap-up

Discuss the journal questions as a class. In addition, discuss the following questions: How is a wetland a unique habitat that is able to support a high diversity of life? Why is it significant that a wetland is highly diverse? *In the Great Lakes watershed, wetlands allow the lakes to support a greater diversity of life. Some organisms, such as insects, spend time in both the wetlands and the lakes. Some lake organisms lay their eggs in wetlands. In the context of this unit, the biodiversity of wetlands is significant because the high level of diversity in a wetland is, in part, what allows it to successfully filter excess nutrients out of the water. It is this process that makes the water cleaner for the lakes and for drinking.*

extension

Choose other types of organisms and investigate their life cycles.

assessment

Rubric on page 247

 We value your thoughts and feedback on Great Lakes in My World. Please let us know about any oversights, errors or omissions you find, or if there are things you or your students particularly like.

Send your comments to: education@greatlakes.org

9 | Living Life Cycles

FIRST NAME																				
LAST NAME																				

Choose one insect from your Bugs in the Mud or Critical Critters journal entries.

[1] Species Name...

[2] In what stage of its life cycle did you find it? (Circle one)

EGG   NYMPH   LARVA   PUPA   ADULT

[3] In what stage(s) does this species live underwater?

....

....

....

[4] What are your research questions about this species?...........................

....

....

[5] In what ways does this species' life cycle depend on the wetland?

....

....

....

....

....

....

....

....

....

....

....

....

APPROVED BY	

9 | Living Life Cycles

GRADE LEVEL
3-6

FIRST NAME																			
LAST NAME																			

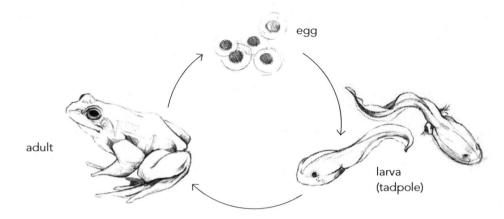

adult — egg — larva (tadpole)

[6] Draw the life cycle of your species like the example above. Use the words from question #2 that describe your species.

APPROVED BY

EXPLORE

10 | Name that Plant

GRADE LEVEL

4-8

45-90 minutes

Developmental Modifications: K-3 students do the clothing classification activity, and use K-3 Journal Pages. Work with a variety of species from the Creature Cards to sort them into categories of plants, birds, insects or fish. Discuss (or create a Venn diagram for discussion) the similarities and differences among the species. Students choose one species about which to create a question and research the answer. Create field guide based on this research.

summary

Students practice classification skills to understand how plants are typically arranged in a field guide. They use information collected to create a field guide to wetland plants. This, in turn, can be used in Mini Wetlands.

objectives

- Sort and classify plants by characteristics.
- Research wetland plants.
- Create pages for a wetland "field guide."

prerequisite

Wetland Observation or students should have visited a wetland and created journal entries about a specific plant. If the class did not visit the wetland, students may choose any Great Lakes wetland plant or the teacher may bring plants to class.

vocabulary

None

setting

INDOORS

subjects

Art, Language Arts, Biology, Ecology

standards

This Great Lakes in My World activity is aligned to the Common Core State Standards and to state learning standards in:

Illinois
Indiana
Michigan
Minnesota
New York
Ohio
Pennsylvania
Wisconsin

This alignment is available on your Great Lakes in My World CD in the "Standards" folder and on-line at http://www.greatlakes.org/ GLiMWstandards.

materials

- Several sets of different leaves (one set per small group)
- Journals
- Art supplies
- Research resources (books, field guides, internet)

background

Field guide: handbook used to identify and learn about specific plants or animals. Pictures are usually involved. Many are arranged according to visual clues. Others are arranged according to evolutionary relationships. Most use some combination of the two. Field guides usually provide basic additional information about the species involved, especially when it aids in identification.

Plant key: an outline of the distinguishing characteristics of a group of species, used as an identification guide. These usually begin by providing two descriptive choices. By choosing the one that best matches the plant in question, the user moves on to a different section of the key, where another pair of choices await. The user continues through a series of choices, until they get to the name of the plant. Pictures are usually not involved.

Each wetland plant has a role. They may provide food or shelter to birds, insects, or other animals, hold soil in place, filter water, or provide a home for important bacteria or fungi. In this activity, students will observe plants in the wetland and learn about their characteristics and specific habitat. This information will be useful in the completion of the final project, the constructed wetland.

For examples of "keys," see:
www.forestry.about.com/library/treekey

procedure

Part One: Identification

1. Explain to students that scientists use a system of classification to organize plants, animals and other natural objects for identification. *Plants, for example, are sorted into groups with similar characteristics. Within like-groups, the differences in plants help distinguish one from another. Field guide books are arranged using a classification system to make it easier for people to find or identify specific plants.*

2. Practice classification skills by having the students organize themselves based on certain characteristics. It may help to move desks out of the way.

Use the following directions for students:

a. *Everyone wearing clothes get up and stand in the middle of the room.*

b. *Everyone in this group wearing short sleeves move to the left side of the room. Everyone wearing long sleeves move to the right side of the room. These categories may need to be modified for your class.*

c. *On the left side of the room, everyone wearing a shirt with buttons move to the front corner of the room, everyone without, move to the back corner of the room.*

d. *On the right side of the room, everyone wearing cotton move to the front corner of the room, everyone not wearing cotton move to the back corner of the room, and so on.*

3. To make this activity more meaningful, have the students choose the classifications themselves each time they move to a new group. They should look for a major divide within the group to help break down the categories.

4. The type of classification done with the class is similar to what scientists do with plants when trying to identify them. Have the students practice on some plants. Break students into small groups. Give each group a set of different leaves. Have the group divide their leaves into two categories, based on an easily observed difference. Then have students divide those two categories in half again, based on characteristics. It does not matter what characteristics the students choose.

procedure continued

Part Two: Field Guide Activity

5. If stations were not used in Wetland Observation, one group of students may have been responsible for observing plants. If this is the case and student drawings from that activity are accurate and clear, break the class into small groups, with one student from the "plant group" in wetland observation in each of the new groups, also known as "jigsaw." The groups will create field guide pages for the plant that the "plant group" student entered into his/her journal during Wetland Observation. If all students rotated through the stations, if students did not go to the wetland, or if the drawings are not usable, simply break the class into groups and have each group choose a wetland plant to study.

6. Students will work in groups, but each student will create his/her own field guide pages.

7. The "plant group" student should share his/her plant journal entry with the rest of his/her group. Students should also take advantage of other resources to gain information on their plants (guide books, internet).

8. In their journals, students should draw his/her plant and answer the questions along the sides of the journal page.

9. When students have completed their pages, collect them and then pass them out randomly so each student has another student's page. Students will assess each other's pages based on the following questions, written on the board. Or, have students come up with the assessment criteria. Students should answer these questions on a separate sheet of paper.

Assessment Criteria (4-8)

a. Are all of the questions answered completely? (one point for each answer - 10 points total) If you feel that there is missing information, indicate what is missing.

b. Is the drawing detailed? (1-3 points for very little detail, 4-6 points for some detail, 7-10 points for lots of detail) If students gave fewer points, they should make suggestions for details that could be added.

wrap-up

1. To create a complete field guide for each student, choose the most accurate and complete entry from each plant group. Photocopy these pages so that there are enough to distribute one of each type of plant to each student.

2. Have the class come up with a classification system with which to organize the field guide. To do this, they first need to come up with one major difference between the plants to divide them into categories. From there, each category would need to be broken down one step further until each plant has its own identity. Students may think back to the classification activity to remember how this is done.

3. The completed field guide can then be used to choose plants for the final project: Mini Wetlands.

extension

The plants students have observed will change through the seasons. If practical, have students observe their plants several other times during the year and take note of the changes. For example, has the plant grown, flowered, or gone to seed? To be sure students find the same plant at each visit, mark each one with a stake on the first field trip. Students may add new information to their field guides after each seasonal observation.

assessment

Rubric on page 248

We value your thoughts and feedback on Great Lakes in My World. Please let us know about any oversights, errors or omissions you find, or if there are things you or your students particularly like.

Send your comments to: education@greatlakes.org

10 | Name that Plant

GRADE LEVEL
4-8

journal pages

FIRST NAME																			
LAST NAME																			

[1] Draw the plant in the middle and fill in the information below. Label any important characteristics on the drawing.

TYPE (circle one)
Woody/Herbaceous

BRANCHING
Opposite/Alternate

FLOWERS
Yes/No
Number of Petals _____
Color _____

SEEDS
Fruit/Nut/Parachute/
Hitchhiker/Other

LEAVES
Color _____
Shape _____
Height _____

OTHER INFORMATION _____
_____
_____
_____

SUNLIGHT
Sunny/Shady

SOIL
Wet/Medium/Dry
Clayey/Sandy/Mixed

LOCATION
Underwater/Emerging
from the water/At the edge of the
water/On land

ABUNDANCE
High Number/Medium/Very Few

APPROVED BY	

10 | Name that Plant

GRADE LEVEL
K-3

journal pages

FIRST NAME

LAST NAME

[1] Animal or plant name: ....

[2] Type of animal or plant: ....

[3] Draw the animal or plant.

[4] Describing words:

....

....

....

[5] Research question(s) about animal or plant:

....

....

....

[6] Answer to question(s):

....

....

....

APPROVED BY

EXPLORE

11 | Working Wetlands

GRADE LEVEL

4-8

45 minutes

*Developmental Modifications: K-3 - Do this as a demonstration and use the K-3 Journal
Page. Students circle 1. larger particles that sink, 2. particles in gravel and 3. plant roots.*

summary

Students create and observe models
that demonstrate how wetlands
clean water through sedimentation,
filtration and absorption.

objectives

- Design models that show how wetlands filter water.
- Discuss the strengths and weaknesses of models.
- Observe and diagram the changes in the model.
- Discuss the characteristics of wetland plants.
- List the key components of a wetland.
- Verbalize why wetlands are important to the Great Lakes.

prerequisite

Value of Wetlands. It is preferable that students have visited a local wetland
site, such as in Wetland Observation.

vocabulary

Sedimentation: removing sediment from water by allowing larger particles to
    sink
Filtration: removing smaller suspended particles by passing water through a
    filter such as sand and gravel absorption: taking in of a substance
Vascular: of or relating to a tube or channel for carrying a body fluid (as blood
    of an animal or sap of a plant)

setting

INDOORS

subjects

Ecology

standards

This Great Lakes in My World
activity is aligned to the Common
Core State Standards and to state
learning standards in:

Illinois
Indiana
Michigan
Minnesota
New York
Ohio
Pennsylvania
Wisconsin

This alignment is available on your
Great Lakes in My World CD in the
"Standards" folder and on-line at
http://www.greatlakes.org/
GLiMWstandards.

materials

- Journals
- Pencils
- Dirt/sticks/debris
- Rocks, sand, gravel
- Celery stalks
- Water
- Clear containers (glass jars or
  plastic bottles) with lids
- Clear containers without lids
- Red or blue food coloring
- Two-liter soda bottles cut in half
  horizontally

background

Wetlands have the ability to clean water that passes through them. The cleansing processes defined here are only part of what is happening in wetlands. For instance, bacteria and fungi play an important role in changing pollutants into beneficial nutrients, as do wetland animals such as fish and snails. Different wetlands have different abilities to clean water, depending on their size, soils, water flow and location. Sedimentation cannot happen in moving water, such as a stream or drain sewer. The water must stop flowing, as in wetlands.

In a wetland, filtration happens when sand, gravel, and soil remove particles in water that passes through. In addition, metals bind with the soil, removing them from the water. Another process in a wetland is absorption. In a wetland, plants absorb nutrients and pollutants through their roots.

procedure

Part One: Sedimentation

1. Discuss experimental design with students, including the importance generating a hypothesis, limiting variables and keeping conditions the same each time.

2. Remind students that wetlands filter water. Ask students to describe how sediment is separated from the water. *They learned in Value of Wetlands that the sediment sinks to the bottom of the wetland.* Tell students that they will demonstrate this process for themselves. Ask students how they might accomplish this with the materials provided. Students should be able to come up with the following demonstration. If not, guide them in that direction.

3. Break students into small groups. Each group should have 1 clear container (approximately 1 liter) with a lid filled 2/3 with water, and some dirt/sticks/debris. Students add the dirt/sticks/debris to the container of water, secure the lid, and shake the mixture so the water is dirty.

4. Students draw the container of water in their journals. Allow the water to sit for 30 minutes. (While students are waiting, they may set up the filtration demonstration.) After 15 minutes, students observe the water and draw what they see. *The sediment in the water should have begun to settle. The water may still look cloudy, but heavier particles will be at the bottom of the container.*

5. After 15 more minutes, students should observe and draw the water again. (While students are waiting, they may set up the next demonstration.) Ask students what has happened to the sediment in the water. What characterizes the sediment at the bottom, versus the sediment still floating? *The water should look clearer, with visible sediment at the bottom of the containers. The densest particles will be at the bottom, the least dense at the top.*

6. Ask students to connect this with what happens in a real wetland. *Since water flows very slowly through a wetland, there is time for sediment to settle to the bottom. This sediment does not move on with the water when the water slowly flows through.*

Part Two: Filtration

1. Each group should have: one soda bottle (no lid), a few rocks (approximately 1 inch in diameter), a half liter of gravel, a half liter of sand, and the container of water with sediment at the bottom.

2. Ask students what in the wetland could remove the remaining sediment from the water. *In Value of Wetlands, students learned that sand and gravel act as a filter to remove particles from the water.* Ask students how they might demonstrate this process with the available materials. Again, students will probably come up with the following procedure, but may need some guidance.

3. Students should first invert the top half of the soda bottle and place the larger stones at the opening. These should not completely block the opening, but should prevent the gravel from falling through.

4. The gravel goes in next, followed by the sand. The inverted soda bottle top may be placed inside of the bottom so that the bottom half will catch the water. A student will need to hold onto the bottles to prevent them from falling. See Journal Pages for diagram.

5. Next, the students should slowly and carefully pour the settled water into the soda bottle. They should try to keep the sediment at the bottom of the container from coming out with the water, if possible. Students observe and record two things: what do they see on top of the sand, and what does the water look like that is coming through the soda bottle?

6. Ask students to explain what has happened. *The sand and gravel act as a natural filter, catching particles suspended in the water. The water coming through the bottle should look much clearer than it did before.*

7. Ask students to connect this process with what happens in a real wetland. *When water passes through sand and gravel, suspended particles are trapped. This may happen when water percolates into the soil, before it reaches the roots of plants, or it may happen as water enters the wetland.*

procedure

Part Three: Absorption

1. There is another way in which wetlands filter water that the students learned about in the activity Value of Wetlands. *Plants absorb pollutants when they take up water through their roots.* Ask students what they would need to see in order to believe this is true. *They need to see the pollutants inside of a plant.*

2. Students will need: two glasses of water, two stalks of celery (with the bottom inch freshly cut off), and blue or red food coloring. Have students look at the base of the celery. They should be able to see small dots, which are the vascular tissues of the plants. These tiny tubes move water and nutrients through the plant.

3. Ask students what they might do with the available materials to demonstrate absorption. *Students should mix a few drops of food coloring into one of the glasses of water, then place one celery stalk in each glass. Students should draw the glasses of water and celery.*

4. The celery will have to sit for a few hours or overnight. Then students should remove the celery from the glasses and slice the stalks in half horizontally. (Teachers should do this for younger students for safety.) Students should see that the holes in the celery that were in the colored glass have turned blue or red. The other celery stalk has not changed. Ask students to explain what has happened. *The celery has absorbed the water in the glasses, including any pollutants in the water (in this case, food coloring). The pollutant is visible in the vascular tissue of the plant.*

5. Ask students to relate this to what happens in a real wetland. *Plants absorb water and pollutants, further adding to the cleansing of the water.*

6. Students should draw the colored celery in their journals.

7. Students use numbers to label the order of the final diagram in the journal pages.
The correct answers are: 2, 7, 4, 5, 3, 1, 6.

wrap-up

1. As a class, discuss how these components might all fit together as a model of a wetland. They might discuss the idea of connecting the containers so that the water flows through the three processes (sedimentation, filtration and absorption). Students should write about this in their journals.

2. Discuss the strengths and weaknesses of this demonstration as a model of a wetland. Have students think about Wetland Observation. Ask students what other components of a wetland are missing. *Wetland plants with roots (not celery), animals (including macroinvertebrates), bacteria, fungi, soil and sunlight.* Students should record a list in their journals.

3. Explain to students that the other components of wetlands also contribute to the cleaning of the water. Some organisms change waste into substances that are usable by other organisms.

assessment

Rubric on page 248

We value your thoughts and feedback on Great Lakes in My World. Please let us know about any oversights, errors or omissions you find, or if there are things you or your students particularly like.

Send your comments to: education@greatlakes.org

11 | Working Wetlands

GRADE LEVEL
4-8

FIRST NAME																					
LAST NAME																					

Sedimentation

[1] Draw the water and sediment.

Water Container at the Beginning	Water Container after 15 Minutes	Water Container after 30 Minutes

[2] What does this procedure demonstrate about wetlands?

....

....

....

....

....

....

....

....

APPROVED BY	

11 | Working Wetlands

FIRST NAME																					
LAST NAME																					

Filtration

[1] Draw the water, sand, gravel and rocks.

[2] What do you see at the top when the
water is poured?

....

....

....

....

....

....

[3] What does the water look like when it
flows out of the bottom?

....

....

....

....

....

....

[4] What does this procedure demonstrate
about wetlands?

....

....

....

....

....

....

....

Water Poured Through
Sand and Gravel

APPROVED BY	

11 | Working Wetlands

GRADE LEVEL
4-8

journal pages

FIRST NAME

LAST NAME

Absorption

[1] Draw the water, celery and food coloring after they have been left over night.

CELERY IN CLEAR WATER

CELERY IN COLORED WATER

Glass of water

Base of the
Celery Stalk

Glass of water

Base of the
Celery Stalk

Water Cleaning

[2] How could the components of sedimentation, filtration and absorption fit together as a model of a wetland? Use words and diagrams in your description.

....

....

....

[3] What components of a real wetland are missing? Make a list below.

....

....

....

APPROVED BY

11 | Working Wetlands

FIRST NAME																		
LAST NAME																		

[1] Wetlands clean water. Put the steps below in the correct order according to the diagram

_____ Rocks trap large pieces of debris and waste.

_____ Cleaner water leaves the wetland.

_____ The sediment traps metals and debris.

_____ Tiny organisms eat the waste.

_____ Sediment falls to the bottom of the wetland.

_____ Water flows into the wetland (past rocks).

_____ The roots of plants suck up the rest of the waste.

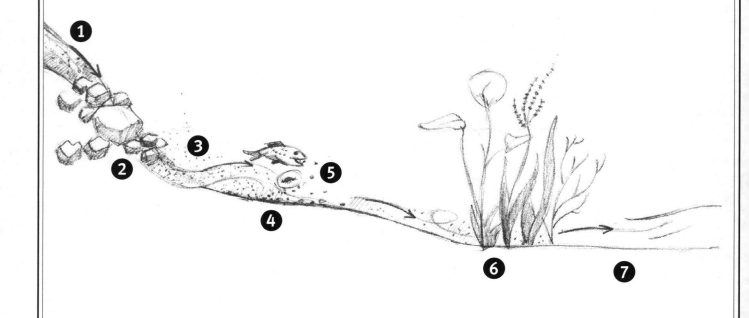

APPROVED BY	

11 | Working Wetlands

GRADE LEVEL
K-3

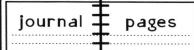

FIRST NAME																					
LAST NAME																					

[1] Circle one place where the wetland cleans water through:
   a. Sedimentation: Heavier particles sink to the bottom.
   b. Filtration: Particles stay in sand, gravel or soil.
   c. Absorption: Plant takes in nutrients and/or pollutants through plant roots.
[2] Draw the missing wetland animals.

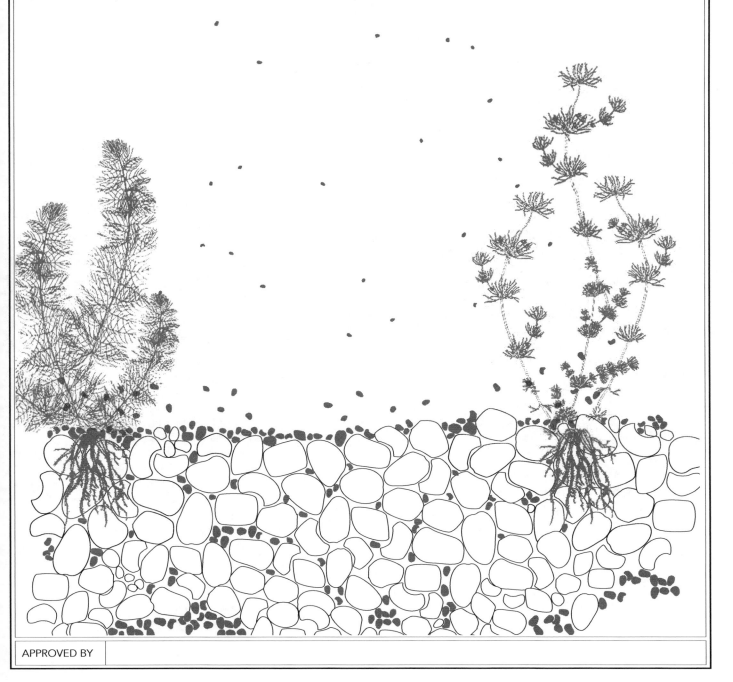

APPROVED BY	

INVESTIGATE: FINAL PROJECT

12 | Mini Wetlands

GRADE LEVEL

4-8

ongoing

Developmental Modifications: For K-3 students, this project requires high teacher supervision and input. Students of this age would not need to compare methods of filtering gray water. They would instead focus on how wetlands are able to clean water, the biodiversity that exists in a wetland, and on basic needs of organisms and how to provide this in a constructed system. Students also focus on the components of a wetland and how they function to create an ecosystem.

summary

Students use information gathered during the unit to design and build a classroom living system that is able to treat "gray water." Initial research includes a trip to a local drinking water treatment plant and learning about living systems.

objectives

- Research the water purification process for drinking water.
- Discuss the importance of water conservation.
- List components of a wetland.
- Research alternative strategies for cleaning water.
- Brainstorm the design of a "constructed wetland."
- Construct a system in which living organisms can survive while filtering gray water.
- Maintain the constructed wetland.

prerequisite

Value of Wetlands and Working Wetlands

vocabulary

Purification: to make or become pure
Living system or "living machine": ecologically engineered natural wastewater treatment and reclamation systems
Gray water: water made dirty through use

setting

INDOORS

subjects

Ecology, Biology, Life Science

standards

This Great Lakes in My World activity is aligned to the Common Core State Standards and to state learning standards in:

Illinois
Indiana
Michigan
Minnesota
New York
Ohio
Pennsylvania
Wisconsin

This alignment is available on your Great Lakes in My World CD in the "Standards" folder and on-line at http://www.greatlakes.org/ GLiMWstandards.

materials

Five to six 19 liter (5 gallon) leakproof drinking water jugs or other clear plastic or glass containers, five to six 1 meter (3 foot), one-half inch inner diameter pieces of transparent vinyl tubing to connect the jugs, keyhole saw, aquarium bubbler ($10-$15), water quality testing kit ($15), two meters (4-6 feet) of one-eighth inch diameter of tubing for bubbler, binder clips, siphoning aid (optional), fish, plants, mud, pond water (from local wetland)

background

On average, Americans each use approximately 168 gallons of water per day. Public drinking water is the second largest use of water in the Great Lakes basin or watershed, following irrigation. Water is also used in industry and energy generation. According to the Michigan Department of Environmental Quality, 90 percent of water withdrawn from the Great Lakes basin comes directly from the Great Lakes. The other 10 percent comes from tributaries and groundwater.

Water withdrawn from the Great Lakes for drinking goes through water treatment plants like the one shown below. For example, the water treatment plant in Chicago processes one billion gallons of water each day, serving five million consumers in the city and its suburbs. The process takes seven hours. Water is drawn from the lake and then treated with carbon to absorb tastes and odors. It is then treated with polyphosphate, chlorine, fluoride, aluminum sulfate and polyelectrolyte. These chemicals kill bacteria, remove micro-organisms and prevent tooth decay. The water then undergoes sedimentation and filtration. Sedimentation is the process of removing sediment from water by allowing larger particles to sink. Filtration is the process of removing smaller suspended particles by passing water through a filter such as sand and gravel. There are similarities and differences between this process and the process that a wetland uses to filter water.

Classroom Living System: The water treatment process that occurs in a natural or constructed wetland can be created on a small scale for the classroom. A living system or "Living Machine," is a series of tanks with live plants, trees, grasses, algae, fish, tiny freshwater shrimp, snails, and a diversity of microorganisms and bacteria. Each tank is a different mini-ecosystem designed to eat or break down waste. Depending on the system, the process can take about four days to turn mucky water crystal clear. It is chemical-free, generally odor-free, and, compared to conventional waste treatment, it costs less financially and ecologically.

A wetland is an example of a living system in nature, which is why these systems are sometime called "constructed wetlands." The interactions of organisms in the microhabitats make it possible for the wetland to filter water. The wastes of one organism are the nutrients of another organism. In order to filter water in the classroom, the complex system of a wetland is mimicked, but on a very small scale. To overcome this problem of size, multiple cells are used in this design, each containing its own microhabitat of aquatic life. Organisms and nutrients may move between the cells until they find their own niche. One cell may contain sediment from the bottom of a pond and benthic organisms, one may contain emergent plants and bacteria, one may contain fish and snails, etc. As in the natural world, greater biodiversity in the classroom living system will aid the system in overcoming environmental challenges.

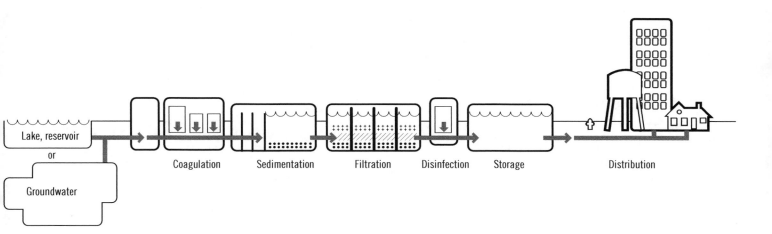

Lake, reservoir or Groundwater | Coagulation | Sedimentation | Filtration | Disinfection | Storage | Distribution

Resources

Ducks Unlimited Educators: http://www.greenwing.org/dueducator/noncssdu_educator.html
For the current U.S. EPA drinking water quality standards, go to the following web site:
   U.S. Environmental Protection Agency: http://www.epa.gov/safewater/mcl.html.
For more information on constructed wetlands, go to the following web site:
   U.S. Environmental Protection Agency: http://www.epa.gov/owow/wetlands/watersheds/cwetlands.html

procedure

Part One
Before constructing a mini wetland (optional):

1. Take a field trip to your local water treatment plant (or have a guest speaker talk on this topic) and take a tour to learn about how the water in your area is purified.

2. Before the field trip, ask students to come up with a list of questions to ask the staff at the treatment plant. If a trip is not possible, have students research on the internet, make phone calls, and write letters to find out the answers to their questions.

If they need ideas, some questions might include:

Where does the water come from? Where does water go when I flush the toilet? What is the water used for? What is the water treatment process? How long does the process take? How much does it cost? How much energy is used? What chemicals are put into the water and for what purposes? How much water is treated each day? How many people use the water from this plant?

Note: For a successful field trip, urge the guide to answer the students' questions in age appropriate language.

3. Ask students to think about how the water treatment plant and wetlands are similar.

wrap-up

1. Discuss the questions and answers as a class.
- What did students learn?
- What concerns do they have about their local water treatment?
- Based on what they know about water treatment, why might it be important to conserve water?

- What are some ways that they can think of to conserve water?
- How does their study of wetlands relate to the water treatment plant?

procedure

Part Two
Construction of a Mini Wetland
This procedure provides an example of one way to construct a living system, but keep in mind that there is not one correct way to set up a living system. This should be decided by the teacher and students based on the type of space available and the specific use intended by the class. It is not possible to guess exactly what animals, bacteria, plants, and protists will end up living and reproducing in your living system—it is best to allow nature to decide this while helping it along by providing a diversity of samples from a wetland.

A. Research and Brainstorming

1. Research living machines and constructed wetlands. Information is provided in the journal pages for students to read. They should also conduct additional research.

2. Break into small groups to discuss and record in journals:

   Based on what students learned on the field trip to a water treatment plant, and in their reading, are there any aspects of traditional water treatment that could be improved upon? If so, what? Choose one problem and write a concise statement about it.

3. Based on the problem the group chooses, formulate an objective. For example, the problem with conventional water treatment is the high level of energy consumption (there are other issues the class might choose to address). The objective is to develop a water treatment method that uses less energy. The objective statement should be directly related to the problem statement.

4. Share group ideas with the class. Either come to a consensus on one objective as a large group, or agree to attempt to meet all of the objectives. Keep in mind that the objectives are to be strived for, and they may not all be met.

5. Show students the (non-living) available materials. Ask students what natural materials and living components might be necessary for the design. Students may refer to their journal pages from Water Cleaning, Wetland Observation, Creating a Field Guide, and Macroinvertebrates.

6. Ask students if they think it is possible to re-create a complex wetland system in one small aquarium. Why or why not? *The amount of space necessary for all of the components of a complex system is greater than an aquarium. This is one of the reasons why constructed wetlands are done in large, outdoor spaces.*

7. Ask students what might be done to overcome this problem. *This is the reason for the use of cells. Each cell is large enough for a part of the system, and when connected, they may interact as they might in a larger wetland system.*

8. Ask students which part of a wetland each cell could represent. *Students should think back to the macroinvertebrates activity—each water sample came from a different microhabitat in the wetland.*

procedure continued

9. Allow students to re-group. This time, students should brainstorm design ideas using 5-6 connected cells as a basis.

- By this point, students should have created a list of possible microhabitats for each cell, and presented potential models for the set-up of the living system.

- Review the provided directions (below) for construction with the class. Determine whether this procedure is best for your class, or if modifications need to be made (based on their research and objectives). Students will be responsible for determining what organisms will be put into the cells.

B. Construction Directions

1. Cut the tops off of the water jugs with the keyhole saw. (Teacher should perform or supervise this task for safety.)

2. Arrange the jugs. You will need a strong surface on which to place the full jugs and bubbler (at the same height). One option is below.

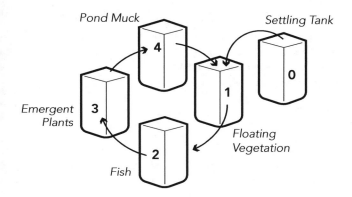

3. Place jugs in an area that gets sunlight. Cells should be placed 20-30 cm (8-12 inches) apart so that students can easily view them and light can get in.

4. Arrange an airlift. The bottom of the airlift tube should be 2-3 cm (one inch) above the floor of the container. Insert the tube from the bubbler up into the bottom of the airlift tube. It should extend up into the airlift tube by about 2 ½ cm (1 inch).

5. Arrange siphon tubes so that they connect the jugs. It may be helpful to attach binder clips to the walls of the jugs, and then attach the siphon tubes to the clips. Siphon tubes should have their input end higher than their output end. The input of each tube should be about one third of the depth of the cell, while the output should be about two thirds of the depth of the cell or more. (The airlift tube is the opposite: the input is low and the output is high.)

6. Fill the cells with water to within 10 cm (4 inches) of the top.

7. Start the airlift by turning on the bubbler. Water should start to bubble from cell 0 to cell 1. Start siphoning from cell 1 to 2, then 2 to 3, 3 to 4, and 4 to 1. Siphoning can be started by using a siphon aid of the type commonly used for siphoning gas (found in auto part stores). Or, you can submerge the entire siphon tube in a tub of water, allow it to fill, plug both ends with your thumbs, then carry it to the cells and submerge it there.

8. Adjust the flow rate between the cells. The water level should remain constant in all cells. If not, you may need to turn down the siphon tubes by constricting them with a clamp or blocking them with putty.

9. Once the system is in place, run it for a few days with only water in it in order to dechlorinate the water and allow time to adjust the flow. Note: any new water added to the system should be allowed to sit out for 24 hours in order to dechlorinate before being exposed to living organisms. Animals should not be added to the system until it has been working smoothly for a few days.

C. Choosing the Cell Contents

1. Students should go back to their journal pages from the following activities: Wetland Observation, Create a Field Guide, Macroinvertebrates, and Life Cycles for reference in choosing organisms for the living system.

2. Break students into four groups and assign each to a cell. Each group should brainstorm a list of organisms and natural materials for their cell.

3. Collect the contents for the cells (either from wetlands, garden centers and/or pet stores) and proceed with the Construction Directions.

- *CELL 0: Settling Tank*

  Your class may choose to have a settling tank as a starting point for the living system. Grey water would be added to this tank, and the sediment allowed to settle before moving on to the next tanks. This tank is separate from the recirculating tanks because water does not need to re-enter the settling tank. Sludge at the bottom of this tank would need to be removed periodically.

- *CELL 1: Floating Vegetation*

  This cell contains floating vegetation (duckweed, water hyacinth, azolla). If you are not able to collect this from your wetland site, similar plants may be found in garden centers that sell aquatic plants. These plants will spread across the cell and can be moved to CELL 2 for the fish to eat later on.

procedure continued

- *CELL 2: Fish*

  Leave this cell empty until the system has been running for a few days. Before the fish are added, gradually mix the system water with the fish water to adjust fish to the temperature. Goldfish from the pet store work well because they are hardy. Fish should be no smaller than ½ inch in diameter. Another fish to consider is the yellow perch (in cool water temperatures). Fish should be purchased from a store rather than collected from a wetland. Students should research what the fish eat. NEVER release non-native species (plant or animal) into a body of water.

- *CELL 3: Emergent Plants*

  This cell contains emergent plants (arrowhead, taro, papyrus, calla lilies). Again, if you are unable to collect these plants from your wetland site, they may be purchased at a garden center. Be sure you have the roots of these plants, as they are the regenerative structures.

- *CELL 4: Pond Muck*

  This cell contains a few cups of pond muck and water collected from your local wetland. The muck will contain microorganisms and macroinvertebrates, which are essential components of the living system. You may also include cattails or other grasses from the wetland in this cell.

- You may wish to include soil, sand, and/or gravel from the wetland in the bottom of the cells for cover for small organisms and plant roots.

D. Observations

- Once the system is running, students should begin to record weekly or monthly observations about its health and diversity. New life can be added as needed which increases the biodiversity, aiding the system.

- Organism observations: the number of plants, leaf sizes, types and numbers of macroinvertebrates present, number of fish, and any other organisms found.

- Waste and nutrient observations: Students should test for ammonia, nitrite and nitrate in each of the cells. Easy-to-use test kits can be purchased from aquarium stores ($15). Ammonia and nitrite are toxic to fish, but can be transformed to nitrate by bacteria, then taken up by plants. Regular observation of these levels will show their movement in the system.

- Water level: Students should keep track of the water level in the system. Some water will be lost to evaporation, and new water may need to be added to compensate for this. Remember, new water should sit out for 24 hours before being added to the system.

wrap-up

1. Use the constructed wetland in the classroom to treat gray water generated by the students. Many of our every day water uses generate gray water, such as brushing teeth, washing hands, doing laundry, etc.

2. After watching the water levels in the system for two weeks, have students determine the amount of new water that the system can handle due to loss through evaporation.

3. Collect waste water (not from the toilets, though—gray water only!) and add to the first cell of the living system.

4. Continue monitoring the system. The water treated in this system should be a suitable quality for release into natural wetlands. However, do not dispose of any fish or plant materials in a body of water. Invasive species that are not native to a system can cause severe problems for that ecosystem.

5. Make any necessary modifications to the system.

6. Celebrate the accomplishment! Host a tour of the site for school dignitaries, or set up a day to offer tours to other classes or the media.

7. Have students write an essay about the creation of this project. The essay should reflect each student's personal experience including thoughts, feelings, ideas and technical details.

sources

Wikipedia - Constructed Wetlands:
    http://en.wikipedia.org/wiki/Constructed_wetland
ConstructedWetlands.org:
    http://www.constructedwetlands.org/cw/
Building a Living Machine:
    http://www.geosociety.org/educate/LessonPlans/
    LivingMachine.pdf

assessment

Rubric on page 248

12 | Mini Wetlands

GRADE LEVEL
4-8

journal pages

FIRST NAME

LAST NAME

Make a list of questions about your local water treatment. Record the answers during the field trip.

[1] ....

....

....

[2] ....

....

....

[3] ....

....

....

[4] Draw a diagram of your local water treatment process. Label the parts of the diagram.

APPROVED BY

12 | Mini Wetlands

FIRST NAME																	
LAST NAME																	

What is wastewater?

Wastewater is water that has been used in homes and businesses. It comes from sinks, toilets, showers, washing machines, and related places. Wastewater contains nitrogen, phosphorus, pathogens, and organic material. Each of these need to be removed via water purification.

How is wastewater cleaned?

- Bacteria transform nitrogen into a harmless gas that can be released into the environment.
- Phosphorus is removed from wastewater by binding with sediments, which are periodically removed.
- Pathogens are removed by micro-organisms and ultraviolet light.
- Organic material is broken down by bacteria through aerobic oxygen-based respiration, and converted into carbon dioxide and water.

Gray Water: Wastewater other than sewage, such as sink drainage or washing machine discharge.

What are some alternatives to traditional water treatment?

Living Systems or Living Machines

Living systems are human-made aquatic ecosystems that naturally purify wastewater with sunlight, plants and animals. Living systems are less expensive than traditional water treatment systems, and are environmentally sound. However, extreme levels of toxins would damage a living machine.

For example, the Living Machine at Oberlin College, Ohio combines conventional technology with natural wetland ecosystems to treat one building's water. Water cleaned by the living machine is reused in the building's toilets.

Constructed Wetlands

A constructed wetland is a human-made wetland of soil and rocks, plants, animals and water for human use. Wastewater enters an inlet filled with crushed rocks, which filters large solids. A film of bacteria and fungi grows on the surface of the rocks and aids in the process. The water then flows across the wetland, pulled by gravity down a slight incline. High earthen walls absorb overflow rainwater. The bed is lined and sealed to prevent leakage into the groundwater. The soil and gravel provides a place for plants to root and absorb metals. Over time, the metals accumulate and need to be removed. The plants absorb pollutants.

Constructed wetlands can be used for treating waste from houses or farms. When used in sewage treatment, they are often attached to conventional systems. They are also used to treat highway and parking lot runoff before it reaches storm drains or sensitive areas. Constructed wetlands are used in the southern United States, Germany and the United Kingdom, among other places.

The advantages of this type of system are: low costs compared with standard treatment methods, simple construction, low maintenance and environmental compatibility. The disadvantage is the slow rate of processing water.

Why can't wastewater be released into natural wetlands and rivers?

Excess nutrients cause plants in the water, especially algae, to grow rapidly. When these plants decay, the decomposition uses up high amounts of oxygen in the water, which kills other organisms. In addition, these rotting plants release any toxins they have absorbed back into the water when they die. There is a limit to how much pollution a natural system can handle before becoming damaged.

Conclusion

Use this document as a base from which to continue your research on living systems and how you might create one in your own classroom.

APPROVED BY	

12 | Mini Wetlands

GRADE LEVEL
4-8

FIRST NAME																						
LAST NAME																						

[1] What aspects of traditional wastewater treatment could be improved upon? Make a list. As a group, choose one problem you'd like to focus on and circle it.

....

....

....

....

....

....

....

....

....

[2] Based on the problem you circled, write a sentence stating the problem. For example: Traditional water treatment methods use too much energy.

....

....

....

[3] Write a goal statement based on your problem statement. For example: Our goal is to design a water treatment method that uses less energy than the current system. Brainstorm how you can achieve this goal.

....

....

....

....

....

....

....

....

....

....

....

....

APPROVED BY	

12 | Mini Wetlands

FIRST NAME																						
LAST NAME																						

[4] Make a list of natural materials that may be needed to create a miniature living wetland system.

[5] Why is it difficult to create a small, complex wetland system in only one container?

[6] What can be done to overcome this problem?

APPROVED BY

12 | Mini Wetlands

GRADE LEVEL
4-8

FIRST NAME

LAST NAME

[7] What wetland microhabitats could be represented by each of the living system cells? Look back to your Critical Critters journal pages for reference: each of the water samples came from a different microhabitat.

[8] Brainstorm possible designs for the classroom living system using five to six cells. List the microhabitat each cell would represent. Would there be other types of cells?

APPROVED BY

12 | Mini Wetlands

FIRST NAME																			
LAST NAME																			

[1] My group is responsible for cell #_____

[2] Make a list of natural materials and organisms that could go into the cell. Refer to your journal pages from Wetland Observation, Name that Plant, Critical Critters, and Living Life Cycles for ideas.

....

....

....

....

....

[3] Write about your personal experience in the creation of this project. What was your initial impression of the project? How did this change over the course of its completion? What ideas did you have? What is your assessment of the outcome?

....

....

....

....

....

....

....

....

....

....

....

....

....

....

....

....

APPROVED BY	

12 | Mini Wetlands

FIRST NAME

LAST NAME

Living System Observations

Date	Organisms (# and types)	Wastes and Nutrients	Water Level (cm from top)

APPROVED BY

INVESTIGATE: FINAL PROJECT

13 | Teaching About Wetlands

GRADE LEVEL
4-8

several class periods

K-3 students focus on reflecting on what they have learned, celebrating their work in the Wetland Unit, and deciding on ways to share their knowledge of the importance of wetlands with the school or larger community. Suggestions include inviting another class to a wetland party and setting up learning stations that highlight important concepts, projects, and presentations that have been done throughout the wetland unit.

summary

Students create an educational piece about a local wetland to share with the community.

objectives

- Identify the key messages students would like to teach their community about wetlands.
- Devise and produce a method to convey an educational message to the community.
- Communicate the importance of a wetland to the community.

prerequisite

Activities in Wetland unit

vocabulary

Regulation: a rule or order telling how something is to be done
Incentive: something that makes a person try or work hard or harder

setting

INDOORS

subjects

Ecology, Language Arts, Social Studies

standards

This Great Lakes in My World activity is aligned to the Common Core State Standards and to state learning standards in:

Illinois
Indiana
Michigan
Minnesota
New York
Ohio
Pennsylvania
Wisconsin

This alignment is available on your Great Lakes in My World CD in the "Standards" folder and on-line at http://www.greatlakes.org/ GLiMWstandards.

materials

- Journals
- Pencils
- Guest speakers from the community

background

There are four ways in which wetlands are protected: regulations, land owner protection (e.g. park districts, organizations like The Nature Conservancy, etc.) economic incentives, and public education. Wetlands are federally protected under the Clean Water Act, which regulates pollution and development permits and licenses. State and local governments may also have their own wetland regulations. Public education about the value of wetlands is a preventative protection measure. The theory behind education is that if people understand and value its wetlands, they are less likely to pollute or develop them.

procedure

1. Pose the following scenario to the class: The students are adults on the city/town council or village board. They are decision-makers in this community. They all have knowledge they have gained about wetlands. They know the values of wetlands for people as well as plants and animals. A proposal has come up to fill the local wetland and use the space as a parking area for the very popular soccer, baseball and football fields next to it. Currently it's become so congested in the current parking lot that people have to park far away, walk long distances and kids are late for their games. Neighbors are complaining, too, about all the cars along their streets. No one uses the wetland, because it's muddy, and some people say that it just breeds mosquitoes and collects trash blown off the road. Would the students be likely to let this proposal go through? Why or why not? Are the students less likely to allow the wetland to be filled now that they understand its values?

2. Tell students that now that they have knowledge about their local wetland, they can either keep it to themselves or share it. Which do they choose, and why? Let students openly discuss any misgivings they would have about getting involved. Discuss ways to work on multi-sided issues, such as gathering facts, talking politely, and respecting a variety of opinions.

3. If the class would like to share their knowledge, break students into small groups and have them brainstorm lists of things they want to teach others. Students should write the lists in their journals. Have each of the groups share a few things from their lists and write them on the board.

4. As a class, look for trends or similarities among things on the class list. Have a discussion to see what students see as a goal for teaching the community. For example, can they agree that they would like to teach that the wetland is of value to the community? If so, what aspect(s) of the wetland would they like to focus on?

5. Students can work in large or small groups to create questions that they will focus on answering in order to educate others. For example: How do wetlands prevent floods in this community? These essential questions will guide the students in the creation of their public education project.

6. Ask students to brainstorm a list of ways in which they could provide information to the community. The list may include things such as the public access television station, a local radio station, newspapers, newsletters, posters, public workshops or classes, signage at the wetland site or flyers. As a class, choose methods of communication from the list to use for this project. Note: The chosen method may involve talking with people from the community to get permission or access to the wetland.

7. Now students can begin creating their public education projects. Students should agree upon a length and scope of the project, and any other parameters needed.

8. Divide the students into groups to work on different aspects of the project. In their small groups, students will devise a way to answer the question in a creative, clear way. There are a variety of forms that this part of the project could take. For example, students may create skits, stories, create exhibits, posters, write essays/letters or a combination.

9. In each group, students should divide their tasks so that each member participates. Students may be creative as long as the outcome is clear, meets the goal, and accurately and completely answers their essential question.

10. Once the groups have completed their project, they should present them to the entire class, another class or the community.

wrap-up

1. If desired, take steps to share the educational projects. This may mean passing out flyers, doing presentations, hanging up signs, or working with a television or radio crew. Make sure you have the proper permission for whatever the class decides to do.

assessment

Rubric on page 248

13 | Teaching About Wetlands

GRADE LEVEL
4-8

journal ≡ pages

FIRST NAME																					
LAST NAME																					

[1] Make a list of what you would like to teach your community about the local wetland.

....

....

[2] What is the class goal of this project?

....

....

[3] What questions will you answer in your project?

....

....

....

[4] Make a list of ways in which your class could communicate with the community.

....

....

....

[5] Describe the project your group will do.

....

....

....

....

[6] What is your role in the project? What will you need to do?

....

....

....

....

APPROVED BY	

13 | Teaching About Wetlands

GRADE LEVEL
4-8

journal pages

FIRST NAME

LAST NAME

[7] How is your project helping wetlands?

....

....

....

....

....

....

....

....

....

....

....

[8] How has learning about wetlands and teaching others about their importance
changed you or made you feel differently about your role in your community?

....

....

....

....

....

....

....

....

....

....

....

....

....

....

APPROVED BY

CONNECT   1 | **Wetland Alphabet**

ELEMENTS	☆☆☆☆	☆☆☆	☆☆	☆
ALPHABET LIST: Student brainstorms a list of wetland-related words that begin with the correct letters of the alphabet. They choose one or more words and write and illustrate the word(s).	Addresses all of the components	Missing one component	Missing two components	Missing three or more components
RESEARCH: Student creates questions related to his/her alphabet word and researches the answers through class activities and research.	Addresses all of the components	Missing one component	Missing two components	Missing three or more components
PRESENTATION: (Grades 3-5): Student shares and explains his/her alphabet book work with younger students, discusses the components of a wetland, and helps younger students create their own alphabet book.	Addresses all of the components	Missing one component	Missing two components	Missing three or more components

CONNECT   2 | **Wetland Song**

ELEMENTS	☆☆☆☆	☆☆☆	☆☆	☆
DESCRIBING WORDS: Student participates in creating a brainstorm list of description words, action/feeling words and facts about a wetland organism.	Addresses all of the components	Missing one component	Missing two components	Missing three or more components
SONG: Student writes a sentence and helps to create a wetland song. Student participates in singing the wetland song with the class.	Addresses all of the components	Missing one component	Missing two components	Missing three or more components

CONNECT   3 | **Mud Painting**

ELEMENTS	☆☆☆☆	☆☆☆	☆☆	☆
DISCUSSION: Student participates in the discussion on collecting natural objects, and renewable/nonrenewable materials. Student uses active listening skills (eye-contact, confirming or referencing others' comments, affirmative gestures or comments).	Addresses all of the components	Missing one component	Missing two components	Missing three or more components
PROJECT: Student collects appropriate objects and wetland mud, and arranges them correctly on the fabric. Student completes journal free write and offers responses during the wrap-up discussion that demonstrate reflection. Personal investment is obvious.	Addresses all of the components	Missing one component	Missing two components	Missing three or more components

EXPLORE   4 | **Groundwater Exploration**

ELEMENTS	☆☆☆☆	☆☆☆	☆☆	☆
MAP: Student uses a map and/or the internet to locate the school, Great Lakes, wetland and watershed on a map. Student finds the regional watersheds and defines "watershed." Student draws a map that includes the school, wetland, tributaries and Great Lake.	Addresses all of the components	Missing one component	Missing two components	Missing three or more components
MODEL: Student helps design the model of "underground," discusses water movement, and hypothesizes about the water's path between the wetland and lake, both above ground and underground.	Addresses all of the components	Missing one component	Missing two components	Missing three or more components
WRITING: Through writing (and illustration), student demonstrates an understanding about the path water might take underground in the watershed.	Addresses all of the components	Missing one component	Missing two components	Missing three or more components

EXPLORE   5 | **Value of Wetlands**

ELEMENTS	☆☆☆☆	☆☆☆	☆☆	☆
MODEL: Student participates in designing and creating the model wetland, discusses it and the significance of wetlands. Student draws diagrams that show how wetlands hold and filter water.	Addresses all of the components	Missing one component	Missing two components	Missing three or more components
POEM: Student listens to and/or reads the poem "Value of Wetlands," and finds 2-3 examples of why wetlands are unique, important places.	Addresses all of the components	Missing one component	Missing two components	Missing three or more components
DISCUSSION: Student is able to articulate lessons and questions that arose from observing the model. Student uses active listening skills (eye-contact, confirming or referencing others' comments, affirmative gestures or comments).	Addresses all of the components	Missing one component	Missing two components	Missing three or more components

EXPLORE   6 | Wetland Observation

ELEMENTS	☆☆☆☆	☆☆☆	☆☆	☆
OBSERVATION: Student participates in initial observation activity and discusses the importance of observation.	Addresses all of the components	Missing one component	Missing two components	Missing three or more components
STATIONS: Student rotates between the 4 stations, making focused observations with words and sketches.	Addresses all of the components	Missing one component	Missing two components	Missing three or more components
SYNTHESIS: Student actively participates in the class discussion to synthesize information from the stations, and records information in his/her journal that indicates the significance of a wetland. Student uses active listening skills (eye-contact, confirming or referencing others' comments, affirmative gestures or comments).	Addresses all of the components	Missing one component	Missing two components	Missing three or more components
CONNECTIONS: Student is able to find 3-6 connections between living and nonliving components of the wetland.	Addresses all of the components	Missing one component	Missing two components	Missing three or more components

EXPLORE   7 | Bugs in the Mud

ELEMENTS	☆☆☆☆	☆☆☆	☆☆	☆
OBSERVATION: Student looks for macroinvertebrates and observes and sorts them at several stations. Student counts and records appropriate data to determine most commonly occurring macroinvertebrate.	Addresses all of the components	Missing one component	Missing two components	Missing three or more components
SKETCH: Student sketches the macroinvertebrates after carefully observing them under a hand lens	Addresses all of the components	Missing one component	Missing two components	Missing three or more components
DISCUSSION: Student identifies the most common macroinvertebrates found and the significance of them to the ecosystem	Addresses all of the components	Missing one component	Missing two components	Missing three or more components

EXPLORE   8 | Critical Critters

ELEMENTS	☆☆☆☆	☆☆☆	☆☆	☆
OBSERVATION: Student looks for macroinvertebrates and observes and sorts them at several stations. Student counts and records appropriate data to determine most commonly occurring macroinvertebrate.	Addresses all of the components	Missing one component	Missing two components	Missing three or more components
SKETCH: Student sketches the macroinvertebrates after carefully observing them under a hand lens and included living conditions in sketch or notes	Addresses all of the components	Missing one component	Missing two components	Missing three or more components
DISCUSSION: Student identifies the most common macroinvertebrates found and the significance of them to the ecosystem and their tolerance level for pollution.	Addresses all of the components	Missing one component	Missing two components	Missing three or more components

EXPLORE   9 | Living Life Cycles

ELEMENTS	☆☆☆☆	☆☆☆	☆☆	☆
QUESTIONS: Student chooses a macroinvertebrate and poses 1-3 questions about it (in addition to the activity questions) using the 5 W's (who, what, where, when and how).	Addresses all of the components	Missing one component	Missing two components	Missing three or more components
RESEARCH: Student researches and answers the questions and uses pictures and text to diagram the life cycle. Student works well with other groups members to collect information.	Addresses all of the components	Missing one component	Missing two components	Missing three or more components
PRESENTATION: Student participates in sharing his/her research with the group and performs a skit of an organisms' life cycle for the class. Student articulates the changes that one organism goes through. Student (5-6) includes details on changes in structure and function, feeding and habitat.	Addresses all of the components	Missing one component	Missing two components	Missing three or more components

EXPLORE   10 | Name that Plant

ELEMENTS	★★★★	★★★	★★	★
PARTICIPATION: Student actively participates in the clothing classification and leaf classification activities, and assesses others' work with care, using the established guidelines.	Addresses all of the components	Missing one component	Missing two components	Missing three or more components
FIELD GUIDE: Student researches their plant, draws an accurate representation of it and answers journal questions completely	Addresses all of the components	Missing one component	Missing two components	Missing three or more components
CLASSIFICATION: Student helps complete a class field guide, articulates what it means to classify organisms, and explains methods and values of classifying.	Addresses all of the components	Missing one component	Missing two components	Missing three or more components

EXPLORE   11 | Working Wetlands

ELEMENTS	★★★★	★★★	★★	★
EXPERIMENT: Student actively helps to design and create the 3 phases of the model that represent how a wetland functions. Student hypothesizes about what will happen in each phase.	Addresses all of the components	Missing one component	Missing two components	Missing three or more components
JOURNAL PAGES: Student completes the journal page for each phase with accurate diagrams and responses that demonstrate an understanding of the concepts. (K-2) Student accurately completed diagrams provided.	Addresses all of the components	Missing one component	Missing two components	Missing three or more components
DISCUSSION: Student articulates how the model is similar to and different from a wetland, and explains the functions of a wetland. Student asks questions and responds to questions from other students and educator.	Addresses all of the components	Missing one component	Missing two components	Missing three or more components

INVESTIGATE   12 | Mini Wetlands

ELEMENTS	★★★★	★★★	★★	★
WATER PURIFICATION: Student creates 2-4 research questions about water treatment and finds answers through a variety of research methods. Student creates a visual representation of the water treatment process and includes information on their own water use, and conservation methods.	Addresses all of the components	Missing one component	Missing two components	Missing three or more components
PARTICIPATION: Student lists components of a wetland and brainstorms a design for a classroom wetland based on an improvement in the water treatment system. Student uses prior activities and other research to create design.	Addresses all of the components	Missing one component	Missing two components	Missing three or more components
IMPLEMENTATION: Student helps to implement a design by working on a specific cell, placing organisms and assuring their needs were met. Student compared cells to actual wetland microhabitats.	Addresses all of the components	Missing one component	Missing two components	Missing three or more components
MONITORING: Student collects data to monitor the constructed wetland. He/she compares past data and monitors the impact of additional water and gray water being added to the system.	Addresses all of the components	Missing one component	Missing two components	Missing three or more components
ASSESSMENT: Student accurately diagrams the processes in the classroom wetland. Student writes an essay that reflects his/her thoughts, experiences and knowledge gained. Student is able to share his/her knowledge with others.	Addresses all of the components	Missing one component	Missing two components	Missing three or more components

INVESTIGATE   13 | Teaching About Wetlands

ELEMENTS	★★★★	★★★	★★	★
REFLECTION: Student actively reflects on what he/she learned, problems wetlands face and how to convey knowledge to others. Student brainstorms educational ideas based on these reflections.	Addresses all of the components	Missing one component	Missing two components	Missing three or more components
GOALS: Student constructs a do-able project with achievable goals while working productively with a team and using past and new knowledge.	Addresses all of the components	Missing one component	Missing two components	Missing three or more components
IMPLEMENTATION: Student works with others to implement and present a project that serves to preserve, educate about, and celebrate wetlands.	Addresses all of the components	Missing one component	Missing two components	Missing three or more components

Human Communities

- In what ways do humans depend on the Great Lakes?
- How do human communities and the Great Lakes affect each other?
- How can a community be healthy and live in balance with the Great Lakes?

Humans (Homo sapiens) have been dependent on the Great Lakes for thousands of years. Humans have the potential to both create and solve problems for the Great Lakes.

unit overview

Students reflect on and examine how human relationships with the environment affect Great Lakes' communities. They study how human and wildlife needs are met within the Great Lakes region. In exploring how urban ecosystems are dependent on water resources, students learn about the interplay and balance essential in maintaining a healthy relationship with the Great Lakes. Students investigate issues that face the Great Lakes and the human role in creating, perpetuating and helping to solve these problems. By looking at communities and how they work, students evaluate their communities, with an eye toward improvements to the system. As a final project, students design a community that takes into account what they learn in this unit.

concepts

⦿ The Great Lakes serve the region in many ways. To fully appreciate this ecosystem, it is important to understand the ways in which plants, animals, people and their communities depend on the lakes.

⦿ Humans can both create and solve problems for the Great Lakes. In order to conserve, preserve and have a healthy relationship with our Great Lakes, we need to understand the impact our actions have on them.

unit activities

1 | What's the Environment?

GRADE LEVEL

4-8

45 minutes

summary

Students explore definitions of the word "environment" that include an urban definition and write about how life in the Midwest would be different without the Great Lakes.

objectives

- Define "environment" in a new way.
- Compare and contrast images of the environment.
- Discuss what makes the environment a valuable place to live.

prerequisite

None

vocabulary

Environment: where we live, work and play

setting

Works well for students in an urban setting, but can be used in any setting, see note in procedure.

INDOORS

subjects

Language Arts, Environmental Science

standards

This Great Lakes in My World activity is aligned to the Common Core State Standards and to state learning standards in:

Illinois
Indiana
Michigan
Minnesota
New York
Ohio
Pennsylvania
Wisconsin

This alignment is available on your Great Lakes in My World CD in the "Standards" folder and on-line at http://www.greatlakes.org/ GLiMWstandards.

materials

- Pencil
- Paper
- Markers
- Crayons
- Images of a city for non-urban students

background

There is evidence that many people think of the environment as a beautiful, wild, natural place, untouched by humans. This can create a sense of disconnect from the perceived environment for urban students. According to the environmental justice movement, the environment is where we live, work and play.

This definition considers all of the settings that humans live in as the environment. It places importance on the places humans live, even those that are not always thought of as valuable. When we realize that where we live is a vital place, an ethic of care for that place may follow.

procedure

1. Ask students to define the word "environment." Have a brief discussion about the word. *For the most part, students are likely to define it as a beautiful, natural place. Do not place more weight on any one student's answer.*

2. Have students use half of a sheet of paper to draw what they think the environment looks like.

3. Write the following definition of "environment" on the board for students to see: Environment: where we live, work and play.

4. Ask students if this changes their mental picture of the environment. How? What is the environment that they live in? How do the Great Lakes fit into their environment? Use this to assess students' pre-conceived notions of the Great Lakes.

5. Have students draw a second picture, illustrating their environment as it fits this new definition.

   Note: For students living in a rural setting, ask them to put themselves in the shoes of a student in an urban setting, once they have seen the definition. According to this definition, what would students draw if they lived in a city? Use images of a city (on accompanying compact disc) to help.

6. Have students share their drawings with partners and explain how they are different or similar to each other's pictures.

wrap-up

1. As a class, students discuss:

   • What was the difference between your two drawings?
   • What do you think of this definition of the environment?
   • How does the definition change or not change what you think about where you live?
   • How are the Great Lakes a part of your environment?
   • Your neighborhood? Your community?

2. The Great Lakes are an essential part of the Midwest environment. Have students imagine that one day they discover the Great Lakes no longer exist and had suddenly disappeared. What would life be like without the Great Lakes? Have students write about a day without the Great Lakes, emphasizing what would be different. How would they and their families and neighbors survive?

3. Students share writing and reflections with each other and the class.

assessment

Rubric on page 309

Contributing author: Anna Byrne

 We value your thoughts and feedback on Great Lakes in My World. Please let us know about any oversights, errors or omissions you find, or if there are things you or your students particularly like.

Send your comments to: education@greatlakes.org

1 | What's the Environment?

GRADE LEVEL
4-8

FIRST NAME																				
LAST NAME																				

Drawing 1

Drawing 2

Free Write: What would life be like without the Great Lakes?

APPROVED BY

CONNECT

2 | Sound Picture

GRADE LEVEL

3-6

 30 minutes

Developmental Modifications: For younger students, talk about the senses, then have students create a drawing that reflects the sounds they hear. They may label components of their drawing, then share and discuss what they have made.

summary

Students create an image based on sounds heard at the lake and then discuss the relationship between people and the Great Lakes.

objectives

- Illustrate sounds heard at the lake.
- Discuss human interaction with the Great Lakes.

prerequisite

None

vocabulary

None

setting

Crowded beach/waterfront area where people and lake noises can both be heard, or in the classroom with pre-recorded sounds.

 INDOORS

 OUTDOORS

subjects

Language Arts

standards

This Great Lakes in My World activity is aligned to the Common Core State Standards and to state learning standards in:

Illinois
Indiana
Michigan
Minnesota
New York
Ohio
Pennsylvania
Wisconsin

This alignment is available on your Great Lakes in My World CD in the "Standards" folder and on-line at http://www.greatlakes.org/GLiMWstandards.

materials

- Pre-recorded sound (if in the classroom - on compact disc)
- Paper
- Pencils
- Journals
- Clipboards

background

People and the Great Lakes are neighbors. A long history has brought and kept humans close to the shores of the Great Lakes. Although it is possible to look at humans and the Great Lakes in isolation, acknowledging the sounds of both entities allow us to think about how the two are intertwined. Because students can use images, shapes and words for their pictures, there may be a wide variety of creative responses to this activity.

procedure

1. Have students listen carefully to the sounds of the Great Lakes combined with a human presence (i.e. use a sound recording (on compact disc) or go to a beach or pier where water-related sounds can be heard). If the class is at an outdoor site, have students find a spot to sit with their eyes closed and listen for 30-60 seconds to the sounds around them. If using sounds on the compact disk, have students respond after each segment

2. After they have listened, have students record the sounds (not what they can see) on the journal page. Students may use drawings or words to reflect what they hear. The images or words should be arranged to reflect what the students heard happening. For example, was the sound in the water, in the sky, on the sand or on the ground? Students may use abstract or concrete representations.

3. Students should have between three and ten images or words on their paper. If using words, students may write their words in shapes that reflect the sounds they hear. *For example, what might the following sounds look like: crashing wave, music playing, cry of a gull, children laughing or the wind?*

4. Have students share their sound picture with a partner or in a small group. While sharing pictures, students may consider: What were some of the things you heard? How does this picture show what you heard? How is what you heard different from what you were able to see?

wrap-up

1. As a class, discuss the following:

   • Have you been to the Great Lakes before?
   • What sounds did you hear?
   • How did the sounds make you feel about the lake?
   • What does the lake sound like without human noises?
   • Do you prefer to be near the lake with or without human sounds? Why?
   • What were some of the similarities and differences between the sound pictures in the class?

assessment

Rubric on page 309

2 | Sound Picture

GRADE LEVEL
3-6

FIRST NAME																					
LAST NAME																					

[1] Use the space below to create a picture of the sounds you hear at the beach or in the recording. For example, if you hear the sound of waves crashing, draw or write what you hear in a place on the page that shows where they are.

[2] How do the sounds make you feel about the lake?

....

....

....

....

....

[3] Do you prefer to be near the lake with or without human sounds? Why?

....

....

....

....

....

APPROVED BY	

EXPLORE

3 | Take a Good Look

GRADE LEVEL

K-4

45 minutes

Developmental Modifications: Use either the K-2 or the 3-4 journal pages.

summary

Students observe the living and non-living items they see at the beach and discuss the relationship of the items to the Great Lakes.

objectives

• List items found at the beach.
• Discuss the relationship of these items to the ecosystem.

prerequisite

None

vocabulary

Organic: things that are or were once alive
Inorganic: things that have never been alive
Habitat: place where an organism lives that includes its food, water, shelter and space

setting

OUTDOORS

Beach

subjects

Geology, Social Studies

standards

This Great Lakes in My World activity is aligned to the Common Core State Standards and to state learning standards in:

Illinois
Indiana
Michigan
Minnesota
New York
Ohio
Pennsylvania
Wisconsin

This alignment is available on your Great Lakes in My World CD in the "Standards" folder and on-line at http://www.greatlakes.org/ GLiMWstandards.

materials

• Pencils
• Journals
• Clipboards,
• Gloves, garbage bags - optional

background

The Great Lakes shoreline is a habitat that is home to many living things. This activity shows the interdependence between the living and nonliving factors where the land and water meet. The unique combination of living and non-living elements creates a dynamic system that requires exploration and observation to understand the interactions that occur there. In order to understand humans' place within this ecosystem, students begin by studying these interactions.

procedure

1. Tell students they will be using their sense of sight to observe what they see at the beach. They will be looking for both living and non-living objects.

2. Take students to the beach to do their observation. Tell students that some of the things they observe may be very small, so they will have to pay close attention. Students can be given gloves and garbage bags to pick up any garbage they find.
Note: Caution students against picking up any sharp objects. Have adult chaperones assist with this.

3. Take 10-15 minutes for pairs of students to observe. *Examples of items they might find:*
Living – ant, bee, spider, bird, grass, flower, humans
Non-living – rock, soil/dirt, buildings, garbage, playground equipment

4. When they come back, ask students what they found. Discuss which are living and which are not living.

5. Have them draw one living and one non-living item in their journals either during the observation of afterwards. Label the items.

6. Fill out and discuss journal questions. For K-2, this can be a discussion only.

7. Discuss: What surprised you about what you saw? How do the living objects depend on the Great Lakes? *Food, water, recreation.* What is the relationship of the nonliving items to the Great Lakes? *Some are natural objects that belong, and some were brought by human hands.* How can you tell humans spend time at the beach? *Footprints, garbage, garbage cans, lifeguard stands, cars.* What makes the Great Lakes an important part of your life? *Include drinking water as a response, if this applies to your community. Emphasize that humans could not survive without drinking water. Freshwater is also necessary for crops to grow. The Great Lakes also enable goods to be shipped to and from the region and are a source of beauty and recreation.* What makes the Great Lakes a special place for you?

wrap-up

1. Back in the classroom, create a class list of the items found.

2. Have students write and draw about their time at the beach.

3. Discuss questions the students have from their visit.

4. Discuss how life would be different if we did not have the Great Lakes. Why are they so important to the people, plants and animals in the region?

assessment

Rubric on page 309

 We value your thoughts and feedback on Great Lakes in My World. Please let us know about any oversights, errors or omissions you find, or if there are things you or your students particularly like.

Send your comments to: education@greatlakes.org

3 | Take a Good Look

GRADE LEVEL
K-2

journal pages

FIRST NAME																				
LAST NAME																				

[1] Draw a picture of a living item you found:

[2] Draw a picture of a non-living item you found:

[3] What maKes the Great LaKes a special place?

....

....

....

....

....

....

....

APPROVED BY	

3 | Take a Good Look

GRADE LEVEL
3-4

journal ≡ pages

FIRST NAME																					
LAST NAME																					

Living Item Questions

[1] List some living things you found.

....

....

....

Choose one item and answer the following questions:

[2] How do you Know this item is living?

....

....

....

....

[3] What does this living thing need in order to survive?

....

....

....

....

[4] What other living things might need the one you have chosen, to survive?

....

....

....

....

[5] Draw the living creature you observed.

APPROVED BY	

3 | Take a Good Look

GRADE LEVEL
3-4

journal pages

FIRST NAME

LAST NAME

Non-Living Item Questions

[6] List some non-living things you found.

Choose one item and answer the following questions:

[7] How do you Know this item is not living?

[8] How might living things use this non-living thing?

[9] Was this item once alive, or part of something that was once alive, liKe a leaf or a shell? Note – Special Vocabulary: Organic: Things that are or were once alive. Inorganic: Things that have never been alive.

[10] Draw the non-living item you observed.

[11] Why are the Great LaKes important to you and your community?

APPROVED BY

EXPLORE

4 | Who Lives In My Community?

GRADE LEVEL

K-4

45 minutes

Developmental Modifications: Kindergartners can complete the first journal page only.

summary

Students discuss the basic needs of living things by identifying what humans, plants and animals require for survival. Students identify the resources the Great Lakes provide for local organisms.

objectives

- List the basic needs of living things.
- Explain what a habitat is.
- Identify several of the common plants and animals of the area.
- Describe why we depend on the Great Lakes.
- Explain why it is important to keep the Great Lakes and the surrounding community clean and healthy.

prerequisite

None

vocabulary

Habitat: a place where an organism lives that includes its food, water, shelter and space
Organism: a living creature, either plant or animal

setting

INDOORS

subjects

Life Science, Social Studies, Language Arts

standards

This Great Lakes in My World activity is aligned to the Common Core State Standards and to state learning standards in:

Illinois
Indiana
Michigan
Minnesota
New York
Ohio
Pennsylvania
Wisconsin

This alignment is available on your Great Lakes in My World CD in the "Standards" folder and on-line at http://www.greatlakes.org/ GLiMWstandards.

materials

- Creature Cards
- Journals
- Pencils

background

Plants and animals have their own communities that enable them to survive, without needing to rely on human communities. Humans have built communities that they share with plants and animals. These communities often overlap in the spaces they occupy and in the ways they support life. For example, some birds nest at the beach, while humans also use the space as recreation. All living organisms have similar needs that they must meet in order to survive. This activity focuses on the importance of keeping the Great Lakes and our communities clean and healthy in order to support all the life that depends on them. Prior to this activity, separate the Creature Cards according to step #6.

procedure

1. As a class answer the following question and write responses on the board:
   What do all animals need to survive?
   Food, water, shelter, space, air and livable temperatures are the components of a habitat and are the essential things that all animals need to survive. Other student responses may include things like specific types of food, air, nests, etc, which all fit under the basic headings of food, water, shelter, and space. Animals also need each other for reproduction.

2. Write food, water, shelter, and space as categories and show how other answers fit into these categories. Explain that these are the things all animals need to survive and items that can always be found in an animal's habitat. Define a habitat.
   For example, a squirrel's habitat is a forest (or, in some cases, a city). Its food is acorns, its shelter is a tree, its space is the area it has to move around, and it has a water source within this area.

3. Repeat this process for plants. *Plants need sunlight, water, nutrients, air and a substrate (place), such as soil. Some plants also need each other or animals for seed dispersal or reproduction.*

4. Discuss how humans and animals have similar needs. Compare human and plant needs.

5. What is a human's space? *Neighborhood, town, city.* What are our communities? *Response will vary.* For this activity, we will consider the Great Lakes as part of the community. How does a human get what it needs to live in that space? *Discuss where we get food, water and shelter.* Who lives in our communities? *Other humans, animals and plants that depend on the resources of the Great Lakes region.*

6. Break students into small groups and give each group several Creature Cards. For an additional card set, print them from the compact disc. It is fine if some of the cards are repeated in more than one group. At least one card should be a species that can be found in or near a human community. *Depending on where the students live, some organisms that live in human communities include: Canada goose, mosquito, herring gull, mallard duck, and black ant. It is possible that students decide that all of the species can live in their community.*

7. Have students separate the cards into species that can be found in their Great Lakes community and those that cannot. They use the information on the backs of the Creature Cards to help decide why an animal may or may not be able to live in their community. *For example, a goose may be able to live in their community if it has water, grass and insects. A fish would not be able to live in their community if there is not a river, pond or lake.*

8. Students should answer journal questions.

9. Have each group choose one species and present to the class why this plant or animal can or cannot live in their communities, keeping in mind the components of a habitat and what is available to the plants/animals in their community.

10. Discuss: Have you seen any of these organisms in or around your community before? Where? How are humans similar to plants and animals? *They are all living beings that live where they can meet their needs.* How do the Great Lakes meet the needs of living species? *They provide water, food, shelter and space.* Do these species live only in human communities or do they overlap into other habitats as well? If so, which ones and why? *Other habitats may include beach, dune, or forest.*

wrap-up

1. Imagine the region without the Great Lakes. How would life be different for humans, animals and plants? What do humans get from the Great Lakes to meet their needs? *Drinking water, goods are shipped (food, clothing, housing materials), some fish are eaten.*

2. Why is it important that we keep the Great Lakes and the areas around them clean and healthy? *Humans and animals depend on the Great Lakes for food, water, goods via the shipping industry and recreation.*

extension

Take a walk in the school neighborhood to look for some of these organisms. Make a list of all organisms you find on your walk.

assessment

Rubric on page 309

4 | Who Lives In My Community?

GRADE LEVEL
K-4

journal pages

FIRST NAME																				
LAST NAME																				

[1] Which plant or animal will your group present to the class?

....

....

....

[2] Draw it:

[3] Does it live in your community? Why or why not?

....

....

....

....

....

APPROVED BY	

4 | Who Lives In My Community?

GRADE LEVEL K-4

journal pages

FIRST NAME

LAST NAME

[4] What does it need to live?

[5] Where does it live?

[6] What do humans have in common with it?

APPROVED BY

5 | Lake Landmarks

45-90 minutes

Developmental Modifications: If students do not create community maps, use a community map to locate landmarks and discuss cardinal directions, aerial view and scale. Students can draw a landmark, locate it on the map and discuss aspects of their community they like or would like to see improved.

summary

Students create a list of the important aspects of the nearest city, and make a map, weaving in the importance of the Great Lakes.

objectives

- List the key components of their community or the nearest city.
- Explain whether different aspects of a community fulfill needs or wants.
- Discuss why the lake is necessary for survival.
- Draw a map of the community that includes key landmarks.
- Reflect on city planning decisions.

prerequisite

Students should be familiar with some of the landmarks in the nearest city and have completed What's the Environment?

vocabulary

Central city: usually refers to the downtown area of a city
City: the city as officially incorporated; does not include suburbs
Megacity: a city with at least 10 million people; various sources define megacities as cities with at least 8, 10, or 12 million people
Metropolitan area: a city and its suburbs
Suburb: usually a residential area located outside of a city or town; some suburbs have commercial districts with offices and shops

setting

INDOORS

subjects

Geography, Social Studies

standards

This Great Lakes in My World activity is aligned to the Common Core State Standards and to state learning standards in:

Illinois
Indiana
Michigan
Minnesota
New York
Ohio
Pennsylvania
Wisconsin

This alignment is available on your Great Lakes in My World CD in the "Standards" folder and on-line at http://www.greatlakes.org/GLiMWstandards.

materials

- World map
- Regional map
- Community map
- Journals
- Pencils

background

Within the next decade, more than half of the world's population will be living in urban areas. In order to create more livable and friendlier communities, we can start by reflecting on the community or urban area in which we live, or which is close by. Understanding the current community allows students to later envision what can be done to revitalize and improve the community.

procedure

1. Have students look at a national or world map. Note what many of the major cities have in common in terms of location. Students will notice that many cities are located near a water resource, in particular, freshwater. Discuss this. *Freshwater is essential for survival. Humans cannot live without it. Being near water can also enable goods to be shipped to and from a city.* If the lake were not here, what other source of drinking water would be nearby? What are groundwater reserves like in your region? How would the population of your community be affected if the lake were not here?

2. Students look at a map of the nearest city or the one that they inhabit. Tell students they are going to be talking about communities. Ask the students: What is the name of the community you live in or near? What word is used to describe the community you live in? If you live in a rural area, focus on a large community/city that is close to you. Define the term that describes your community. *You may define it in the way that works best for this activity. Some helpful definitions are included in the Vocabulary section.*

3. Ask the students: What does a community (or city) need in order to work well for the people who live in it? Think about what exists in your own community. As a class, brainstorm a list of the key elements. *The list might include: supermarket, fresh water, places to live, roads, government, port or harbor, post office, beaches, parks or other outdoor space, shops (can be specific), movie theater, gas stations, public transportation.*

4. Have students divide the list into categories: 1) Necessary for survival or 2) Makes life fun or more interesting. Items necessary for survival will include those related to food, water, shelter, and space. Discuss the question: How are wants and needs different?

5. Make a mark next to items that are related to your Great Lake. *This might include: drinking water, water treatment plant, homes and businesses (materials for these may have been shipped via the lake), industry may use water from the lake, outdoor space may be located near the lake, beaches are along the shoreline.* Discuss the question: Is the lake necessary for human survival? *Yes.* What does it add to the community? *Humans cannot live without freshwater. It is absolutely essential for drinking and for growing crops for food. The lake adds other benefits to the community including beauty, recreation, means for shipping.*

6. Out of the items on the list, which do students consider personal landmarks? *A landmark is a place that holds significance for an individual or the community, or serves as a visual marker for finding your way.*

7. Individually, have students create a map that includes several elements from the original list. Post a community map to guide students. Note: This activity is an opportunity to introduce students to the concepts of scale, aerial view, and contour maps as appropriate.
   The sketch should include:
   - The lake – shoreline and water
   - Two to three elements necessary for human survival
   - Two to three personal landmarks (can be elements that make life more fun or interesting)
   - School and/or student's place of residence
   Starred items indicate personal landmarks. The sketch should have at least three, including the students' place of residence, and their school.
   - Labeled landmarks and labeled cardinal directions (north, south, east and west)
   - Optional - Add 1 or 2 imaginary landmarks to your map. Label them.

wrap-up

1. Students discuss the following questions as a class. Why are the landmarks on your map important? How is the lake important to your community? What do you like about your community? What do you think could be improved in your community? How would changes impact the lake or other natural areas in the community? Your local government made decisions when planning your city. What do you have to think about when planning a city? (Note: This topic is related to the activities My Community and Create-a-Community.)

extension

Students can write research papers about different cities around the Great Lakes, present them to the class and discuss similarities and differences in the cities, and their relationships with the Great Lakes.

assessment

Rubric on page 310

5 | Lake Landmarks

GRADE LEVEL
4-8

journal pages

FIRST NAME																				
LAST NAME																				

[1] Create a map that includes elements from your original list and includes:
- Your Great Lake: shoreline and water.
- Two to three elements necessary for human survival.
- Two to three elements that make life more fun or interesting.
- Three personal landmarks, including your home and/or your school (put a star next to items that indicate personal landmarks.)
- Label all of the landmarks.
- Label north, south, east and west.

APPROVED BY	

5 | Lake Landmarks

GRADE LEVEL
4-8

journal ≣ pages

FIRST NAME																			
LAST NAME																			

[2] How is the lake important to your community?

....

....

....

....

....

....

[3] What do you like about your community?

....

....

....

....

....

....

[4] What do you think could be improved in your community?

....

....

....

....

....

....

[5] Your local government made decisions when planning your community. What do you
have to think about when planning a community?

....

....

....

....

....

....

....

APPROVED BY	

EXPLORE

6 | Litter Tag

GRADE LEVEL

3-6

30 minutes

summary

Students play a tag game to understand the harmful effects litter has on Great Lakes organisms.

objectives

- Discuss how garbage harms wildlife.
- List ways that humans can help solve this problem.

prerequisite

Sound Picture or What's the Environment?, Who Lives In My Community? and Take a Good Look

vocabulary

None

setting

INDOORS   OUTDOORS

subjects

Environmental Science, Social Studies

standards

This Great Lakes in My World activity is aligned to the Common Core State Standards and to state learning standards in:

Illinois
Indiana
Michigan
Minnesota
New York
Ohio
Pennsylvania
Wisconsin

This alignment is available on your Great Lakes in My World CD in the "Standards" folder and on-line at http://www.greatlakes.org/ GLiMWstandards.

materials

- Cigarette butt
- Balloon with string
- Fishing line
- Plastic bag

background

When litter is put in the environment, either intentionally, or by accident, it generally has negative effects. In the Great Lakes, litter can decrease tourism, diminish community pride, and cause harm to plants, animals and people.

Data collected from garbage collected along the shoreline of the Great Lakes shows the most frequently found items. Some of the top items found (by number of pieces picked up) are listed below, along with some of the problems associated with them.

Cigarette Butts: Cigarette filters are the most numerous item found during beach cleanups. Filters are made of a plastic, cellulose acetate, which can take up to five years to break down and even longer to decompose. Children at play on the beach can put cigarette filters in their mouths. A study has also been done showing that the chemicals in cigarettes can be harmful to microorganisms that support other wildlife.

Balloons: Balloons and their ribbons entangle animals and are sometimes ingested, when mistaken for food, causing injury or death. Balloons can also pose a problem for boaters if their propellers get tangled up in the string.
Food and Food Packaging: Bags can entangle animals or be accidentally ingested by them, causing injury or death. Leftover food may attract additional wildlife to the beach, resulting in increased animal droppings, which can lead to high bacteria levels in the water. High bacteria levels are a reason for beach closings.
Beverage bottles (glass, aluminum, plastic): This could indicate the need for recycling containers on the beach. Broken glass and sharp points on aluminum can injure people as well as wildlife.
Fishing line: Fishing line can entangle animals, which can cause injury to wildlife.

procedure

1. Ask students what they like best about going to the beach. Ask them what some of the problems are that they see at the beach. Eventually, they should get to litter that they have seen there. Ask students what kind of problems litter might cause. Use background information to help them get a complete picture.
2. Ask students to think of ways to help solve this problem. *Pick up the garbage, or do not leave it in the environment in the first place. Humans are both the problem and the solution.*
3. In an outdoor area or a gym, divide the students into four groups representing litter, birds, fish and humans. For a class of 26 there should be four humans, four litter, nine birds and nine fish. Have the students decide which type of

litter, bird or fish they will be. Explain that the litter will be chasing the birds and fish, trying to tag them. Once a bird or fish is tagged, they are frozen.
4. After one minute, the humans will come into the game to "rescue" the tagged fish and birds. When rescuing a bird or fish, two humans must hold hands with the animal in the middle and yell, "One, two, three fish (or bird) free!" And then, after several minutes, choose one or two humans to be Beach Captains. The Beach Captains can still free the animals with the other humans, but now they can chase the litter, too. If the litter is tagged, they must sit out. The game ends when the beach captains tag all the litter, or sooner, if students are tired. If time allows, switch roles and play again.

wrap-up

1. Bring the group back together and ask students to talk about what they learned or what the game made them think about with regard to litter and the Great Lakes.
2. Discuss the following questions: Do animals really get caught in litter? *Yes, plastic bags, string and netting cause many problems for wildlife.*

How realistic is it to say that litter "chases" animals? *Animals do not generally suspect that litter will hurt them. It can take animals by surprise when litter entangles them.* How can humans help solve this problem? *By picking up after themselves, telling others the harm that litter can do.*

extension

If the students consider litter to be a problem in their community, have the class consider what actions they could take to help solve this problem.

- Participate in the Alliance for the Great Lakes' Adopt-a-Beach™ program.
- Send notes home about the International Coastal Cleanup, which occurs on the third Saturday of every September.
- Students put their litter solutions into action.

assessment

Rubric on page 310

Contributing author: Steve Jerbi

7 | Garbage Investigation

GRADE LEVEL
4-8

45-90 minutes

Developmental Modifications: Use the K-3 journal page for this activity. Young children will need close supervision at the beach and should exercise extreme caution with sharp objects. When picking up garbage, always wear gloves. If appropriate, graph the data as a class.

summary

Students analyze beach trash, discuss the problems posed by it and propose solutions to these problems.

objectives

- Discuss the difference between natural and human-made objects.
- Sort, record, graph, compare, and discuss garbage data.
- Problem-solve about garbage issues.

prerequisite

Sound Picture or What's the Environment?, Who Lives In My Community? and Take a Good Look

vocabulary

None

setting

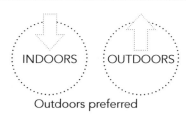

INDOORS   OUTDOORS

Outdoors preferred

subjects

Environmental Science, Ecology, Social Studies, Math

standards

This Great Lakes in My World activity is aligned to the Common Core State Standards and to state learning standards in:

Illinois
Indiana
Michigan
Minnesota
New York
Ohio
Pennsylvania
Wisconsin

This alignment is available on your Great Lakes in My World CD in the "Standards" folder and on-line at http://www.greatlakes.org/ GLiMWstandards.

materials

- Pencils
- Journals
- Data sheet
- Graph paper
- Garbage
- Sturdy gloves for each student
- Tarp (if indoors)
- The Ocean Conservancy's data (on cd)

background

Beaches are a place to recreate, exercise, socialize, see wildlife and find solitude. They attract tourists and can be an immense draw for those who live near them. Due to human impact, beaches can suffer from a number of issues, including problems associated with shoreline garbage.

Caution: Students will touch garbage in this activity. Exercise caution when touching garbage! Students should wear gloves. Garbage can be emptied onto a plastic tarp or plastic bag to minimize the mess. If there is a potential for sharp objects, the teacher should sort them out, or responsible, older students can do the sorting. Students should wash their hands when they finish this activity.

Beach litter problems

Cigarette Butts: Cigarette filters are the most numerous item found at Coastal Cleanup. Filters are made of a plastic, cellulose acetate, which can take up to five years to break down and even longer to decompose. Children at play on the beach can put cigarette filters in their mouths. A study has been done showing that the chemicals in cigarettes can be harmful to microorganisms that support other wildlife.

Balloons: Balloons and their ribbons entangle animals and are sometimes ingested when mistaken for food, causing injury or death. Balloons can also be a problem for boaters if their propellers get tangled up in the string.

Food and Food Packaging: Bags can entangle animals or be accidentally ingested by them, causing injury or death. Leftover food may attract additional wildlife to the beach, resulting in increased animal droppings, which can lead to high bacteria levels in the water. High bacteria levels are a reason for beach closings.

Beverage bottles (glass, aluminum, plastic): Broken glass and sharp points on aluminum can injure people as well as wildlife.

Fishing line: Fishing line can cause wildlife to become entangled, potentially leading to injury or death.

Ways to address problems created through beach litter

Service Learning: Service learning integrates community service work into classroom learning and curriculum. Community issues such as dirty beaches or beach closings can be addressed through service learning. When integrated into a curriculum, Adopt-a-Beach™ and Coastal Cleanup are examples of service learning.

Adopt-a-Beach™: Join the Adopt-a-Beach™ program to create positive change for your beach through litter monitoring and water quality testing along the shorelines of the Great Lakes. The Alliance for the Great Lakes provides support and structure for Adopt-a-Beach™ through documentation, an online database and guidance. Adopters make up to five beach visits per year. Participants analyze data and take action to improve their beach. See the Adopt-a-Beach™ activity in this unit orhttp://www.greatlakes.org/adoptabeach.

The International Coastal Cleanup: Coastal Cleanup is an annual, international volunteer event that takes place on the third Saturday of September. In Illinois, Indiana, Michigan and Wisconsin, it is part of the Alliance for the Great Lakes' Adopt-a-Beach™ program (September Adopt-a-Beach™). To get involved in IL, IN, MI or WI, contact the Alliance for the Great Lakes at adoptabeach@greatlakes.org. In other states or countries, contact the Ocean Conservancy to get involved: http://www.oceanconservancy.org.

procedure

Part One

1. Give the students one minute to think about an experience they have had on a beach or near the shore. In pairs, have students share their experience with each other for one or two minutes.
2. Ask students, if they have been to the beach, what they like about it. Take a few answers. Ask students what problems they have seen at the beach. *The list of answers might include: too crowded, no lifeguards, garbage, dirty, too cold, big waves, too hot.* Acknowledge all of these answers as possible. Focus on the garbage issue. Ask students: *What do we mean when we say the beach is dirty? This can mean garbage in the water and on the shoreline.* How does garbage get to the beach? *Human hands are behind garbage on the beach. People can leave trash at a beach or it can be left elsewhere, then be blown or washed onto the shore.*

3. Investigation: What do students think is found at beaches? Tell students they are going to investigate what is really found at beaches. Depending on classroom scheduling, here are two options:

   a. Bring in a bag of garbage found on a Great Lakes beach.
   b. During a class field trip to the beach, have students pick up garbage and bring the bag to class.

4. Have students collect data on the garbage they find. Garbage can be sorted as a class, or divided up and sorted by small groups of students. Use the sorting chart provided. To add interest, add a few natural objects that might be found at the beach (feathers, rocks, driftwood...) into the mix of garbage for later discussion.

procedure continued

5. Complete and discuss the questions on journal pages. Also, discuss the following: Is this all considered garbage? *Some items you find can be recycled. Discuss the benefits of recycling and/or reusing an object (such as a toy that is found at the beach). If you have put natural objects in with the garbage, discuss the fact that natural objects belong in the ecosystem.*

   How are natural objects different from those produced by people? *When natural objects decompose or break down in the ecosystem, they give back to the area in the form of nutrients for decomposers, insects and scavengers. They belong along the shoreline.*

   What problems could garbage create on the beach? *Web Option: This question can be answered on the Alliance for the Great Lakes's web site: www.greatlakes.org or the class can brainstorm ideas. Information is included in Background. Garbage items can cause problems for humans and wildlife. Trash on beaches can: cause people to care less about beaches or feel unhappy about their community, transform a beach into an eyesore, cause health issues, and entangle animals or be accidentally eaten by them, which can cause sickness or death for the animals.*

6. What can we do to help solve the problem of garbage on the beach? *Carry out what you carry in to beaches, picking up extra garbage at the beach, and educate others about beach litter issues.*

   Solution List: Based on the class discussion, have students make a list of possible solutions. Students create a list of three items they can do to help reduce garbage on the beach. Students share this list to compile a class solution list.

Suggested Solutions:

A. *Take responsibility: Always pick up your garbage, even the small pieces and food waste. Garbage can cause problems for humans and wildlife.*

B. *Join the Alliance for the Great Lakes's Adopt-a-Beach™ Program. Schools and community groups are invited to adopt. The program includes a commitment of five visits per year for litter cleanup and monitoring. As a program participant, you can also monitor water quality.*

C. *Volunteer at Coastal Cleanup, an international event that takes place the third Saturday of every September. It is coordinated by the Alliance for the Great Lakes in Michigan, Illinois, Wisconsin, and Indiana, and internationally by the Ocean Conservancy. For a list of state coordinators, see the Ocean Conservancy's web site: http://www.oceanconservancy.org*

D. *Pick up extra garbage. Bring an extra garbage bag with you when you go to the beach and spend some time making the area cleaner than when you arrived. This sets a great example for others at the beach.*

E. *Talk to local and state officials: Encourage your local and state officials to enforce litter laws and support them with proper disposal containers and adequate staff.*

F. *Educate others. Explain the problems associated with shoreline trash to other people. Help them see how important it is for us each to take responsibility for our actions.*

Part Two

1. Graph the data that you have collected while sorting garbage.
2. Graph the Coastal Cleanup data provided.
3. Compare the graphs. Your beach visit data and the data collected in Coastal Cleanup 2004. Choose a single site or use data for a state. Remember that you are comparing your site to one that is likely different in size and volunteer numbers.

4. Discuss as a class:
   - What is similar about what was found?
   - What is different about what was found?
   - What might account for any differences?
   - Discuss what makes graphing a useful tool. *Graphing is a useful tool for comparison because if allows people to see a visual representation of data.*
   - What conclusions can you draw from these sets of data?

wrap-up

1. Schools, classrooms, families and individuals can take action about the problem of beach garbage by participating in Adopt-a-Beach™. Your school can integrate the idea of "service learning" into the curriculum by addressing the beach issues in this activity. To get involved: Contact the Alliance for the Great Lakes about Adopt-a-Beach™.

extension

Explore what happens to the garbage in your school or community. Where does it go? Is some of it recycled? Landfilled? Investigate some of the problems associated with solid waste management. What are ways that these problems can be addressed within your school or community?

assessment

Rubric on page 310

7 | Garbage Investigation

GRADE LEVEL
4-8

FIRST NAME																					
LAST NAME																					

[1] In the chart below, Keep tracK of the garbage you find:

ITEM DESCRIPTION	TALLY

APPROVED BY	

7 | Garbage Investigation

FIRST NAME																							
LAST NAME																							

[2] What did you find the most of? Where did it come from?

....

....

....

[3] What did you find the least of?

....

....

[4] What category was the most popular for items that you found? (Check one)

❋ Recreational Activities (evidence of people having fun at the beach)

❋ Fishing/Boating (trash from commercial fishing or boat/vessel activities)

❋ Smoking-related (cigarette filters, lighters, packaging)

❋ Dumping (old appliances, batteries, car parts, tires)

❋ Eating (food wrappers, food packaging, napkins, utensils)

[5] What surprised you about what you found?

....

....

....

....

[6] What problems might be created by shoreline trash? List two to four problems.

....

....

....

....

[7] What three solutions do you think will help solve the problem of beach litter?

....

....

....

....

....

APPROVED BY	

7 | Garbage Investigation

GRADE LEVEL
4-8

FIRST NAME

LAST NAME

[8] MaKe a bar graph of the data you collected:

Number of Items

Type of Items

If you have many items, you may want to group them in the following categories:
- Recreational Activities
- Food-related
- Fishing/Boating
- SmoKing-related

APPROVED BY

7 | Garbage Investigation

GRADE LEVEL
4-8

FIRST NAME																						
LAST NAME																						

[9] Make a bar graph of The Ocean Conservancy data:

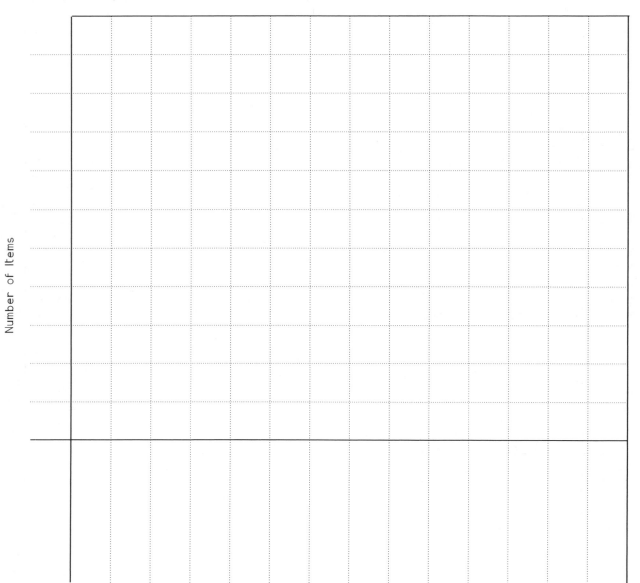

Number of Items

Type of Items

If you have many items, you may want to group them in the following categories:

- Recreational Activities
- Food-related
- Fishing/Boating
- Smoking-related

APPROVED BY

7 | Garbage Investigation

GRADE LEVEL
K-3

journal ≡ pages

FIRST NAME																					
LAST NAME																					

[1] Draw the object you found most often.

[2] How many did you find?
....
....

[3] Draw the most unusual object you found. Label it.

[4] Draw a clean beach. Include any animals and plants you think might live there.

APPROVED BY	

INVESTIGATE

8 | Beach Mysteries

GRADE LEVEL
4-8

90 minutes

summary

Students learn about bacteria as an indicator of beach water quality for swimming. In groups they solve hypothetical problems associated with beaches. Then students write persuasive essays on the issue.

objectives

- Discuss the effect of harmful bacteria on swimming conditions at beaches.
- Diagram three reasons for beach contamination.
- Explain solutions for beach health problems.
- Write a persuasive essay about beach health.

prerequisite

Garbage Investigation, Litter Tag

vocabulary

Bacteria: single-celled organisms, free-living or parasitic, that break down the wastes and bodies of dead organisms, making their components available for reuse by other organisms

Sewage overflow: sewage that is discharged into waterways

Stormwater: water that accumulates on the ground during a rain event

setting

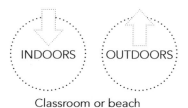

INDOORS   OUTDOORS

Classroom or beach

subjects

Environmental Science, Human Health, Social Studies, Language Arts

standards

This Great Lakes in My World activity is aligned to the Common Core State Standards and to state learning standards in:

Illinois
Indiana
Michigan
Minnesota
New York
Ohio
Pennsylvania
Wisconsin

This alignment is available on your Great Lakes in My World CD in the "Standards" folder and on-line at http://www.greatlakes.org/GLiMWstandards.

materials

- Healthy Beaches Action Guide (on cd) or visit http://www.greatlakes.org/HealthyBeachesActionGuide
- Journals
- Pencils
- Clipboards (if outside)

background

Beaches can bring great advantages to shoreline communities, providing recreation, gathering places and beauty. It is important to keep them clean and healthy. Although this activity is about beach closings, emphasize to students that the Great Lakes beaches can be wonderful places for swimming and recreation. However, based on the rise of beach closings due to bacteria issues, it is important that communities become informed about beach closings. The information in this activity should enable students and their families to better understand how to appreciate their beaches and keep them healthy so they can be enjoyed.

Beach Closings: Local health departments are forced to close beaches or declare "swimming bans" when bacteria levels are high. As monitoring programs start in communities, beach closings happen with increasing frequency. Leftover food may attract additional wildlife to the beach, resulting in increased animal droppings, which can lead to high bacteria levels in the water.

Closures are prompted because of the health risks posed by the bacteria, viruses, other germs and algae blooms, which come from sewage overflows, untreated stormwater runoff, animal waste, boating wastes and malfunctioning septic systems. Sewage treatment plants in some large cities were not originally built for the increased number of people that now live there. Each day a beach is closed, according to a 2004 study, The Economic Costs of *E. coli* Beach Closings, communities can lose thousands of dollars in revenue.

Recreational water quality monitoring: Beaches are run by governmental agencies that try to keep the shoreline safe for human use. In many cases these agencies monitor the water quality by testing bacteria levels. When levels are too high, areas that have monitoring programs will close the beaches.
Health Issues: When a beach is closed, everyone who uses nearshore areas for recreation – including divers and swimmers – is at risk when bacteria are present. Bacteria and other germs in contaminated sand and water can cause vomiting, diarrhea, stomachaches, nausea, headaches, fever, giardiasis, rashes, and pink eye.

E. coli: *E. coli* is the bacteria used to determine if a beach should be closed. It is found in human and animal feces. *E. coli* is a common bacteria used for science experiments in thousands of schools and laboratories around the world. You have it living inside your intestines right now, as does every other human, and many other organisms. *E. coli* has hundreds of genetic variants; only a very few of these can make humans sick. The *E. coli* agencies search for in beach testing is not necessarily what makes humans sick, but it indicates the presence of fecal contamination (and possibly other pathogens that ARE harmful).

There is only one particular strain of *E. coli* harmful to human health, and it is relatively uncommon. However, *E. coli* is easy to test for and is an indicator of other potentially harmful bacteria that can exist under the same conditions. When *E. coli* is found in high levels, beaches are closed because bacteria harmful to human health may be present.

Algae: Excess nutrients, particularly phosphorus and nitrogen, can contribute to algae blooms, which may harbor potential human pathogens such as Salmonella. Algal blooms in water, if allowed to remain to the point of decay, can adversely impact water quality. Though small amounts of plant material are a natural part of coastal areas, large accumulations should be removed promptly by raking the plants ashore and moving them above the high water line.

procedure

1. Ask for a show of hands to find out how many students in your group swim regularly at a Great Lakes beach. Discuss as a class: Can beaches be dirty if there is no garbage to be seen? How? Take a few responses.
2. Are beaches in your area ever closed or do they have swimming bans? *This depends on whether or not your area has a recreational water quality monitoring program. Beaches in some areas are closed when bacteria levels exceed Environmental Protection Agency standards.*
3. Why does this happen? Create a list of ideas to assess students' prior knowledge about why beaches close. *Note: If beaches are not monitored or closed in your area due to high bacteria levels, let students know that this happens in other areas of the Great Lakes.*
4. Use the background information to explain bacteria in general and *E. coli* in particular, and the health issues they present.

5. Have students work in small groups to solve beach mysteries on journal pages. Students may use the Alliance for the Great Lakes' Prescription for a Healthy Beaches: http://www.greatlakes.org/HealthyBeachesActionGuide (or see copy on compact disc).

Answers to Beach Mysteries
#1. How did the bacteria get there? *After the gulls have eaten, they may leave droppings behind on the beach.* E. coli *bacteria is found in human and animal waste.* How can we help solve this problem? *Don't leave litter behind. Any litter can cause harm. Food-related litter can attract wildlife in greater numbers than might normally live at or near the beach. Wildlife waste may contribute to high bacteria levels at the beach.*

procedure continued

#2. How did the bacteria get there? *When a lot of precipitation (rain or snow) falls, the water treatment plant may not be able to process and clean all the water as quickly as it accumulates. If this happens, water treatment plants may release untreated sewage into the lake. E. coli may be found in the untreated sewage. This can cause elevated bacteria levels. As for the phone call, beach managers are often notified of sewage overflows.*

How can we help solve this problem? *Encourage your local municipality to make sure your water treatment facility is big enough to handle all of the water from your community. Do not contribute extra water to the system during a heavy rain. This may mean waiting to run your dishwasher or do your laundry.*

#3. How did the bacteria get there? *Dog waste may be contributing to E. coli or other bacteria in the water if the dog owners do not responsibly pick up after their pets.*
How can we help solve this problem? *Always pick up after your pet. Encourage other animal owners to do the same.*

#4. How did the bacteria get there? *When rain reaches the ground during a rain event, it is called stormwater. As it accumulates, stormwater flows to the lowest point. In a Great Lakes community, this is often the lake. Stormwater carries bacteria and other pollutants from a variety of sources including animal waste from domestic and wild animals, as well as fertilizers. Stormwater flows from the surrounding surfaces (streets, parking lots, lawns, agricultural areas) over sand and into the lake. This can cause elevated levels of bacteria to be detected. Some communities funnel stormwater into the Great Lakes through pipes called outfalls, which can contribute to the bacteria levels. Nationally, stormwater is the most frequent cause of beach closings.*

How can we help solve this problem? *Encourage your community to incorporate "green spaces" such as rain gardens, wetlands, or a pond system near hard surfaces so the rain runoff can be absorbed and filtered instead of flowing directly into the Great Lakes. Other ideas include using hard surfaces that allow water to pass through (permeable paving) and planting native grasses in "green borders" around parking lots.*

6. Discuss the mysteries in a large group. Have students present their answers to each other.
7. Create! After students have solved the Beach Mysteries, have them create and label a diagram that shows at least three to four ways bacterial pollution can get to the beach. Students should include solutions to the problems in their diagrams
8. Discuss as a class: What are solutions to beach health issues? Have students share the responses in their diagrams. Remember that while monitoring can indicate that there is a problem, it doesn't identify or eliminate the source. Source elimination is the ultimate solution. How will students' knowledge of beach health issues change their future behavior at the beach?
9. As a follow-up, have students write a persuasive essay about human responsibility with regard to beach health. This can include the following:
   a. Your area may or may not have a program for monitoring the recreational water quality for beach health purposes. Why should such a program exist in your community?
   b. Humans can change their behaviors to improve water quality. What should or shouldn't people do to help improve water quality?

wrap-up

1. Play Mysterious Bacteria to finish the activity.
2. Students sit in a circle with their eyes closed. Choose one student to be the "beach bacteria." Tap this student on the shoulder and have everyone re-open his or her eyes. The student uses the knowledge from the activity to decide what source s/he is from (*sewage overflow, seagull waste, stormwater runoff*)
3. Have the students walk around the room, shaking hands with each other. When the "bacteria" student shakes hands, s/he squeezes the other students' hand, indicating the spread of the bacteria.
4. When a student is "contaminated," s/he dramatically falls to the ground, indicating sickness.
5. Other students can guess who the "bacteria" student is. If they are wrong, they are out of the game.
6. Once the student is identified, the other students can ask yes or no questions to determine the student's selected source of contamination.

7. After the game, explain that it is currently very difficult to determine the source of bacteria in the water, much like it was difficult to determine which student was the harmful bacteria and what their source was.

extension

1. Research the status of recreational water quality in your area by inviting a beach manager as a guest speaker to your classroom.

2. Have the students decide if they would like to take action to improve beach health in their community by:
   • Participating in the Alliance for the Great Lakes's Adopt-a-Beach™ program, which enables students to create positive change for their beaches through litter clean-up and monitoring and water quality monitoring.
   • Turning the persuasive essays regarding beach health into a class "letter to the editor" for your local paper.

assessment

Rubric on page 311

8 | Beach Mysteries

journal ≡ pages

FIRST NAME																				
LAST NAME																				

[1] Facts: A high level of bacteria is not detected at the beach. A flock of seagulls spot some food and wrappers left behind by humans. They land on the beach to eat and inspect the garbage. A boat sails by in the distance. Two kayakers paddle up to the shore, which startles the birds. They fly away. Several hours after the seagulls arrived, water samples are taken. When they come back from the lab, results show there is a high level of bacteria in the water near the beach.

Questions: How did the bacteria get there?

....
....
....

How can we help solve this problem?

....
....
....
....

[2] Facts: The beach is clean. A high level of bacteria is not detected. That night a huge rainstorm takes place. It rains hard all night long. You think it is a great night to stay in and do laundry and your dishes, so your family runs both the washing machine and the dishwasher. You listen to music while doing homework, then go to bed. The next day, the beach is closed because the beach managers have received a call from the water treatment plant. Based on the call, the beach managers know there will be high levels of bacteria in the water.

Questions: How did the bacteria get there?

....
....
....
....

What did the mysterious phone call tell the beach managers about why the beaches should be closed?

....
....
....

How can we help solve this problem?

....
....
....
....

APPROVED BY	

8 | Beach Mysteries

FIRST NAME																		
LAST NAME																		

[3] Facts: A few friends meet on the beach in the morning to walk their dogs. The dogs run along the shoreline and into the water, fetching sticks for an hour. A jet-ski zooms by in the distance and several motor boats pass by at high speeds. When the group with the dogs leaves, there is dog waste visible along the water's edge. The next day, the beach is closed because the beach managers have detected high levels of bacteria at the beach.

Questions: How did the bacteria get there?

....

....

....

....

....

How can we help solve this problem?

....

....

....

....

....

[4] Facts: During a walk around your neighborhood, you see dog waste on the ground, ants walking on the sidewalk and into the grass and hear birds singing in the trees. After it rains that night, the beaches are closed. You remember that the dog waste was not close to the beach, but in the grass across the street from it. It was not really a heavy rain, and you know that there was not a "sewage overflow," but there are still high levels of bacteria when the beach managers get the results back from a water sample they take after the rainy night.

Questions: How did the bacteria get there?

....

....

....

....

How can we help solve this problem?

....

....

....

....

....

APPROVED BY	

8 | Beach Mysteries

GRADE LEVEL
4-8

journal pages

FIRST NAME																					
LAST NAME																					

[5] Create and label a diagram that shows at least three ways bacterial pollution can get to the beach. Include solutions to the problems you indicate in the diagram.

APPROVED BY

8 | Beach Mysteries

GRADE LEVEL
4-8

FIRST NAME																			
LAST NAME																			

[6] Write a persuasive essay or letter to the editor about human responsibility with regard to beach health. You may include the following ideas:

a. Your area may or may not have a program for monitoring the recreational water quality for beach health purposes. Why should such a program exist in your community?

b. Humans can change their behaviors to improve water quality. What should or shouldn't people do to help improve water quality?

APPROVED BY	

INVESTIGATE

9 | Adopt-a-Beach™

GRADE LEVEL
4-8

ongoing: field trips plus classroom work

Developmental Modifications: Adopt-a-Beach™ can be done with younger students. Young children will need close supervision at the beach and should exercise extreme caution with sharp objects. When picking up garbage, always wear gloves.

summary

Students adopt a beach along the Great Lakes shoreline and visit it two to five times to collect litter and other data. Students enter their data into an online database. Students complete a project to further improve their beach.

*Note: Contact the Alliance for the Great Lakes to get involved with the Adopt-a-Beach™ program.

See http://www.greatlakes.org/adoptabeach for more information.

objectives

- Discuss how people can help their community.
- Reflect on why beaches are a special amenity.
- Collect data on litter, water quality and physical characteristics at a beach.
- Analyze data for trends and patterns.
- Create solutions based on identifiable concerns.

prerequisite

Garbage Investigation and Beach Mysteries

vocabulary

None

setting

INDOORS   OUTDOORS

Adopted beach and in classroom

subjects

Environmental Science, Social Studies, Math

standards

This Great Lakes in My World activity is aligned to the Common Core State Standards and to state learning standards in:

Illinois
Indiana
Michigan
Minnesota
New York
Ohio
Pennsylvania
Wisconsin

This alignment is available on your Great Lakes in My World CD in the "Standards" folder and on-line at http://www.greatlakes.org/GLiMWstandards.

materials

- See Adopt-a-Beach™ checklist (on cd)
- Other Adopt-a-Beach™ materials (also on cd)

background

The Alliance for the Great Lakes' Adopt-a-Beach™ program is a service learning and citizen science program. Through this program, groups collect data on litter and water quality during a series of, ideally, five visits. They then use the data to create positive change at the beach.

Service learning integrates community service into curriculum, and connects schools with agencies and neighborhoods. These experiences build an understanding of a community, enrich learning and help youth develop personally, socially and academically. Service learning incorporates such steps as: research, investigation, analysis, action, reflection and celebration.

The Alliance for the Great Lakes' Adopt-a-Beach™ program is an easy and fun way for groups to connect with part of the Great Lakes' shoreline: their favorite beach. Adopters generally commit to five visits per year. During the visits, adopters use special forms to collect data on three different aspects of their beach.

procedure

Part One: Collecting and Analyzing Data

1. Gather information on Adopt-a-Beach™ through www. greatlakes.org and email questions to: adoptabeach@greatlakes.org

2. Select a beach to adopt and send your visit schedule to the Alliance for the Great Lakes. They will send you a participation form to fill out. If your group cannot commit to all five visits, consider asking another group to share the beach visits and data collection.

3. Use the equipment checklist (on cd) to gather the necessary supplies.

4. Pre-visit Reflection: Have the students answer the first set of journal questions.

5. Go to your adopted beach and collect data on the three forms:
   - Beach Assessment (once per year): During the first visit of each year, groups take a careful look at the existing physical characteristics of the site.
   - Litter Monitor (each visit): At each visit, litter is collected, recorded, and recycled or disposed of properly.
   - Water Quality Monitor (each visit): Using a simple test, investigate bacteria levels in the water. High bacteria levels can cause beach closings and swimming bans.

6. Once back from each beach visit, have students answer the second set of journal questions. Provide one copy of this page for each visit. Discuss as a class.

7. Tally all data and, if your beach is on a Great Lake, enter it into the Adopt-a-Beach™ database. The database allows groups to compare findings and reflect on improvements. This data is available to the public as well. Use online database to respond to question #6.

8. Review and analyze the data over the course of your visits, looking for trends and issues on your beach. Graph the data in order to gain a greater understanding of beach garbage issues. Find creative ways to display your data, through graphs, posters and presentations. Ideas for ways to help the beach will surface as students analyze their data.

Part Two: Taking Action

1. Use the information gathered to help create positive change at the beach by asking: What are some of the problems this beach has? How could we help solve beach problems? What solutions do the students come up with for issues they encounter? *Solutions may range from educating others within the school about keeping beaches healthy to trying to get additional garbage cans or educational signage at the beach. This could involve educating others, writing a letter with suggested improvements to your municipality or a community leader, or many other positive actions.*

2. After at least two visits, have students complete and share the third journal page. Use this as an opportunity to teach students about choosing projects carefully. Many projects are bigger than groups realize, and fail because of it. Teach students to select a manageable project that they can succeed at.

wrap-up

1. Have students share their knowledge and experiences with others in the school and community.

2. Stage a celebration that includes others who will appreciate learning about your adopted beach and what the students did for it.

assessment

Rubric on page 311

9 | Adopt-a-Beach™

FIRST NAME																					
LAST NAME																					

Answer these questions BEFORE your first beach visit.

[1] How often do you visit the beach?

....
....

[2] When you visit the beach, what do you do there?

....
....
....

[3] What do you like best about the beach?

....
....
....

[4] What factors determine beach conditions?

....
....
....

[5] When was the last precipitation (rain, snow, hail) and how might this impact the beach?

....
....
....
....

[6] What ideas do you have for creating positive change at the beach?

....
....
....

[7] What are you looking forward to as part of Adopt-a-Beach™?

....
....
....
....

APPROVED BY	

9 | Adopt-a-Beach™

GRADE LEVEL
4-8

journal   pages

FIRST NAME																					
LAST NAME																					

Answer these questions AFTER each beach visit.

[1] Describe how the beach looked when you arrived.

....

....

....

[2] What did you like best about your beach visit?

....

....

....

[3] What surprised you about the visit to the beach?

....

....

....

[4] What did you learn from the data you collected?

....

....

....

[5] What was the most frequently found trash item?

....

....

[6] How does your data compare to past visits you have made, or to data other
    groups around the lake have collected?

....

....

....

[7] Based on your data, what ideas do you have for creating positive change at this beach?

....

....

....

....

APPROVED BY	

9 | Adopt-a-Beach™

GRADE LEVEL
4-8

journal pages

FIRST NAME																			
LAST NAME																			

Answer these questions after at least 2 visits.

[1] What are your favorite ideas for ways to create positive change at the beach?

....

....

....

....

....

[2] Choose one you would like to carry out.

....

[3] What resources (time, money, etc.) are needed for this project?

....

....

....

[4] What challenges might you face while working on this project?

....

....

....

[5] How will you overcome these challenges?

....

....

....

[6] List the first steps you think the class should take.

....

....

....

....

APPROVED BY	

INVESTIGATE		GRADE LEVEL	
10 | Taking Action		**4-8**
45-90 minutes |

summary

Students analyze data from a beach scenario, plan a presentation and decide on actions for improving the health of the beach and present their projects.

objectives

- Analyze data to reach conclusions.
- Develop plans from those conclusions.
- Identify and role-play the participants in beach health scenarios.

prerequisite

Garbage Investigation and Beach Mysteries. This activity can be done in conjunction with Adopt-a-Beach™ to help students practice data analysis.

vocabulary

E. coli: bacteria (Escherichia coli) occurring in various strains, live as harmless inhabitants of the human lower intestine, are used in public health as indicators of fecal pollution, or produce a toxin causing intestinal illness

Bacteria: single-celled micro-organisms that live in soil, water, organic matter, or the bodies of plants and animal and are important because of their role in food webs and as a cause of disease

Stormwater: water that accumulates on the ground during a rain event

setting

INDOORS

subjects

Environmental Science, Math, Language Arts

standards

This Great Lakes in My World activity is aligned to the Common Core State Standards and to state learning standards in:

Illinois
Indiana
Michigan
Minnesota
New York
Ohio
Pennsylvania
Wisconsin

This alignment is available on your Great Lakes in My World CD in the "Standards" folder and on-line at http://www.greatlakes.org/GLiMWstandards.

materials

- Data chart
- Pencils

background

Collecting data can be an interesting and worthwhile endeavor for students. However, the real interest and potential for critical thinking is in understanding what the data means. This activity allows students to practice analyzing and synthesizing data relating to beach health. When done in conjunction with Adopt-a-Beach™, this activity can serve as a way to get students to interpret data and understand how to look for trends and possible cause-and-effect relationships in information.

procedure

1. Give the students the following scenario: A local middle school has adopted a nearby beach. They have made four visits throughout the fall and spring looking at the shoreline and surrounding area, the type and amount of litter, and the presence of *E. coli* bacteria. They are ready to analyze their data and create an action plan to create positive change at their beach. Where should they start?

2. Give the students the data in the journal pages. Data on litter and water quality was collected each time, on separate charts. Have them compare the visits based on the data and use the journal questions to make note of their observations. As a class, discuss the data. *This may include noticing problems with overflowing trash cans, consistent seagull waste, and a possible sewage overflow on the second visit.*

3. Introduce the idea of taking action to help the beach. Divide students into groups and have each group pick one problem on which they will focus their attention. *Problems might include overflowing trash cans, consistent seagull waste, possible sewage overflows, lack of educational signage, stormwater runoff from the paved parking lot. What type of project can students create that will address these issues?*

4. Have students develop an action project to address the issue, including a presentation of results to each other in "roles" of city officials.

wrap-up

1. Have each group take turns presenting their action project while the other group role-plays the group hearing the results.

2. After both groups have presented, evaluate the presentations. Did the students prefer presenting or hearing the presentation? What did the other group do well? What could they do better? If your classroom were to really arrange a meeting, what other things should be considered?

extension

- Students take results from Adopt-a-Beach™ or Garbage Investigation and create an action plan to help their beach.
- Use this activity as a model for presenting actual data to community decision-makers.
- Have the class participate in the Alliance for the Great Lakes' ongoing Adopt-a-Beach™ program: www.greatlakes.org or the International Coastal Cleanup, which occurs on the third Saturday of every September: www.oceanconservancy.org.

assessment

Rubric on page 311

Contributing author: Steve Jerbi

We value your thoughts and feedback on Great Lakes in My World. Please let us know about any oversights, errors or omissions you find, or if there are things you or your students particularly like.

Send your comments to: education@greatlakes.org

10 | Taking Action

GRADE LEVEL
4-8

FIRST NAME																			
LAST NAME																			

Taking Action

Help! The following data has been collected at a beach nearby. The students who collected it need help figuring out what it all means.

The Results: In additional data, it was noted that the trash cans were overflowing, had no lids and there were no recycling containers. The trash cans are located near the beach entrance. There is no designated eating area. There are no signs about the problems that litter creates on a beach. The parking is on a paved lot 100 yards from the beach. There is no border between the parking lot and the beach sand. The local park district is responsible for maintaining this beach.

Litter Monitoring

	First Visit 9/22	Second Visit 10/14	Third Visit 4/22	Fourth Visit 5/14
Weather	Sunny	Rainy	Sunny, Windy	Partly Cloudy
Air temp	82	68	64	72
Beach users	51-200	1-50	51-200	51-200
Litter condition	Relatively clean	Not very clean	Dirty, lots of litter	Relatively clean
Trash Cans	Overflowing	--	Overflowing	--
Dogs	No dogs unleashed	Yes, all on leashes	Yes, some not leashed	Yes, some not leashed
Animal Waste	Seagull	Seagull	Seagull, Dog	Seagull
Water Smell Strange?	No	Yes, raw sewage	No	No
Restrooms	Very Clean	Locked	Locked	Dirty walls/ buildings
Cigarettes	124	74	223	62
Food Wrappers	79	112	57	123
Aluminum Cans	12	16	8	10
Glass Bottles	5	24	6	12

APPROVED BY	

10 | Taking Action

GRADE LEVEL
4-8

journal ≡ pages

FIRST NAME																			
LAST NAME																			

Water Monitoring

	First Visit 9/22	Second Visit 10/14	Third Visit 4/22	Fourth Visit 5/14
Weather	Sunny	Rainy	Sunny, Windy	Partly Cloudy
Beach users	50-100	1-20	50-100	100-200
Toddlers	1-20	0	1-20	21-49
Gulls	1-20	1-20	21-49	1-20
Geese	0	1-20	0	0
Water Smell Strange?	No	Yes, raw sewage	No	No
Date of Last Precipitation	9/3	10/13	4/19	4/30
E. coli count	3 colonies	12 colonies	6 colonies	10 colonies
Other Coliform	14 colonies	32 colonies	11 colonies	17 colonies

Looking at the Data

[1] What observations can you make based on this data?

....

....

....

....

[2] What problems might be indicated by the data?

....

....

....

[3] What suggestions do you have for helping this beach become a healthier place?

....

....

....

....

....

APPROVED BY	

10 | Taking Action

GRADE LEVEL
4-8

journal pages

FIRST NAME																			
LAST NAME																			

Helping Out

[4] What beach problem is your group working to solve?

....

....

....

[5] What is your plan or "action project" for addressing this issue?

....

....

....

....

[6] How will you present this "action project" to the class?

....

....

....

....

Presentations

[7] Did you prefer presenting or hearing the presentation? Why?

....

....

....

[8] What did your group do well?

....

....

....

....

[9] What could your group have done better?

....

....

....

....

APPROVED BY	

INVESTIGATE: FINAL PROJECT

11 | My Community

GRADE LEVEL
K-4

several hours, depending on the group

summary

Students create a model of a Great Lakes community and recognize its relationship to the local Great Lake.

objectives

- Define a community.
- List the buildings that most communities have.
- Reflect on how people's needs and wants influence the community.
- Discuss the Great Lake's role in the community.
- Map the community.
- Discuss how positive changes can be made within a community.

prerequisite

Take a Good Look, Sound Picture, Who Lives In My Neighborhood?, Litter Tag

vocabulary

Amenity: nice features or offerings. For example, a town's amenities may include a central park or a community theater

setting

INDOORS

subjects

Social Studies, Environmental Science, Language Arts

standards

This Great Lakes in My World activity is aligned to the Common Core State Standards and to state learning standards in:

Illinois
Indiana
Michigan
Minnesota
New York
Ohio
Pennsylvania
Wisconsin

This alignment is available on your Great Lakes in My World CD in the "Standards" folder and on-line at http://www.greatlakes.org/ GLiMWstandards.

materials

- Pencils
- Journals
- Art supplies
- Small milk cartons or boxes (2 for each student)
- Large piece of blue paper

background

Communities have great influence on how we live. The design, location, quality, quantity and character of a community's amenities determine property values, civic pride, neighborliness and quality of life. In creating a model of their community, students will need to think about many aspects of community life. In this activity, students will work to show how the local Great Lake is integrated into their community.

procedure

1. Students see a large piece of blue paper on the floor of their classroom when they come in. Tell them it represents their Great Lake.

2. Discuss the word community. What does it mean? *A group of people connected by a common characteristic; frequently, the people of a town. Their classroom is an example of a community, as is their town. Ask students what a town needs in order to be a town. Communities often have buildings and other amenities.* Create a class list by reviewing some of the buildings and services in their town.

3. Tell students they will be building their own Great Lakes community. Discuss which buildings should be close and which can be farther from the lake. During the discussion ask students which businesses they want to own and find out where they would like their house to be. Give students a milk carton (or other object) to signify their business and their house. Have students decorate these.

4. Discuss what else, besides humans, lives in and around the Great Lakes. *Plants and animals.* Ask students how they will make sure there is room for plants and animals, and encourage students to create parks and outdoor spaces that offer natural habitats.

5. Students may want to build roads, a harbor, a power company, etc. Let older students know about alternatives for generating power that include standard and environmentally friendly options (*wind, solar or another*). Encourage them to think about ways to make the community eco-friendly, while expanding it to a size they want. Throughout the building process, encourage students to think about how human wants and needs influence the human-built environment.

6. Complete and discuss the journal pages.

7. Build in "Lake Think" time as the class works on this project. Ask students how the community needs the lake and how the community they are creating affects the lake. Why is it important to keep the lake clean and healthy? How can they help do this?

8. Option for grades 3-4: After students build their Great Lakes community, have them work alone or in small groups to map it. Depending on their level of knowledge, students can incorporate cardinal directions, scale, relative size and an aerial perspective.

wrap-up

1. Discuss: How does this community compare to your own community? What do you like about this community? Would you like to live in the community you have created? Why or why not? What are the benefits of living near a Great Lake? How can people in the community help keep the Great Lake healthy?

extension

Discuss: Are there any problems in your community that the class would like to change?
What are some steps the class could take to help these changes take place?

assessment

Rubric on page 312

 We value your thoughts and feedback on Great Lakes in My World. Please let us know about any oversights, errors or omissions you find, or if there are things you or your students particularly like.

Send your comments to: education@greatlakes.org

11 | My Community

GRADE LEVEL
K-4

journal ⌇ pages

FIRST NAME																					
LAST NAME																					

[1] What is your business?

....
....
....
....

[2] What does your house look like?

[3] What kinds of plants and animals live around the lake?

....
....
....
....
....

[4] Why is it important to keep the lake clean and healthy?

....
....
....
....

[5] What do you like about this community?

....
....
....
....
....

APPROVED BY	

11 | My Community

GRADE LEVEL
K-4

FIRST NAME																			
LAST NAME																			

[6] Draw a map of your community. Label the lake, your house, and your business.

APPROVED BY

INVESTIGATE: FINAL PROJECT

12 | Create-a-Community

GRADE LEVEL
5-8

several
hours

summary

Students take on roles in small groups to create a Great Lakes community that places equal importance on social, economic and ecological values.

objectives

- Define a sustainable community.
- Discuss elements to consider in community planning.
- With a team, plan a sustainable community.
- Discuss how students might make positive changes within their communities.

prerequisite

What's the Environment?, Lake Landmarks, Beach Mysteries

vocabulary

Community: a) the people living in an area; also the area itself; b) groups of living things that belong to one or more species, interact ecologically, and are located in one place (such as a bog or a pond)

Sustainable: a) relating to a method of using a resource so that the resource is not depleted or permanently damaged; b) relating to a lifestyle involving the use of sustainable methods; sustainable society

setting

INDOORS

subjects

Environmental Science, Social Studies, Language Arts

standards

This Great Lakes in My World activity is aligned to the Common Core State Standards and to state learning standards in:

Illinois
Indiana
Michigan
Minnesota
New York
Ohio
Pennsylvania
Wisconsin

This alignment is available on your Great Lakes in My World CD in the "Standards" folder and on-line at http://www.greatlakes.org/ GLiMWstandards.

materials

- Pencils
- Journals
- Art supplies
- Large paper or poster board for each group
- Triple beam balance and an object to weigh, such as a pencil or pen

background

Communities shape the way the world works. In creating a community, students will need to think about many aspects of community life. In this activity, students will work to create "sustainable communities." These are communities in which equal importance is placed on social, economic and ecological values. The 1996 Sustainable Communities Task Force Report defines sustainable communities as "...cities and towns that prosper because people work together to produce a high quality of life that they want to sustain and constantly improve. They are communities that flourish because they build a mutually supportive, dynamic balance between social well-being, economic opportunity, and environmental quality."

During the beginning of this activity, it is helpful to plan a visit from someone in community planning or parks and recreation to give some background information about these topics to the students.

procedure

1. Give students an object to weigh on a triple beam balance. When they have the object in equilibrium, discuss: What does it mean for something to be "in balance?" When we talk about living in "balance," what does that mean? How does this term compare with the word "sustainable?" In applying the term "balanced" or "sustainable" to a community, first define "community." What are the core components of a community? Use Lake Landmarks activity as a point of reference.

2. Discuss the term "sustainable community." Do you live in a sustainable community? What does it mean to place equal value on social, economic and ecological values? What would be the pros and cons to living in a place that does this? Brainstorm the elements that might exist in a balanced or sustainable community.

3. Ask for examples of what has to be planned for in order to create a sustainable community. Some examples might be: How would you create energy that is less polluting than using fossil fuels? How would you work to reduce prejudice in the community? How are decisions made within a community? Who decides how sustainable a community is?

4. Divide students into groups of four. Tell them they will design their own communities. Show students the rubric so they know how they will be evaluated.

5. Each student adopts a role within the group (see list of roles in students journal pages). Another option is to have this be a student-led activity in which the students come up with the roles and the questions to be answered.

6. Have students begin to plan their communities and answer the questions. This can be done in class or as homework.

7. Students work together in their groups to plan and map a community on large paper or poster board.

wrap-up

1. Have student groups present their communities to each other.

2. Discuss the following questions as a class. Would you like to live in the community you have created? Why or why not?

3. What elements from your created community would you like to see in your real community? Why? Choose one idea and work with students to figure out how the class might take steps toward making this really happen in your own community.

4. Students evaluate each other's work using the rubric provided or one that the students create themselves, based on the criteria for the project.

assessment

Rubric on page 312

12 | Create-a-Community

GRADE LEVEL
5-8

FIRST NAME

LAST NAME

[1] What is a sustainable community?

[2] What is your role in your Create-a-Community group? See choices on next pages. Why did you choose this role?

[3] What is the economic driving force for your community? See Community Regulations.

[4] Answer the questions assigned to you on the appropriate page, depending on your role in your group. See next pages. Use additional paper to answer questions if needed.

APPROVED BY

12 | Create-a-Community

GRADE LEVEL
5-8

FIRST NAME

LAST NAME

Zoning Ecologist: In charge of the way public land is used.

[1] Where will there be parks and wild spaces?

....
....
....

[2] How will these spaces be taken care of? Will you use herbicides and pesticides?
    Why or why not?

....
....
....

[3] How does the community include space for wildlife? Why is (or isn't) this important?

....
....
....
....

[4] How does the community contribute to the safety of humans and wildlife that live in the area?

....
....
....
....

[5] What type of vegetation will be planted there? (Hint: What is the difference between native
    and non-native species? Advantages and/or disadvantages? Edible or non-edible flora?)

....
....
....

[6] Where will the beach be? Where will the harbor be? How will they be kept clean?

....
....
....

[7] How will your Great Lake be affected by your responsibilities?

....
....
....

APPROVED BY

12 | Create-a-Community

GRADE LEVEL
5-8

FIRST NAME

LAST NAME

Resource Manager: In charge of the way the community uses and maintains its resources.

[1] Where will drinking water come from? How will it be cleaned? Where will it go after it is cleaned?

[2] How will people's homes be heated and cooled?

[3] Where will electricity come from?

[4] How does the community use resources so that they will last indefinitely?

[5] How does the community minimize waste?

[6] How does the community produce minimal air, water, and land pollution?

[7] How will your Great Lake be affected by your responsibilities?

APPROVED BY

12 | Create-a-Community

GRADE LEVEL
5-8

FIRST NAME

LAST NAME

Planning Commissioner: Coordinates the way the land is used, ensures that two people do not use an area of land for different purposes.

[1] Where will you place the required buildings?

....
....
....
....

[2] What additional buildings will the community have?

....
....
....
....

[3] How many houses/apartment buildings will you need? Where will they be?

....
....
....
....

[4] If the town population doubles in size in 5 years, how will everyone's housing needs be met?

....
....
....
....

[5] How will you ensure that residents have adequate and convenient green space?

....
....
....
....

[6] How will your Great Lake be affected by your responsibilities?

....
....
....
....

APPROVED BY

12 | Create-a-Community

GRADE LEVEL
5-8

journal pages

FIRST NAME

LAST NAME

Head of Cultural and Recreational Affairs: Responsible for fun and educational entertainment and recreation in the community.

[1] What Kind of outdoor recreation will be available? How will people be able to enjoy nature all year round?

....
....

[2] How will people learn while having fun?

....
....
....

[3] What Kind of entertainment will be present in the community?

....
....
....

[4] Where will the entertainment be?

....
....
....

[5] How does the culture support equality among different races, genders, and ages?

....
....
....

[6] What are healthy and fun options for all different Kinds of people?

....
....

[7] How will your Great LaKe be affected by your responsibilities?

....
....
....

APPROVED BY

12 | Create-a-Community

GRADE LEVEL
5-8

FIRST NAME

LAST NAME

Community Regulations
(This list can be given to students or they can help in its creation through brainstorming)
Community must be adjacent to a Great Lake
Minimum population = 300 people
Community must have at least:
1 beach
1 water treatment plant
1 harbor for boats
1 facility for generating power
1 post office
1 school
1 bank
1 restaurant
1 government building
1 grocery store
1 economic driving force (This can include original reason it came to be settled, or a current company or industry. It could also include tourism, farm services, due to a large number of nearby farms, or a factory due to a large source of raw material.)

[1] After you have answered the questions, work with your group to create a map on poster board of the community you plan and design. Sketch your community design below.

APPROVED BY

CONNECT 1 | What's the Environment?

ELEMENTS	☆☆☆☆	☆☆☆	☆☆	☆
DISCUSSIONS: Student participates in class discussions both before and after drawing his/her interpretation of the word "environment." Student uses active listening skills (eye-contact, confirming or referencing others' comments, affirmative gestures or comments).	Addresses all of the components	Missing one component	Missing two components	Missing three or more components
DRAWING: Student draws his/her interpretation of the environment both before and after class discussion. Changes in thought are reflected in the second drawing. Student's drawing reflects attention to detail and shows personal investment.	Addresses all of the components	Missing one component	Missing two components	Missing three or more components

CONNECT 2 | Sound Picture

ELEMENTS	☆☆☆☆	☆☆☆	☆☆	☆
SOUND PICTURE: Student listens quietly to sounds of a Great Lakes beach. S/he uses words and/or images to reflect what is heard. Student includes words to describe the images, as necessary.	Addresses all of the components	Missing one component	Missing two components	Missing three or more components
DISCUSSION: Student shares his/her drawing with a partner or small group. S/he participates in the discussion about the class sound pictures. Student discusses the interaction between humans and the Great Lakes and his/her personal connection to the lake.	Addresses all of the components	Missing one component	Missing two components	Missing three or more components

EXPLORE 3 | Take a Good Look

ELEMENTS	☆☆☆☆	☆☆☆	☆☆	☆
OBSERVATION: Student observes and makes note of various living and non–living objects at the beach, and then draws and labels a living and non-living item.	Addresses all of the components	Missing one component	Missing two components	Missing three or more components
SHORT ANSWER: Student answers questions about the items, discusses the relationship between living and non-living items to the ecosystem, and participates in the class discussion, connecting human impact with the Great Lakes. Student includes evidence of personal response to the lake.	Addresses all of the components	Missing one component	Missing two components	Missing three or more components

EXPLORE 4 | Who Lives In My Community?

ELEMENTS	☆☆☆☆	☆☆☆	☆☆	☆
DISCUSSION: Student brainstorms the basic needs of organisms and compares them to human needs. Student gives examples of how human needs are met, and distinguishes between needs and wants.	Addresses all of the components	Missing one component	Missing two components	Missing three components
GROUP WORK: Student works with others to determine which plants and animals live in the community. Student helps select and present one organism to the class and explain how the organism's needs are met (or not met) within the context of the community.	Addresses all of the components	Missing one component	Missing two components	Missing three or more components
JOURNAL QUESTIONS: Student responds to journal questions completely. Student uses sentences and pictures in journal answers. Student demonstrates an understanding of the basic needs organisms share.	Addresses all of the components	Missing one component	Missing two components	Missing three components

EXPLORE   5 | Lake Landmarks

ELEMENTS	★★★★	★★★	★★	☆
DISCUSSION: Student brainstorms key elements of the community, categorizes them as wants vs. needs, and indicates their connection to the Great Lakes.	Addresses all of the components	Missing one component	Missing two components	Missing three or more components
MAP: Student creates a community map that contains: the lake, necessary places, personal landmarks, their home and school (imaginary landmarks optional). Key is included. Map and key are neat, clear and understandable.	Addresses all of the components	Missing one component	Missing two components	Missing three or more components
DISCUSSION: Student articulates the importance of landmarks in their community and how the lake is an integral component to the area. Student explains what s/he likes about the community, how the lake benefits the area, and improvements they might foresee in the community. Student explains how changes might impact natural areas and discusses possible elements in city planning.	Addresses all of the components	Missing one component	Missing two components	Missing three or more components

EXPLORE   6 | Litter Tag

ELEMENTS	★★★★	★★★	★★	☆
DISCUSSION: Student lists the types of litter found at the beach and hypothesizes about the problems it can cause. Student uses active listening skills (eye-contact, confirming or referencing others' comments, affirmative gestures or comments).	Addresses all of the components	Missing one component	Missing two components	Missing three or more components
GAME: Student participates in the game, takes on roles and acts according to the directions.	Addresses all of the components	Missing one component	Missing two components	Missing three or more components
WRAP-UP: After the game, student is able to re-focus and reflect on how the game made him/her think about litter and the Great Lakes. Student brainstorms ideas for class action, as appropriate.	Addresses all of the components	Missing one component	Missing two components	Missing three or more components

INVESTIGATE   7 | Garbage Investigation

ELEMENTS	★★★★	★★★	★★	☆
DISCUSSION: Student actively participates in initial discussion on litter, and then discusses data by focusing on frequently found items, and problems and solutions related to beach litter. Student uses active listening skills (eye-contact, confirming or referencing others' comments, affirmative gestures or comments).	Addresses all of the components	Missing one component	Missing two components	Missing three or more components
JOURNAL: Student answers journal questions thoroughly by drawing on data collected, brainstorming litter problems and creating a list of solutions to the these problems.	Addresses all of the components	Missing one component	Missing two components	Missing three or more components
GRAPHING: Students graphs 2 sets of data. Student discusses differences and similarities and draws conclusions based on the data.	Addresses all of the components	Missing one component	Missing two components	Missing three or more components

INVESTIGATE 8 | Beach Mysteries

ELEMENTS	☆☆☆☆	☆☆☆	☆☆	☆
MYSTERIES: Student works with other students to respond to activity questions. Student helps share one scenario and group response. Student listens to other mysteries and participates in the discussions. Student uses active listening skills (eye-contact, confirming or referencing others' comments, affirmative gestures or comments).	Addresses all of the components	Missing one component	Missing two components	Missing three or more components
DIAGRAM: Student draws a diagram that shows at least 3 ways bacterial pollution enters the lake. Diagram is understandable and labeled. Student discusses diagram and articulates how knowledge may shape his/her future behavior.	Addresses all of the components	Missing one component	Missing two components	Missing three or more components
GAME: Student participates in Mysterious Bacteria game by listening to and following rules, participating as necessary, and trying to guess the "mystery" student.	Addresses all of the components	Missing one component	Missing two components	Missing three or more components

INVESTIGATE 9 | Adopt-a-Beach™

ELEMENTS	☆☆☆☆	☆☆☆	☆☆	☆
PRE-VISIT: Student responds to pre-visit questions regarding expectations, ways to help a community, and project goals. Student helps plan the beach visit.	Addresses all of the components	Missing one component	Missing two components	Missing three or more components
DATA COLLECTION: Student collects data on the assigned forms, picks up trash on the beach, and takes part in water quality monitoring, as appropriate. (over multiple visits)	Addresses all of the components	Missing one component	Missing two components	Missing three or more components
IN-CLASS: Student helps to enter data, analyze trends and patterns in data, and brainstorm possible solutions for the class to undertake. (over multiple visits)	Addresses all of the components	Missing one component	Missing two components	Missing three or more omponents
ACTION: Student helps to display data in a creative way. Student takes part in class action to create positive change at the beach.	Addresses all of the components	Missing one component	Missing two components	Missing three or more components
REFLECTION: Student responds to journal questions regarding his/her participation and response to the service learning project.	Addresses all of the components	Missing one component	Missing two components	Missing three or more components

INVESTIGATE 10 | Taking Action

ELEMENTS	☆☆☆☆	☆☆☆	☆☆	☆
DATA ANALYSIS: Student compares beach visit data and makes note of observations and possible problems. Student shares observations in group discussion and listens to well to other's ideas.	Addresses all of the components	Missing one component	Missing two components	Missing three or more components
PROBLEM SOLVING: Student lists ways to address one of the problems noted and creates a project to address this issue. Student plans a presentation about the project.	Addresses all of the components	Missing one component	Missing two components	Missing three or more components
PRESENTATION: Student works with group to present their "action project" to the class. Student cooperates with others in the group. Student shares responsibilities and clearly articulates how the project will address the issue identified.	Addresses all of the components	Missing one component	Missing two components	Missing three or more components

INVESTIGATE 11 | **My Community**

ELEMENTS	☆☆☆☆	☆☆☆	☆☆	☆
DISCUSSION: Student actively participates in the class discussion on communities, brainstorms components of a community, and discusses appropriate distances from the lake for certain items.	Addresses all of the components	Missing one component	Missing two components	Missing three or more components
PARTICIPATION: Student chooses a home and/or business and an appropriate location for it. Student decorates it.	Addresses all of the components	Missing one component	Missing two components	Missing three or more components
WRAP-UP: Student presents his/her part of the community to the class. Student articulates humans can keep the local Great Lake healthy, and compares the created community to their own.	Addresses all of the components	Missing one component	Missing two components	Missing three or more components
MAPPING: (if age appropriate) Student works with others to create a map of the created community, taking into consideration cardinal directions, relative scale, and aerial perspective.	Addresses all of the components	Missing one component	Missing two components	Missing three or more components

INVESTIGATE 12 | **Create-a-Community**

ELEMENTS	☆☆☆☆	☆☆☆	☆☆	☆
DISCUSSION: Student actively participates in the discussion about sustainable and balanced communities, community planning and components of a community.	Addresses all of the components	Missing one component	Missing two components	Missing three or more components
PARTICIPATION: Student adopts a role, responds to corresponding questions, and works with others to plan and create a community on paper. Student shows ability to work in a group by participating in group discussions, affirming teammates' ideas, and completion of his/her share of the work.	Addresses all of the components	Missing one component	Missing two components	Missing three or more components
DISCUSSION: Student articulates how the lake plays a role in the community and how human wants and needs influence a community. Student identifies ways that humans can keep local Great Lake healthy, and compares the created community to his/her own.	Addresses all of the components	Missing one component	Missing two components	Missing three or more components
COMMUNITY MAP: Map contains required components, is neatly labeled, includes a key, shows input from all group members.	Addresses all of the components	Missing one component	Missing two components	Missing three or more components

Unit 5
History

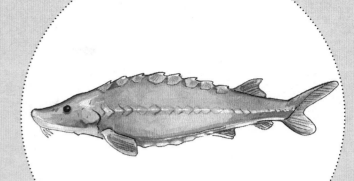

? essential questions

- **Why have people chosen to live near the Great Lakes?**
- **How have the Great Lakes and the different groups of people who have lived near them affected each other?**
- **What were the major groups of people that lived here, and how did they interact with the region?**
- **How can study of Great Lakes historical cultures positively influence the current Great Lakes culture?**

The lake sturgeon (Acipenser fulvescens) has remained largely unchanged for 100 million years. Humans and most other animals that live today did not even exist when the sturgeon first swam.

unit overview

A variety of human groups have established different types of relationships with the Great Lakes throughout history. This unit looks at how people's needs have been met by the Great Lakes region during human history and how this has affected the area. Students make cultural comparisons while exploring the lake-related influences, as well as contributions different groups have made to the region, and look at how this influences our present-day existence. In addition to making cultural comparisons, students explore the Great Lakes fishery, water quality and shipping to comprehend how present-day relationships with the Great Lakes have been established and can be improved. As a final project, students create a newspaper or poster that investigates a Great Lakes time period and group of people to better understand the legacy left by that group.

concepts

⦿ Human groups live in places that meet their needs. Over time, a region and the people that live there influence each other and reflect or create the changes that occur in the area.

⦿ By learning the history of an area, humans can better understand their present identity and can make more thoughtful decisions regarding future cultural goals.

unit activities

CONNECT	EXPLORE	INVESTIGATE

1 | Who Needs the Lakes? p. 315
GRADE LEVEL 4-8 (modifications included)
Students role-play a representative from Great Lakes history, explain this role to other students, and create a timeline.

2 | Now and Then p. 324
GRADE LEVEL 3-6
(additional journal pages for 3-4 and 5-6)
Students brainstorm lists of how the Great Lakes play a role for humans, both today and in the past. They create an illustration and write a story that reflects why their lake is important to them now and why it was important to people in the past.

3 | Beaches Over Time p. 329
GRADE LEVEL K-4 (modifications included)
Students use their senses to discover what is at the beach, read a poem to discover how the beach might have changed over time and discuss what makes the Great Lakes shoreline an important place.

4 | Seasons Change p. 333
GRADE LEVEL 3-6 (modifications included)
Students read an account about the seasonal lifestyle of the Ojibwe (Chippewa). They compare and contrast this lifestyle with their own through discussion and illustration.

5 | Ways of Life p. 338
GRADE LEVEL 4-8
Students use Venn diagrams to compare and contrast different groups that lived in the Great Lakes watershed, including two main groups of Native Americans and European settlers.

6 | Boats of Many Sizes p. 345
GRADE LEVEL 3-6
Students match boats to the correct description, work in small groups to create a boat timeline, discuss costs and benefits of Great Lakes shipping and reflect on shipboard living.

7 | 200 Years of Change p. 350
GRADE LEVEL 4-8
Students role-play different scenes that characterize the impact of European settlement on the Great Lakes in order to gain an understanding of some interactions that help to define Great Lakes history.

8 | Something's Fishy p. 356
GRADE LEVEL 6-8
Students work in groups to examine a time period's interaction and influence on the Great Lakes fishery. They categorize the events of the time period and then present the information to the class, using discussion and diagrams to synthesize information and come to a historical understanding of the Great Lakes fishery.

9 | Water Quality Over Time p. 365
GRADE LEVEL 6-8
Students circulate through stations to answer questions, learn about the history of water quality in the Great Lakes watershed and discuss their conclusions with the class.

Final Projects

10 | A Day in the Life p. 373
GRADE LEVEL K-3
Students create a poster that reflects a different cultural time period within the Great Lakes region. They draw pictures and write about the daily life of the people and how that population viewed and used the lakes.

11 | Sign of the Times p. 377
GRADE LEVEL 4-8
Students create newspapers that reflect different time periods within the Great Lakes region. They research and write articles that show how different populations viewed the lakes and how their lifestyles affected the health of the lake system.

CONNECT

1 | Who Needs the Lakes?

GRADE LEVEL
4-8

45 minutes

Developmental Modifications: For younger students, consider using the role cards from only one time period and have students create illustrations of the person doing what is described on the card.

summary

Students role-play a representative from Great Lakes history, explain this role to other students and create a timeline.

objectives

- Role-play a character from the past.
- Describe the ways historical groups would have depended on the Great Lakes.
- Create a timeline of significant historical time periods in the Great Lakes region.

prerequisite

None

vocabulary

Industrialist: a person involved in work for some useful purpose
Prehistoric: existing in times before written history

setting

INDOORS

subjects

Social Studies, History, Environmental Science

standards

This Great Lakes in My World activity is aligned to the Common Core State Standards and to state learning standards in:

Illinois
Indiana
Michigan
Minnesota
New York
Ohio
Pennsylvania
Wisconsin

This alignment is available on your Great Lakes in My World CD in the "Standards" folder and on-line at http://www.greatlakes.org/ GLiMWstandards.

materials

- Journal
- Writing utensil
- Tape
- Long paper for the timeline (1.5m or 5ft minimum)
- Background information - copy for each student or group
- Role cards

background

The humans who have lived in the Great Lakes watershed have shaped the eventful history of the five lakes. Although many different types of people have lived in, and continue to inhabit the region, this activity focuses on groups of people who have made some of the significant historical contributions that have shaped the area. This information is for teachers and for students to use to prepare for their roles and as background information for the entire history unit.

---

1 | Paleo-Indians: 10,000 - 12,000 years ago

Who were they?
Scientists believe that Native Americans descended from Asian people who walked across the Bering Strait (a narrow waterway between Siberia and Alaska), on what would have been a land or ice bridge. It is also possible that some people came to North America by boat. It is thought that sea levels were lower at this time, which would have made a land bridge possible. At the end of the Ice Age, about 12,000 years ago, these nomadic hunters moved into the Northeast Woodlands. Their descendants built great mounds of earth as burial chambers and monuments to their gods. About 1600 years ago (400 A.D. or C.E), the mound-building culture gave way to the Mississippian culture.

Why did they come to the area?
This is not known.

When did they come to the area?
It is thought they arrived about 10,000 years ago.

What was their impact on that area?
Within a few thousand years, they divided into hundreds of groups, speaking many different languages. They hunted mammoths and lived a nomadic lifestyle. About three thousand years ago, they began raising squash, corn, sunflowers and tobacco.

---

2 | Prehistoric tribes: 1600 years ago (400 A.D. or C. E.)

Who were they?
People of the Northeast Woodland are descendants of the Mississippian culture. This was comprised of perhaps 250,000 people (although some estimates are a great deal higher), making up about 100 different tribes, who once occupied the Northeastern Woodlands. This region included the present U.S. area of New England and extended westward to include the Great Lakes. The states included are: Michigan, Wisconsin, Indiana, Illinois, Ohio, Pennsylvania, New York, Iowa, Minnesota, Kentucky, Virginia, West Virginia and portions of the Canadian provinces of New Brunswick, Quebec and Ontario.

These Native Americans (sometimes called American Indians), spoke versions of two major languages, Algonquian (Algonkian) and Iroquoian. Another large group, the Winnebago (in present-day Wisconsin), spoke a Siouan language. Today descendants of a number of these tribes live in the region and some still speak their native languages. Some live on reservations, but most Northeast Woodland people now live scattered throughout the general population.

Why did they come to the area?
Native Americans used the resources of the area, such as meat, animal hides, water and native plants for survival.

When did they come to the area?
They are thought to be descendants of the Mississippian culture. The most recent tribal groups we refer to as Native Americans date from 400 A.D or C.E. Native Americans themselves have a separate set of beliefs about how they originated. Many Native American tribes have a separate view on their origin. Some tribes say that the first parents originated from underground or from the sky.

What was their impact on that area?
It is frequently said that Native Americans knew how to live comfortably with nature, while preserving its resources for future generations. They hunted, fished, grew crops and developed extensive civilizations throughout the region.

background continued

3 | Early European explorers: 1550-1650

Who were they?
They were primarily French and included:

Samuel de Champlain (1567-1635)
A French explorer and navigator who mapped much of northeastern North America and started a settlement in Quebec.

Jean Nicolet (also spelled Nicollet) (1598 - 1642)
A French explorer who was the first European to travel through the Great Lakes area and lived among Native Americans, visiting Lake Michigan and possibly reaching the Mississippi River.

Father Jacques Marquette (1637-1675)
A French Jesuit priest and explorer. He started an Ojibwe mission at the western end of Lake Superior.

Louis Joliet (1645-1700)
Born in Québec City and explored the Canadian wilderness, including the Great Lakes area. Joliet expanded the fur trade westward and did extensive mapping.

René-Robert Cavelier, Sieur de La Salle (1643-1687)
A French explorer. He was sent by King Louis XIV (14) to travel south from Canada and sail down the Mississippi River to the Gulf of Mexico. He explored Lakes Michigan, Huron, Erie and Ontario.

Why did they come to the area?
They came for reasons including: to do missionary work, to seek wealth and new resources and to expand the territory of their home country by claiming new land.

When did they come to the area?
Some early explorers and sailors arrived in the 15th and 16th centuries, with increasing numbers in the 17th century (1600s).

What was their impact on that area?
Native American life began to change dramatically in the 17th century when French, English and Portuguese explorers started to actively hunt mink and beaver in the north woods. In the 1600s, beaver hats became very popular in Europe. Traders persuaded Native Americans to hunt beaver, otter, raccoon, marten, lynx and ermine in exchange for cloth and metal tools. The result of this relationship was that the animals Native Americans had depended upon became scarce. And, after a few decades, Native Americans had grown increasingly dependent on Europeans for their survival.

4 | Voyageurs: 1580-1640

Who were they?
Fur traders employed by a fur company to transport goods to and from remote stations, especially in the Canadian Northwest; from French "voyager," meaning "to travel"

Why did they come to the area?
They came to work for the fur trade business

When did they come to the area?
They arrived in the late 1500s – early 1600s. By the early 1600s, the French had explored the forests around the St. Lawrence Valley and had begun to exploit the area for furs.

What was their impact on that area?
Native American life began to change dramatically in the 17th century when early explorers began to actively hunt mink and beaver in the north woods. In the 1600s, beaver hats became very popular in Europe. European traders (primarily French) persuaded Native Americans to hunt beaver, otter, raccoon, marten, lynx, and ermine in exchange for cloth and metal tools. The results of this relationship were that the animals Native Americans had depended upon became scarce. And, after a few decades, Native Americans had grown increasingly dependent on Europeans for their survival.

background continued

Role 6 is on the next page

5 | Settlers: 1800s

Who were they?
They were primarily farming immigrants in search of new land for their crops

Why did they come to the area?
They came to find land to farm in order to make a living. As populations grew, dairying and meat production for local consumption began to dominate agriculture in the Great Lakes Basin. Specialty crops, such as fruit, vegetables and tobacco, grown for the growing urban population, claimed an increasingly important share of the lands suitable for them.

Canals allowed farmers to be able to export their crops, which meant that farmers were able to expand their operations beyond a subsistence level. Wheat and corn were the first commodities to be packed in barrels and shipped abroad. Grist mills - one of the region's first industries - were built on the tributaries flowing into the lakes to process the grains for overseas markets.

When did they come to the area?
By the mid-1800s, most of the Great Lakes region where farming was possible was settled.

What was their impact on that area?
The rapid, large-scale clearing of land for agriculture brought rapid changes to the ecosystem. Soils stripped of vegetation washed away to the lakes. As a result, fish habitats and spawning areas were destroyed. Today, we know that when fertilizer runoff reaches waterways it stimulates the growth of algae and other water plants. When the plants die and decay, they deplete the oxygen in the water. Lack of oxygen leads to fish die-offs, and the ecosystem changes as the original plants and animals give way to more pollution-tolerant species. Chemical pesticides and herbicides find their way to rivers and lakes, which affects plant and animal life, and threatens human health.

7 | Caretakers of the Great Lakes: 1970s

Who were they?
These people are individuals and organizations that recognized the need to clean up the Great Lakes.

Why did they come to the area?
They were living here and saw that human pollution and development had taken their toll on Great Lakes water quality. They wanted to help address these problems.

When did they come to the area?
Most people were already living here when they decided to help the Great Lakes. The 1970s was a positive turning point for Great Lakes health.

What was their impact on that area?
Both Canadian and U.S. governments have attempted to address the pollution issues. In the early 1970s, The Clean Water Act and Endangered Species Act were the first attempts at helping.

In 1978, the two governments signed the Great Lakes Water Quality Agreement, a document that added to the protections of the Great Lakes. Activists formed organizations and pressed for cleanup and protection of the Great Lakes. Resource officials established programs to fund, monitor, clean up and protect the Great Lakes basin from further degradation. Although there has been some progress and improvement in Great Lakes water quality, there is still a long way to go to restore the Great Lakes to health again. Pollution-prevention measures are being combined with cleanup to deal with pollution in the Great Lakes. The cleanup of the Great Lakes region will require continuous expenditure by, and cooperation among, state, provincial, tribal and federal agencies, local governments and industry.

background continued

6 | Early Industrialists: mid-1800s

Who were they?
They were people involved with logging, shipping, commercial fishing, canal building and manufacturing.

Why did they come to the area?
They came to make a living. Nearly all the settlements that grew into cities in the Great Lakes region were established on the waterways that transported people, raw materials and goods. The largest urban areas developed at the mouths of tributaries because of transportation advantages and the supply of fresh water for domestic and industrial use. Historically, the major industries in the Great Lakes region have produced steel, paper, chemicals, automobiles and other manufactured goods. Descriptions of some industries are as follows:

Logging
Logging operations in the Great Lakes basin originally involved clearing the land for agriculture and building houses and barns for the settlers. By the 1830s, commercial logging began in Upper Canada, Michigan, Minnesota and Wisconsin.

Paper Industry
Paper-making from pulpwood developed slowly. The first paper mill was built on the Welland Canal in the 1860s. Eventually Canada and the U.S. became the world's leading producers of pulp and paper products.

Canal-building
People came to help build canals such as the Erie Canal, the Lachine Canal and the Welland Canal. Once built, canals enabled people and goods to be brought to and from the region. Canals carried settlers west and freight east.

Shipping
Shipping enabled people and goods to be readily transported throughout the region.

Fishing
Fish were important as food for the region's native people, as well as for the first European settlers. Commercial fishing began around 1820 and expanded about 20 percent per year. The largest Great Lakes fish harvests were recorded in 1889 and 1899 at some 67,000 tonnes (147 million pounds).

When did they come to the area?
They came in the 1800s.

What was their impact on that area?
These industries helped the region to grow to become what it is today. However, all of these industrial activities produce vast quantities of wastes. During most of the 19th century industrial wastes were dumped into the waterways. Eventually, problems started when drinking water supplies became contaminated with urban-industrial effluent. In the mid-1850s, the threat to public health from unhealthy water prompted some cities to adopt practices that seemed to temporarily solve the problem. Some additional effects from industry included:

Logging
The trees that were logged were hundreds of years old and so were not soon replaced. Clear-cutting was the usual practice. Without proper rehabilitation of the forest, soils were readily eroded from barren landscapes and lost to local streams, rivers and lakes. In some areas of the Great Lakes watershed, reforestation has not been adequate and today, as a result, the forests may be a diminishing resource.

Paper Industry
The pulp and paper industry contributed to mercury pollution and added other chemicals to the water.

Canal transportation
Canals caused the Great Lakes to become the transportation hub of eastern North America.

Shipping
Today, the three main commodities shipped on the Great Lakes are iron ore, coal and grain. Transport of iron ore has declined, but steel-making capacity in North America is likely to remain concentrated in the Great Lakes region. Coal moves both east and west within the lakes, but coal export abroad has not expanded. As a result of economic decline, the Great Lakes fleet of over 300 vessels is being reduced through the retirement of the older, smaller vessels.

Fishing
By the 1880s some preferred species in Lake Erie had declined. Catches increased with more efficient fishing equipment, but the "golden days" of the commercial fishery were over by the late 1950s. Over-fishing, pollution, shoreline and stream habitat destruction, and accidental and deliberate introduction of invasive species such as the sea lamprey all played a part in the decline of the fishery.

procedure

1. Advance preparation: Tape up a long piece of paper to create a class timeline. Create a timeline on the paper by writing the title and length of time for each time period and group of people. There will be some overlap.
2. Tell students you will be studying the history of the Great Lakes. Ask them to explain why it is important to study history.
3. Give each student a role card. Organize students in groups by time period. There will be six groups. The seventh group, Caretakers of the Great Lakes, can be discussed as part of the large group discussion during the Wrap-Up. Have students go over the description of their group and time period together, reading it aloud. This can also be read individually. Have them record the different people in their group. They may give themselves a name, if their character does not already have one.

4. Have students circulate around the room introducing themselves to each other in character. They should explain why they depend on a Great Lake. Students record each person they meet, the time period that person comes from and their connection to the lake.

sources

People of the Northeast Woodlands, Linda Thompson, 2004
Great Lakes Atlas
http://www.epa.gov/glnpo/atlas/glat-ch3.html

wrap-up

1. Bring students back together in their groups. Have them describe the types of people they met.
2. In chronological order, have a spokesperson from each time period group generally describe the group of people, the impact their group had on the lake and where their group falls on the timeline.
3. Discuss the final group that was not given roles: Early Caretakers of the Great Lakes. Who were these people and why were they important?

In order to understand the complete picture, it is important to let students know about the positive actions humans have taken, and continue to take, to protect to restore the health of the ecosystem.

4. Have students work individually to answer the journal questions. While students are working, have one group at a time can go up to the timeline and tape their cards in the appropriate location on it. Discuss the journal questions.

extension

1. Use this timeline throughout the unit so that students can add to it as they gain information.
2. This activity can be turned into a guessing game, if students give each other limited information or clues, asking the other student to determine their role and time period.
3. Have students research the following environmental heroes from the Great Lakes region.

assessment

Rubric on page 384

Some environmental heroes in the Great Lakes region:
Dr. Henry Cowles (1869 - 1939) Indiana: Professor and scientist in the Indiana Dunes whose studies included "succession."
Dorothy Buell (1886 - 1977) Indiana: Helped form Save the Dunes Council in 1952 and mobilized citizens to push for the creation of the Indiana Dunes National Lakeshore
Lee Botts (1928 -) Indiana: Environmentalist, founder of Openlands, the Lake Michigan Federation (now the Alliance for the Great Lakes) and Indiana Dunes Environmental Learning Center
Rachel Carson (1907 – 1964) Pennsylvania: Environmental writer, author of Silent Spring
Sigurd Olsen (1899 – 1992) Minnesota: Environmental activist and writer, author of Singing Wilderness
Aldo Leopold (1887 - 1948) Wisconsin: Environmental writer and science professor, author of Sand County Almanac
Gene Stratton-Porter (1863 - 1924) Indiana: Environmental writer and photographer

If you know of a Great Lakes hero to suggest for this list, contact the Alliance for the Great Lakes.

Role Cards

1. Paleo-Indian	2. Prehistoric Tribesperson	3. Explorer	4. Voyageur	5. Settler	6. Early Industrialist
1. Paleo-Indian 10,000 years ago Helped to gather wild foods and prepare them	**2. Prehistoric Tribesperson** 1500 A.D. Algonquin: Potowatomi Woman: Gather wild foods, tan hides, sew and weave, make pottery	**3. Explorer** Samuel de Champlain (1567-1635) French explorer and navigator, mapped much of northeastern North America, started a settlement in Quebec	**4. Voyageur** Early 1600s French fur trader: Traded goods with Native Americans to bring their beaver pelts back to France	**5. Settler** Fruit farmer Early 1800s Farmer who grew fruit trees (apples, cherries) and sold to the local market and to nearby cities	**6. Early Industrialist** Logger Mid 1800s Logger who cut down trees and sent them down the Great Lakes for building homes
1. Paleo-Indian 10,000 years ago Helped build a huge mound of earth in the shape of a serpent, as a burial mound	**2. Prehistoric Tribesperson** 1500 A.D. Algonquin: Ojibwe Young Girl: chop and carry wood, learn to cook and sew, gather wild fruits	**3. Explorer** Father Jacques Marquette (1637-1675) French Jesuit priest and explorer, started an Ojibwe mission at the western end of Lake Superior	**4. Voyageur** Early 1600s Child: Born of a fur trader who married an Ojibwe tribeswoman, learned skills from both parents	**5. Settler** Dairy farmer Mid 1800s Farmer who raised cows for milk, butter and cheese for the region	**6. Early Industrialist** Paper maker Late 1860 Started a paper mill that used wood pulp to make paper for newspapers and books
1. Paleo-Indian 10,000 years ago Hunted mammoth and other game for eating, used the hides for clothing and homes	**2. Prehistoric Tribesperson** 1500 A.D. Iroquois Man: Hunted deer, fished and prepared land for women to plant	**3. Explorer** Louis Joliet (1645-1700) Born in Québec City, explored the Canadian wilderness, including the Great Lakes area	**4. Voyageur** Early 1600s *Coureur de bois* ("woods runner"): independent traders who lived with the Native Americans	**5. Settler** Vegetable farmer Early 1800s Farmer who grew vegetables for local markets	**6. Early Industrialist** Canal builder 1820 Helped complete the Erie Canal so that people and goods could go to and from the area
1. Paleo-Indian 10,000 years ago Worked on building huge mounds of earth as a monument to gods worshipped by your tribe	**2. Prehistoric Tribesperson** 1500 A.D. Winnebago (now known as Ho-Chunk) Young Girl: helped to do family farm work	**3. Explorer** René-Robert Cavelier, Sieur de La Salle (1643-1687) French explorer sent by King Louis 14th, explored Lakes Michigan, Huron, Erie and Ontario	**4. Voyageur** Early 1600s Voyageur: French-Canadian who paddled the canoes and carried the bundles of fur	**5. Settler** Grain farmer Mid 1800s Farmer who grew grain which was ground at mills and exported along canals	**6. Early Industrialist** Boat captain Mid 1860s Captained ships that transported goods and people around the Great Lakes
1. Paleo-Indian 3,000 years ago Grew squash, gourds and sunflowers as part of the first farming efforts	**2. Prehistoric Tribesperson** 1500 A.D. Huron Child: Learned canoeing for fishing and transportation and farming for food	**3. Explorer** Jean Nicolet (1598 - 1642) French explorer, first European to travel through the Great Lakes area, lived with Native Americans in Ontario, Canada	**4. Voyageur** Early 1600s *Hivernant:* "winterer," a more experienced voyageur who spent the winter months trading with tribes	**5. Settler** Meat production Mid 1800s Raised cattle for meat for the local market and shipped to cities	**6. Early Industrialist** Fisherman 1890 Part of the commercial fishing industry that provided food for the region

1 | Who Needs the Lakes?

GRADE LEVEL
4-8

FIRST NAME																								
LAST NAME																								

[1] What is your role and time period?

....

....

....

[2] What was happening during your character's time period?

....

....

[3] Who are the others in your time period?

....

....

[4] List the types of people you meet, their time period and how they were dependent
on the Great Lakes.

Name of Group	Time Period	Connection to the Great Lakes

APPROVED BY	

1 | Who Needs the Lakes?

GRADE LEVEL
4-8

FIRST NAME																					
LAST NAME																					

[5] How do people today use the lake and surroundings differently than they did in the past?

[6] How might people feel differently or similarly about the lake now than they did in the past?

[7] How does the way humans regard the Great Lakes help or harm them?

APPROVED BY

CONNECT

2 | Now and Then

GRADE LEVEL

3-6

45 - 60 minutes

Developmental Modifications: Follow Wrap-Up for appropriate age group.

summary

Students brainstorm lists of how the Great Lakes play a role for humans, both today and in the past. They create an illustration and write a story that reflects why their lake is important to them now and why it was important to people in the past.

objectives

- List the ways the Great Lakes are important to people today.
- Brainstorm a list of ways the Great Lakes were important to people of long ago.
- Document the importance of the lakes in the present and in the past.

prerequisite

Who Needs the Lakes? if age appropriate

vocabulary

Industry: businesses that provide a particular product or service
Irrigate: to supply with water
Recreation: a way of refreshing mind or body

setting

INDOORS : OUTDOORS

Classroom or lake

subjects

Social Studies, History, Language Arts

standards

This Great Lakes in My World activity is aligned to the Common Core State Standards and to state learning standards in:

Illinois
Indiana
Michigan
Minnesota
New York
Ohio
Pennsylvania
Wisconsin

This alignment is available on your Great Lakes in My World CD in the "Standards" folder and on-line at http://www.greatlakes.org/ GLiMWstandards.

materials

- Paper
- Writing utensils
- Colored pencils
- Markers

background

The Great Lakes region has played host to many different groups who have lived in the region over time, all drawn here by the powerful lure of fresh water. The Great Lakes are a direct source of drinking water and also provide food, support wildlife and have provided a means of livelihood for many through industry, shipping, canal building and farming. From Native Americans, explorers, voyageurs, miners, immigrants and settlers, the region has provided for many groups and has seen different interactions with each.

There are similarities and differences between the ways we use the Great Lakes now and the ways the lakes were used in earlier times. This activity serves as a means for students to begin thinking about the different ways people throughout history have interacted with the Great Lakes. If done before *Who Needs the Lake?*, it can also provide a means of assessing students' prior historical knowledge. Otherwise, they can build off knowledge gained from the previous activity. Encourage students to think about how the Great Lakes are and have been an asset to the watershed's people. If students have little historical context, focus on the ways that the lakes serve basic human needs. Ask them to think about the human needs that remain the same over time.

procedure

1. Have students work on the journal pages to create a list of the roles the Great Lakes play in their lives. Explore this by asking them what experiences they have had at the lake. *Responses might include recreation and other items on the list below.*
2. Have students add to their list, including ways their community uses the Great Lakes.
   - *Recreation - going to the beach, taking walks, having picnics, fishing, building sandcastles, swimming*
   - *Drinking water*
   - *Irrigation for crops*
   - *Shipping imports and exports and access to world markets*
   - *Industry - using water in the manufacture of various products*
3. Ask students what types of people they think have lived in the region over time. *Native Americans, French and British explorers, voyageurs, fur trappers, European settlers*

4. Tell students that people have been living near the Great Lakes for thousands of years, starting with Native Americans, then European explorers and settlers. Ask students in what ways these people may have depended on the Great Lakes. Students create a separate list that shows their ideas for this. *Depending on the time frame the students choose, their lists may include some of the items in #2, above, and may also emphasize:*
   - *Fishing for food*
   - *Passenger boats that bring immigrants to the region*
   - *Transportation of people and/or goods from one place to another*
5. Students compare their lists of the past and present. As a class, discuss the following: What is similar about the ways that people may have used the lakes over time? What is different about the ways that people may have used the lakes over time?

wrap-up

Grades 3-4

1. Have students choose a favorite thing to do at or near the lake. Illustrate that activity either in a single image or as a storyboard (series of images). Accompanying the image, they should also write about why the lake is a place of value to them and about why the Great Lakes were important to people who lived here long ago.
2. Have students share their images and writing with each other.

Grades 5-6

1. Students individually choose one group of people and write in first person about a day in that life. What do they imagine their lives would have been like during that time and with the responsibilities of that person? How is this different from your life today? Have students include an illustration, if time.
2. Have students share their stories with each other.

extension

Students can draw two pictures and write about them. One picture should be of a favorite way they use the Great Lakes and an explanation of why they enjoy this activity.

The second picture should show people of long ago using the Great Lakes.

assessment

Rubric on page 384

2 | Now and Then

GRADE LEVEL
3-6

journal pages

| FIRST NAME | | | | | | | | | | | | | | | | | |
| LAST NAME | | | | | | | | | | | | | | | | | |

[1] Make a list of ways you use the Great Lakes.

[2] Make a list of ways your community uses the Great Lakes.

[3] Who are some groups of people who have lived in the Great Lakes watershed throughout history?

[4] How might they have used the Great Lakes?

[5] How are the ways people used the lakes long ago different from today?

[6] How are they similar?

APPROVED BY

2 | Now and Then

GRADE LEVEL
3-4

journal pages

FIRST NAME																					
LAST NAME																					

[7] Draw images that show your favorite way to use the Great Lakes. Write about why the Great Lakes are important to you now and why they were important to people long ago.

APPROVED BY

2 | Now and Then

GRADE LEVEL
5-6

journal pages

FIRST NAME																						
LAST NAME																						

[7] Choose one group of people and write in first person about a day in that life.

Address the following:
a. What do you imagine your life would have been like during that time and with the responsibilities of that person?
b. How is this different from your life today?
c. Include an illustration on a separate sheet of paper, given time.

APPROVED BY	

3 | Beaches Over Time

GRADE LEVEL

K-4

45 minutes

Developmental Modifications: Focus on "trash timeline" as age appropriate.

summary

Students use their senses to discover what is at the beach, read a poem to discover how the beach might have changed over time and discuss what makes the Great Lakes shoreline an important place.

objectives

- Use senses to make observations at the beach.
- Differentiate between natural and human-made objects.
- Discuss historical differences in beach use over time.
- Discuss the importance of the Great Lakes to humans over time.

prerequisite

None, but this activity can be done with activities from the Human Communities units: Litter Tag, Garbage Investigation, and Adopt-a-Beach™

vocabulary

Vessel: boat
Algae: a type of plant that lives in water
Pier: a platform where boats are tied up
Haven: a safe place
Mussel: a mollusk with a hinged double shell; Great Lakes examples include the fingernail clam, the invasive zebra and quagga mussels

setting

OUTDOORS

outdoors, at a beach

subjects

Biology, Environmental Science, Social Studies

standards

This Great Lakes in My World activity is aligned to the Common Core State Standards and to state learning standards in:

Illinois
Indiana
Michigan
Minnesota
New York
Ohio
Pennsylvania
Wisconsin

This alignment is available on your Great Lakes in My World CD in the "Standards" folder and on-line at http://www.greatlakes.org/ GLiMWstandards.

materials

- Journals
- Pencils
- Clipboards
- Garbage bags and gloves (optional)

background

The Great Lakes shoreline has seen many changes over time. During a beach visit, students will see a "snapshot" of the beach at a specific moment. During this activity, they will compare what they currently see with what might have been seen at earlier points in time. This will enable students to imagine a historical context and gain a new perspective for the beach.

A brief history of some commonly found garbage items is listed in this activity. Older students will better understand this timeline. For younger students, focus more on discussing the poem and the difference between natural and human-made objects. See "Trash Timeline" on the compact disc for an expanded version of the history of garbage, or go to BFI-Kids Trash Timeline:

http://www.bfi-salinas.com/kids_trash_timeline_frames.cfm

....

resources

BFI-Kids Trash Timeline
http://www.bfi-salinas.com/kids_trash_timeline_frames.cfm

A Timeline of Soft Drink History
http://inventors.about.com/library/weekly/aa091699.htm

A History of Plastics
http://www.americanchemistry.com/s_plastics/doc.
   asp?CID=1102&DID=4665

....

Highlights from Trash Timeline

1810: (Tin can) Tin can patented.

1860: (Newspaper) American newspapers are printed on paper made from wood pulp fibers rather than rags.

1868: (Plastic) The Hyatt brothers manufacture "celluloid," the first commercial synthetic plastic. It replaces wood, ivory, metal and linen in such items as combs, billiard balls, eyeglasses and shirt collars.

1892: (Bottle cap) William Painter invented the crown bottle cap.

1899: (Glass bottle) The first patent issued for a glass blowing machine, used to produce glass bottles. However, glass containers have been blown since ancient times.

1929: (Aluminum foil) Aluminum foil is invented.

1936: (Paper packaging) Milk products are now commonly sold in paper packaging.

1943: (Aerosol can) The aerosol can is invented by two researchers at the U.S. Department of Agriculture.

1944: (Styrofoam) Styrofoam is invented.

1957: (Aluminum can) The first aluminum cans used.

1960: (Styrofoam cup) Bead molded polystyrene cups are introduced. They provide better insulation for hot drinks.

1960: (Plastic bag) Bread is sold bagged in polyethylene rather than wrapped in waxed paper.

1960: ("Pop tops") Easy open tops for beverage cans are invented.

1970: (Plastic bottle) Plastic bottles are used for soft drinks.

1980: (Plastic straw) Polypropylene is introduced for drinking straws. Other materials had been used in the past to make straws.

....

procedure

1. Have students sit in a circle at the beach or near the lake and close their eyes. Direct them to use their senses of hearing and smell to take in all the information they can about where they are. Tell them they will have their eyes closed for 30 (or more) seconds. After students open their eyes, they should share what they heard and smelled.

2. Ask what kind of feelings students had while they had their eyes closed. Older students may be more comfortable recording their answers, not sharing them aloud. *Some answers may include: peaceful, calm, relaxed, or anxious, depending on the student's past experiences with the Great Lakes.*

3. Now ask students how what they heard and smelled might have changed from 300 years ago. Ask them what would have been or lived here long ago. *Depending on where you are, things may or may not have changed significantly. However, some areas of the shoreline have been reconstructed so that there are now cities. Many of the wetlands that were once here have been removed during development of the shoreline. Would people have felt the same way 300 years ago? Possibly. Answers will vary.*

4. Read the poem Beaches Over Time. This can also be read prior to the visit, if it is easier for students to focus in the classroom. Talk about the things mentioned in the poem and tell students they can look for many of these things on the beach. Now the students will be using observation to discover what is on the beach and reflect on how it might have changed over time.

5. Students take 15 minutes, either on their own, or with a partner, to walk around the beach making observations. Students make a list of what they see, and use symbols to indicate whether items are natural or human-made. While they are walking, have them think about whether these same objects would have been here long ago. Younger students can make mental, instead of written, notes about what they see and make the list as a class.

6. Suggestion: Bring garbage bags and gloves to clean up the garbage that is found on the beach. It can be used for the Garbage Investigation activity in the Human Communities unit.

wrap-up

Bring students back together for a discussion.

1. Students share some of the items on their list. *Items might include feathers, sand, rocks, sticks, cigarette filters, plastic bottles and aluminum cans.*
2. Which of these items is natural and which is human-made? *Separate the items with the students, or in small groups. Discuss how different types of garbage indicate different types activities at the beach including picnics, fishing and playing.*

   Caution: Only adults should handle sharp objects. Everyone should wear gloves when touching garbage.

3. Discuss which objects students found that were mentioned in the poem. How do students think the Great Lakes have changed over time? How were they special for people in the past? How are they special for people now?

For older students (grades 3-4)

4. What is here that might not have been here 300 years ago? *Generally, more human made garbage: cigarette filters, aluminum drink cans, plastic items, fast food containers.*
5. What is not here that might have been here 300 years ago? *Goods and containers from shipwrecks, remains of a campfire or other evidence of people camping there, such as bones or shells, Native American fishing nets or boats.*
6. What makes the beach a unique and important place for us now? *Drinking water, beauty, animals and plants that depend on the Great Lakes, transportation, recreation.*
7. What might have made it a unique and important place for others long ago? *Many of the same reasons, but for different lifestyles.*
8. How might people long ago have viewed the Great Lakes differently from how we view them now? *They might have seen them as more of a food source than we do today. They might have viewed them as bigger since they did not have aerial or satellite photos. Answers will vary.*
9. What can students do to keep the beach healthy for the future? *Keep garbage off the beaches, educate others about what a special place we live near, stay informed of changes in the community that might harm the beaches, take appropriate action if the beach or other parts of the shoreline are threatened.*

assessment

Rubric on page 384

Beaches Over Time

My friend and I went
To the beach today,
To run around
In the sand and play.

We jumped in the waves
That lapped on the shore,
And dug in the sand
To make castles galore.

I found strings of
Algae, shiny and green,
To border my castle
That sheltered my queen.

Fingernail clam shells
Made windows and doors,
And small, rounded
   pebbles
Tiled the floors.

As I looked out
For treasures washed on
   the shore,
I found that the beach
Was hiding much more.

Bubble gum wrappers
And cans of soda pop
Told me that others
Had sat in this spot.

That was not long
Before I came here today
But what about kids
Who came long ago to
   play?

Would a Native American
Have found here instead
Fishing nets floating
In green algae beds?

Were old fire rings
And birch bark canoes
Left by hunters
Of the water blue?

Would a child of
Settlers living here
Have witnessed ships
Sailing from the pier?

And if I dove now
Into the water deep,
Would I find a ship
On the bottom, asleep?

A large vessel that
Carried spices and tea
That sank in the stormy
Freshwater sea?

Now it might rest
Not far from my fort,
A haven where fish
And mussels cavort.

This beach could be
Full of stories to tell,
Like the pearly colors
Inside of a shell.

If I let my mind wander
Beyond my sand castle
   gate,
I might hear the tale
Of old times by this lake.

Author: Anne Richardson

3 | Beaches Over Time

GRADE LEVEL
K-4

journal pages

FIRST NAME																				
LAST NAME																				

[1] What did you find at the beach? Make a mark next to the natural objects.

[2] Draw a picture of one item you found. Label it. Is it a natural object or did humans make it?

[3] What made the Great Lakes a special and important place for people long ago?

[4] What makes the Great Lakes a special place for you now?

APPROVED BY	

4 | Seasons Change

GRADE LEVEL
3-6

45 minutes

Developmental Modifications: For younger students, read the story aloud and have them draw an illustration after each season section is completed.

summary

Students read an account about the seasonal lifestyle of the Ojibwe (Chippewa). They compare and contrast this lifestyle with their own through discussion and illustration.

objectives

- Read a story about the Ojibwe seasonal lifestyle.
- Respond to questions about seasonal living.
- Create an illustration that depicts the lifestyle of the Ojibwe during a certain season.
- Compare and contrast students' lifestyles with the Ojibwe's seasonal lifestyles.

prerequisite

Now and Then, Beaches Over Time or Who Needs the Lakes?

vocabulary

Wigwam: cone-shaped Native American home
Toboggan: sled

setting

INDOORS OUTDOORS

Classroom or outdoors

subjects

Social Studies, History, Language Arts, Science

standards

This Great Lakes in My World activity is aligned to the Common Core State Standards and to state learning standards in:

Illinois
Indiana
Michigan
Minnesota
New York
Ohio
Pennsylvania
Wisconsin

This alignment is available on your Great Lakes in My World CD in the "Standards" folder and on-line at http://www.greatlakes.org/ GLiMWstandards.

materials

- Crayons
- Markers
- Pencils
- Paper
- Seasons Change story (included)

background

Native American tribes have lived in the Great Lakes region for more than 10,000 years. Quite a variety of tribes lived in the region, each with its own customs. As Europeans flooded into North America, tribes were pushed west. As each tribe was pushed further west into new territory, it oftentimes clashed with the tribe occupying the land it was being pushed onto. This story focuses on a tribe that lived in the Great Lakes region, before these cultural clashes began.

For thousands of years, the Great Lakes tribes survived and flourished in the region, dealing with the challenges of the changing seasons. Each season brought about different responsibilities and actions necessary for survival. Native American tribes depended heavily on the Great Lakes for fish, plants and drinking water. They also hunted animals that ate and drank from the Great Lakes. Our own lifestyles are affected much less by the seasons. The story *Seasons Change* enables students to reflect on the Native American lifestyle and discover how it is similar to and different from their own lifestyles. The story is based on the lifestyle that would have been common to many Great Lakes tribes, especially the Ojibwe (Chippewa) tribe.

procedure

1. In a large group, ask students:
   How do we know what season we are in? *Weather, temperature, months, clothing.* What helps people survive cold weather in the Great Lakes region? *Houses, insulation, heat, warm clothing.* What helps people survive hot weather in the Great Lakes region? *Houses, insulation, air conditioning, screens to keep out the bugs, running water, refrigerators.* How do our lives change when the seasons change? *We wear different clothes, carry out different outdoor activities, eat different foods, work on different projects.*

2. Explain to students that Native Americans lived here and had lifestyles that did not have all the comforts we have today. Read to students or have them read the account of how an Ojibwe or Iroquois tribe lived in each season. After each season stop and ask students to think about how their lives are similar to and different from the life of the child in the story.

3. Complete and discuss the journal pages. Additional discussion questions include:
   What did you like or dislike about this lifestyle?
   How might you be a different person if you had grown up with this type of lifestyle?
   How much do surroundings influence peoples' identities?

See History section of resource list on the compact disc for books on this topic.

wrap-up

1. Students should choose one (or more, if time allows) season to illustrate. Each student imagines she or he has been transported back in time to the Native American seasonal way of living and create an illustration, series of images, or comic strip, that shows his or her life with a Native American tribe. They should convey what would be different and difficult for them, as well as what might be similar to their lives now.

2. Have students share their work with a partner or small group.

extension

Have students create an illustrated book, using this story or a variation they research and write. Read it to younger students, showing the illustrations the students have made.

resources

Native Americans of the Great Lakes, Stuart A. Kallan, 2000
People of the Lakes, Roberta Conlan, Time-Life Books, 1994

assessment

Rubric on page 385

4 | Seasons Change

FIRST NAME																			

LAST NAME																			

Spring

Finally, the days are getting longer and warmer! There is still ice over the lake, but it is starting to thaw. Today I even saw a few plants sprouting out of the soil.

Last week we returned to the woods that we live in every spring. It's filled with big, beautiful maple trees, which we use to make maple syrup. This year I helped make cuts in the trees and then put in the spouts. This makes the sap inside the tree flow into the birch-bark pail I put under the spout. When we have a lot of sap, we boil it to turn it into maple syrup, and sometimes even maple sugar. We eat maple syrup on many different foods. It is the main way we sweeten food, so it is an important item for us! After we finish making maple sugar, we will have a maple dance and celebration where there will be a feast and a ceremony to give thanks to the maple tree.

While the women cook the maple sap, the men go fishing. My brother and father lay on the thick ice next to holes they cut in the ice. They look into the hole and when a fish comes by, they spear it and pull it out. Sometimes they use nets to catch the fish. When they bring the fish to the women, we roast and boil them to eat, but we also have to dry many of them to save for later in the year.

Summer

After maple sugaring, we move to our summer village. Not all tribes plant crops, but we do. Each family in the village has its own garden. The men break up the soil and then we plant corn, bean and squash seeds that we saved from last year. After planting, a leader in our tribe asks the spirits for a bountiful harvest.

While we wait for the crops to grow, we gather nuts and wild plants we can eat including my favorites: wild gooseberries, raspberries and blueberries. We dry many of them for eating in fall and winter. We also catch and dry more fish that come from the Great Lakes. We don't have any other way to preserve our food for later.

We don't think about food all the time. We also make the things we need each day, such as clothing, baskets, floor mats, wall coverings, animal traps and fish nets. We make some of these things from plants such as bulrushes and cat-tails that grow near the Great Lakes.

Summer isn't our only hunting season; we hunt deer all year long. We eat their meat and use their bones and antlers for tools, and their hides for clothing. In summer we prepare the hides for clothing. This year I am learning to make moccasins, the soft shoes we wear.

In late summer, we all go out to gather wild rice, which grows in the marshy parts of the lakes. We camp near the wild rice with many other families. After the harvest, we have another festival, like our maple sugar festival. It's good to say thank you to the lakes that give us so much!

We dry and bury some of the rice to eat next year. We also have to harvest all the food from our garden. Much of our corn and squash is dried and stored for the long winter.

Autumn

In autumn, we spend a lot of time preparing for the winter, which we know will come quickly. It will be very cold! The men hunt, trap and fish while we prepare for our winter move. Snow begins to fall, and the lakes start to freeze on the surface. This means we can't use our canoes anymore. So, like other Ojibwe families, we use a sled called a toboggan to reach our winter hunting grounds. Dogs help some of us pull the toboggans. Since we can't all fit in the toboggan, some of us wear snow-shoes and walk.

As we get ready for winter, I think about where I live. I love it here. The Great Lakes give us so much – everything from food to drinking water. It's a good place to live, even though it gets cold in the winter!

Winter

In winter, we hunt animals to survive. We eat their meat, and their thick winter coats make warm clothes for us. We hunt moose, elk, deer, bear, wolves, foxes, rabbits, beavers and duck. Can you guess why it is easiest for us to hunt and find animals in the winter?

In winter, we live in wigwams. These have a framework of poles pounded into the ground in a circle. The poles are tied to-gether at the top and covered with bark or reeds. We live close to other families so that we can help each other and visit each other's wigwams, where we spend a lot of time! Winter can be very hard, especially with such cold temperatures, high winds and all that snow on the ground. We have to cover our wig-wams with two layers of mats to keep out the wind.

Even though it's cold, I love nights in winter. Before we go to sleep, we sit around the fire playing games. The women make clothes and do weaving, while the men repair tools and weap-ons. This is also a time when we tell stories. A family member will beat the drum quietly while we listen to the story. Many of our stories are about the plants, animals and Great Lakes that we need to survive.

The Great Lakes look different in the winter, all white and cov-ered with snow and ice. We stay close by our lake because we know we need it all year round for drinking water, and for the plants and animals that live in and near the lakes.

APPROVED BY	

4 | Seasons Change

FIRST NAME

LAST NAME

Answer the questions.

[1] How did the people in the story depend on the Great Lakes?

[2] How is this similar to or different from the way you depend on the Great Lakes?

[3] What were some of the changes that happened with each season?

[4] How is this story different from your own life?

[5] How is this story similar to your own life?

APPROVED BY

4 | Seasons Change

GRADE LEVEL
3-6

journal pages

FIRST NAME																				
LAST NAME																				

[6] Create!

Imagine that you are living with the Ojibwe tribe in this story. Make a picture or a storyboard that shows you living with the tribe. In the pictures, show what is different for you and what is familiar.

APPROVED BY	

EXPLORE

5 | Ways of Life

GRADE LEVEL

4-8

45 minutes

summary

Students use Venn diagrams to compare and contrast different groups that lived in the Great Lakes watershed, including two main groups of Native Americans and European settlers.

objectives

- List some of the Native American tribes of the Great Lakes region.
- Describe the tribe that lived in the students' region prior to European settlement.
- Use Venn diagrams to compare and contrast Native Americans and the first European settlers that lived in the region.
- Conceptualize sets and subsets.

prerequisite

Who Needs the Lakes? or Now and Then

vocabulary

Breechclouts: a cloth worn about the hips as clothing
Clan: extended family group within a tribe
Dialect: A regional variety of a language differing from the standard language
Totem: An animal symbol that has meaning for a person
Venn diagram: A chart with intersecting circles used to compare and contrast characters, stories, plots, etc. May be used to show the differences and similarities between two characters, things, or books

setting

INDOORS

subjects

Social Studies, History

standards

This Great Lakes in My World activity is aligned to the Common Core State Standards and to state learning standards in:

Illinois
Indiana
Michigan
Minnesota
New York
Ohio
Pennsylvania
Wisconsin

This alignment is available on your Great Lakes in My World CD in the "Standards" folder and on-line at http://www.greatlakes.org/ GLiMWstandards.

materials

- Pencil or pen
- Map of Great Lakes Native American tribes
- Journal
- Extra copies of Venn diagram

background

Native Americans have lived in the Great Lakes region for more than 10,000 years, which is when the last ice age ended. When the first Europeans arrived in the early 17th century (1600s), Native Americans had their own thriving and vibrant civilization. Their culture was rich in religion, self-government and history. In their societies, Native Americans had roles including: farmers, hunters, politicians, artisans, warriors and healers.

There were dozens of tribes and related clans in the Great Lakes area, but the region was generally populated by two broad groups of Native Americans. One group was the Six Nations of the Iroquois (IR-uh-kwoy), who lived around Lake Ontario in the northeastern part of the region in what is now the United States and Canada. The other group consisted of the Algonquian (al-GAHN-kwian) language tribes, who lived in the western region around the Great Lakes.

Europeans first began to arrive in the Great Lakes region in 1615 as explorers. In the 1720s, Europeans began to settle in the area, bringing with them a different way of living that would ultimately clash with the Native American tribes. The French explorers who first visited the Great Lakes, beginning with Lake Huron in 1615, found native peoples who were living comfortably with their environment and were economically self-sustaining. These Europeans brought implements of iron—needles, fishhooks, hatchets, traps and guns—items that the native peoples immediately saw could make their lives easier, and they began trading furs and skins for these implements. The pelts of fur-bearing animals, especially beavers, were most sought after by the European traders. Many natives abandoned their traditional work and became dependent on trade. Such was the basis of the Indian trade over which wars were waged and the history of the Great Lakes region was shaped. The native peoples of the upper lakes often traveled hundreds of miles by canoe down the Ottawa and St. Lawrence rivers to Three Rivers or Montreal, where they exchanged their furs for goods they desired. Beginning around 1660, the traders established themselves over the western Great Lakes wilderness.

1. Tribes of the eastern Great Lakes - Six Nations of the Iroquois (also called the Iroquois Nation or the Iroquois League) included six tribes: Mohawk, Cayuga, Oneida, Onondaga, Seneca and Tuscarora. The Iroquois called themselves Hodenosaunee, meaning, "People of the Longhouse." The tribes spoke different dialects of the Iroquoian language but had similar customs and traditions.

   *Huron: Members of the Huron tribe were enemies of the Iroquois, but shared language and customs.

2. Tribes of the western Great Lakes – speakers of the Algonquian language included nine tribes: the Ottawa, Ojibwe (also called the Chippewa), Potawatomi, Winnebago, Menominee, Sauk, Fox, Miami and Huron. Estimates vary widely, but some suggest that there was a population of at least 250,000 Native Americans (some estimates are much higher) occupying the Upper Great Lakes.

3. Tribe of western Lake Michigan - non-Algonquian speakers Winnebago – lived in eastern Wisconsin (near modern day Green Bay), spoke the Siouan language.

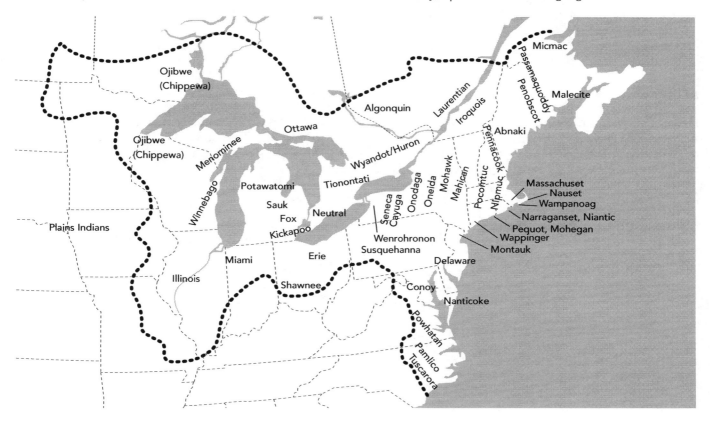

procedure

1. Ask the students who were the first people to live in the Great Lakes region. *Native Americans. They belonged to specific tribes and groups.*

2. Use the map provided to determine which tribe(s) lived in the area your school and community are located in.

3. Explain that the tribes in the Great Lakes can be generally categorized as either the Iroquois or the Algonquian. Was the tribe in your area part of the Iroquois, Algonquian or another group?

4. Ask students what they know about Native Americans. Explain that some Native American groups have lived in the Great Lakes area for more than 10,000 years. Have students read the information in their journal pages, describing the main Native American groups that lived around the Great Lakes. Notice how the two general groups are different and similar.

5. Discuss the European settlers who later came to the region in the 1700s. Where were they from? *France, England, Holland.* Why were they coming to the region? *European explorers were originally searching for a path to the Orient through the Great Lakes. Once they saw what the area had to offer, drinking water, timber, furs, hunting areas, they began to settle in the Great Lakes region in increasing numbers, bringing settlers and early industrialists.* Additional information found in Who Needs the Lakes?

6. Have students create Venn diagrams to compare and contrast the Algonquian and Iroquois tribes, and the earliest European settlers. If students need more space for writing, give them additional copies of the Venn Diagram.

wrap-up

1. Discuss the Venn diagrams. What are some similarities and differences? Even though two groups are Native American tribes, what are some of the things that make them different? What are differences that might cause conflict between these groups? What are similarities that might strike up a relationship? What did you find most interesting when comparing the groups? Have you ever been in a situation where you found out that you had more in common with someone than you initially thought? How can acknowledging the things you have in common be important?

2. How did the different groups depend on the Great Lakes? How do you think each group thought about the Great Lakes?

extension

Students work in small groups to research a specific Native American tribe. In the group, students are responsible for different aspects of the project: recreation, food, clothing, family life, government, seasonal changes, spiritual practices.

resources

Native Peoples of the Great Lakes Region
http://www.great-lakes.net/teach/history/native/native_1.html
Native Americans of the Great Lakes, Stuart A. Kallen, 2000

assessment

Rubric on page 385

 We value your thoughts and feedback on Great Lakes in My World. Please let us know about any oversights, errors or omissions you find, or if there are things you or your students particularly like.

Send your comments to: education@greatlakes.org

5 | Ways of Life

GRADE LEVEL
4-8

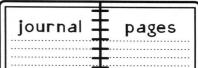

journal ⫴ pages

FIRST NAME																					
LAST NAME																					

Read the information below. Create a series of Venn diagrams that compare and contrast the Algonquian tribespeople, the Iroquois tribespeople and the early European settlers.

WESTERN GREAT LAKES TRIBES

[1] Algonquian

Needs were met
The forests and the Great Lakes provided food, water, shelter and clothing.

Lifestyle
Nomadic or semi-nomadic. They moved as a group, depending on the season, to meet their needs.

Appearance
Dress
Clothing made of skins of deer, bear and beaver. Men and women wore moccasins, leggings and robes. Clothing was decorated with painted bands of red and brown.
- Women wore skirts that reached their knees. In the summer, they did not wear shirts, but in the winter they did.
- Men wore breech-clouts and shirts with detachable sleeves.

Hair
- Women wore their hair well-combed and oiled and in a single tress down the back that was tied with an eelskin.
- Men wore their hair different ways. Some shaved half of the head, many left the hair long and hanging, others left a strip of hair along the midline of the head.

Body Decoration
- Women were not painted or tattooed. They wore necklaces of shells and beads around their necks and waists.
- Most of the men painted their faces and bodies with a variety of designs that were mostly black and red, with some green and purple. The colors were from minerals and vegetables, and mixed with sunflower oil and bear fat. Some men tattooed their bodies with images of animals.

Shelter
They lived in simple, portable wigwams, although some lived in summer homes similar to the Iroquois longhouses. Each clan had its own lodge.

Skills
Women were excellent basket makers. They made baskets from natural materials such as corn husks and decorated them with woven designs. Kitchen utensils and wooden bowls were also made and carved for decoration. Women also embroidered and wove.

Marriage customs
Marriage did not take place between people of the same tribe, meaning that it took place between members of different tribes.

Roles
Women built wigwams, gathered wood, tanned hides and cooked food. Men were hunters and warriors. Women were responsible for most of the chores.

Social Structure
Each tribe was divided into two groups. Each group had either a land or a sky animal symbol, called a totem. Each family had a specific totem such as Eagle, Pigeon, Bear, Wolf, Snake, Deer or Fish. Earth and sky totems lived in separate areas, according to clan. Each clan had its own specialty. Specialties included: referee in arguments and warriors who policed the village. A person looked to their totem for guidance on how to live their life.

[2] Iroquois

Needs were met
The forests and the Great Lakes provided food, water, shelter and clothing.

Lifestyle
Sedentary - They did not move as a group, depending on the season, to meet their needs.

Iroquois description continued on the next page

APPROVED BY	

5 | Ways of Life

| FIRST NAME | | | | | | | | | | | | | | | | | | | |
| LAST NAME | | | | | | | | | | | | | | | | | | | |

Iroquois description continued

Appearance
Dress
Clothing made of animal skins and plant fibers.
In the summer, some wore nothing at all.

Hair
The women's hair was worn in one long braid down their back. The Iroquois men wore a scalp lock or a piece of hair going down the neck.

Body Decoration
Faces painted red, black and yellow.

Shelter
Lived in longhouses that were 18-25 feet wide and 50-150 feet long. They were windowless and several different families lived within one longhouse.

Skills
Women were excellent basket makers. They wove baskets from natural materials such as corn husks and decorated them with designs. Kitchen utensils and wooden bowls were also made and carved for decoration. Women also embroidered and wove.

Marriage customs
Marriage did not take place between people of the same tribe.

Roles
Men hunted, and provided protection. Women gathered wild foods, cooked, made baskets and clothing and cared for the children. All property in the village belonged to women.

Social Structure
As early as 1570, the Iroquois tribes were organized into the Iroquois League. They created 13 laws in order to live in peace and unity. Leaders of the League (Grand Council) were men, selected by each tribe's women. Tribes believed: "in all of your…acts, self-interest shall be cast away…Look and listen for the welfare of the whole people, and have always in view not only the present, but also the coming generations… the unborn of the future nation."

[3] Early European Settlers

Needs were met
The forests and the Great Lakes provided food, water, shelter, and clothing.

Lifestyle
Sedentary - They did not move as a group, depending on the season. They stayed in the houses they built for themselves.

Appearance
Dress
Clothing made of animal skins and plant fibers.

Hair
The women's hair was worn up, down or in braids. Men wore their hair long.

Body Decoration
Women wore jewelry and some had pierced ears. Some wore make-up on their lips, cheeks and eyes. They generally did not have tattoos.

Shelter
Lived in houses made from local wood. Generally, one family lived in a house, but relatives of the family might also have lived there.

Skills
Women cooked, cleaned and helped with farming. Women also sewed, embroidered and wove.

Marriage customs
Marriage took place mostly between people of the same cultural background.

Roles
Men hunted, traded, farmed and provided protection. Women gathered cultivated and wild foods, cleaned, cooked, made clothing and cared for the children. All property in the towns belonged to men.

Social Structure
They came from different countries; mostly France at first, then England. These countries had different established governments. Once in North America, the American government was established after the American Revolution in 1776. The Canadian government was established by gradual constitutional change spread over many years.

| APPROVED BY | |

5 | Ways of Life

GRADE LEVEL
4-8

FIRST NAME

LAST NAME

List what is similar in the spaces that overlap and what is different in the spaces that do not overlap.

Algonquian

Iroquois

Early European Settlers

APPROVED BY

5 | Ways of Life

GRADE LEVEL
4-8

FIRST NAME

LAST NAME

Look at the Venn diagrams.

[1] Even though two groups of people are both Native American tribes, what are some of the things that make them different?

....

....

[2] Which groups were most similar to each other?

....

....

[3] What are differences that might cause conflict between these groups?

....

....

[4] How did the different groups depend on the Great Lakes?

....

....

....

[5] How do you think each group felt about the Great Lakes?

....

....

....

[6] What did you find most interesting when comparing the groups?

....

....

....

[7] When have you been in a situation where you found out that you had more in common with someone than you first thought?

....

....

....

[8] How can acknowledging the things you have in common with someone be important?

....

....

....

APPROVED BY

EXPLORE

6 | Boats of Many Sizes

GRADE LEVEL

3-6

45 minutes

Developmental Modification: For younger students, stay focused on the boats and have older students discuss some of the changes associated with the shipping industry.

summary

Students match boats to the correct description, work in small groups to create a boat timeline, discuss costs and benefits of Great Lakes shipping and reflect on shipboard living.

objectives

- Describe how Great Lakes ships meet people's current and historic needs.
- List some of the different boats historically used in the Great Lakes region and the goods they transported.
- Describe how technology decreases shipwrecks.
- Explain how shipping has changed the Great Lakes ecosystem.

prerequisite

Who Needs the Lakes?, Now and Then, Ways of Life

vocabulary

Capacity: ability to hold or contain
Freight: goods or cargo carried by ship, train, truck, or airplane
Invasive species: animal or plant that is not native to an area

setting

INDOORS

subjects

Social Studies, History, Language Arts, Environmental Science, Technology

standards

This *Great Lakes in My World* activity is aligned to the Common Core State Standards and to state learning standards in:

Illinois
Indiana
Michigan
Minnesota
New York
Ohio
Pennsylvania
Wisconsin

This alignment is available on your *Great Lakes in My World* CD in the "Standards" folder and on-line at http://www.greatlakes.org/ GLiMWstandards.

materials

- Boat names and descriptions, one for each student
- Pencils
- Journals
- Map that includes the Great Lakes

background

The Great Lakes have a long history of shipping. Goods and people have arrived to the region by boat for several centuries, including the early Great Lakes explorers and the first settlers. A large shipping industry continues to thrive in the Great Lakes and actively sees goods shipped in and out of the region. This activity explores the historical importance of shipping by examining particular boats used in the region.

Canoes: The maritime history of the Great Lakes begins with the Native Americans. Birch bark canoes were the most adaptable and useful canoes built by Native Americans. They were lightweight, easily maneuverable, could hold a relatively heavy weight, and could even be repaired during the course of a journey, using materials close at hand. It is not known when the Native Americans first began building canoes, but tribes have lived in the region and used the waterways for an estimated 10,000 years.

Voyageur boats: By the 1600s French fur traders had begun to adopt the canoe as a way to explore and expand their trapping/trading business. To adapt to their needs, the voyageurs lengthened and expanded the traditional canoe to increase its capacity. The French fur companies used these great freight canoes in similar ways to today's modern trucks. The largest of the voyageur boats was called *canots de maitres*. Voyageurs piloted these canoes, which ranged from 7 to 11 meters (25 to 36 feet) in length and carried 1,016 to 3,048 kilograms (1 to 3 tons) of cargo and a crew of 4 to 8 people.

Schooners: The canoe-shaped boats gradually gave way to larger wooden boats and sailing ships. Even in the 1830s, canoes were still in popular use. However, with the building of the Illinois and Michigan Canal, which took place from 1836 to 1848, Chicago became a budding port city. Up until the 1880s, schooners made up the bulk of the sailing fleet and were responsible for growth in the grain and lumber trades. By the late 1880s, steamships had begun to take the lead in the grain trade, although schooners continued to play an important role in the lumber trade well into the 20th century. Great Lakes schooners were seldom longer than 60 meters (200 feet). As many as 500 schooners would weather the winter in the Chicago River to take advantage of the city's numerous shipyards, in order to make boat repairs for the next shipping season.

Steamships: Steam power brought reliability to the transportation of people and products on the lakes. Whereas sailing ships were subject to the weather, steamships were able to operate on a tighter schedule, which better suited the region as it was becoming more industrialized. The first steamboats were paddle wheel vessels. In 1841, Great Lakes shipbuilders began to experiment with propeller-driven ships. Eventually, the propeller-driven ships became dominant on both the Great Lakes and in the oceans. Although some iron-hulled boats began to make an appearance, the abundance of forest products in the region meant that wooden-hulled ships were built into the 19th century. Beginning in 1889, steel-hulled ships began to make an appearance. This style ruled the lakes in the 20th century as passenger ships, package steamers and bulk carriers. Initially, sails remained on many barges, to help them speed along in good weather. However, it became increasingly difficult to find crews who were skilled with sailing vessels.

Freighters: Today, the traffic on the Great Lakes includes passenger, package freight and bulk freight. Of passenger boats, the largest are 116 meters (380 feet) and have a speed of over 32 kilometers per hour (20 miles per hour). They carry no freight. On Lake Michigan many passenger boats run out of Chicago, and on Lake Ontario there are several large and fast Canadian steamers on routes from Toronto. The transportation of goods in enclosed parcels (package freight business) is principally local. By far the greatest number of vessels on the lakes are bulk freighters. The modern bulk freighter is a vessel 183 meters (600 feet) long, capable of carrying 14,000 tons. This type of vessel can be loaded in a few minutes, and unloaded in six or eight hours. The bulk freight generally follows certain well-defined routes; iron ore is shipped east from ports on both sides of Lake Superior and on the west side of Lake Michigan to rail shipping points on the south shore of Lake Erie. Wheat and other grains from Duluth find their way to Buffalo, as do wheat, corn and other grains from Chicago. Wheat from the Canadian north-west is distributed from Fort William and Port Arthur to railway terminals on the Georgian Bay, to Buffalo, and to Port Colborne for shipment to canal barges for Montreal, and coal is distributed from Lake Erie to all western points. The shipping trade is assisted by both Canadian and U. S. governments by a system of aids to navigation that mark every channel and danger. There are also life-saving stations at all dangerous points.

Lakers: To handle Great Lakes cargo, a special type of vessel has evolved, called the North American "laker," the largest being 335 meters (1,013 ft.) long, capable of carrying up to 70,966 tons of iron ore or 45,552.5 tons (1,700,00 bushels) of grain in one trip.

procedure

1. While looking at a map of the Great Lakes, ask students how they think people travel now in the Great Lakes area. *Train, car, bus, boat.* How do students think people traveled in the past? *Prior to cars and trains, horses, boats and foot were the primary means of getting around.*

2. How have boats helped people meet their needs on the Great Lakes? *Hundreds of years ago, boats were the primary way that people arrived to the Great Lakes region. Boats were and are still a major way that goods are transported in this region.*

procedure continued

3. Hand out boat names to half the class, so that several students are assigned each type of boat. Give the other half of the class descriptions and pictures of each type of boat, without the names. They find a partner to match the picture to the description. Give each student two copies of the image or the description, so they can give one copy to their partner. Each student should have a complete set.
4. Make several groups so that at least one boat type is represented in each group. Have students determine the chronological order of their boats and then report to each other about the significance of each boat.
5. As a class, create a chronological timeline of the types of boats in this activity.
6. Ask students how shipping has helped people of the region meet their needs. List some of the goods transported in the past by boat. *People, timber, grain.* How do we continue to depend on shipping in the present? *Iron ore, coal, grains.*

wrap-up

1. For older students, discuss some of the changes that are associated with the shipping industry. Address the fact that there have been many shipwrecks on the Great Lakes. List a few that have happened in your region, if you are familiar with them. Just as boats have changed over time, the technology onboard the boats has changed as well. What advances have been made to decrease the number of shipwrecks? *Lighthouses, radio, radar, coast guard.*
2. How has shipping caused changes in the Great Lakes ecosystem?
a. *Canals, which have physically changed the Great Lakes, were built in order to accommodate and expedite shipping in the region.*
b. *Canals allowed a number of invasive (non-native) species, including the sea lamprey and alewife to enter the system.*
c. *Ships have accidentally brought invasive species that are unintentional stowaways into the region in ballast water. Ballast water is used to help ships balance their weight and is taken up in one body of water in a different part of the world and can be released in another body of water, such as the Great Lakes. Species that have entered the Great Lakes this way include the Eurasian ruffe, zebra mussels, round goby, spiny water flea, fish hook water flea.*
3. Students choose one boat and take 10 or more minutes to respond to the following: Choose one of the boats you have learned about and describe a day or journey on that boat on your Great Lake. *Being out on the Great Lakes can be very beautiful and give an interesting perspective to the shoreline. The Great Lakes, however, can be a challenging place for boating. Sometimes the voyages can be very long and the weather can make the trips difficult and even dangerous.*
4. Students share their writing with a partner.

extension

The long history of shipping in the region includes many shipwrecks. Have students create a presentation with a visual component on Great Lakes shipping and a documented Great Lakes shipwreck. Projects could include a research paper/poster that details the shipwreck: the cargo, where the ship was coming from, where it was going, what caused the shipwreck, number of passengers, rescue attempts, an estimate of the value of the cargo and what it might be worth today or historically accurate, fictional journal entries written by someone onboard that include the ship sinking. As a wrap-up, students can present their project to the class.

Possible shipwrecks include:

Lake Michigan: Lady Elgin, Eastland, Phoenix, Carl D. Bradley, Chicora, Alpena, Our Son, Andaste, Louisiana, Selah Chamberlain, George F, Williams, Frank O'Connor Steamer, Christina Nilson

Lake Superior: Henry B. Smith, Western Reserve, Edmund Fitzgerald, Kamloops, Bannockburn, Benjamin Noble, C.F. Curtis, Sevona, Pretoria

Lake Erie: Marquette and Bessemer, G.P. Griffith, Atlantic, Merida, Dean Richmond, Admiral, Sachem, Atlantic, Dean Richmond, Trade Wind, Tug Smith

Lake Huron: Kaliyuga, Clifton, Hunter Savidge, Dunderdug, Troy Steamer, Emma L. Nielson, John A. McGean, Daniel J. Morrell

Lake Ontario: Homer Warren, Roberval, Mary Kay, Hamilton, Scourge, Noronic

sources

Voyageur History
    http://www.learning.gov.sk.ca/
Love to Know Encyclopedia:
    http://www.whiteoak.org/learning/voyageurs.html
Chicago Maritime Society
    http://www.chicagomaritimesociety.org/

assessment

Rubric on page 385

background

Cut here

Canoe

The boat history of the Great Lakes begins with the Native Americans who built birch bark boats. These boats were lightweight, easy to maneuver and could hold a relatively heavy weight. They could even be repaired during the course of a journey, using materials close at hand. It is not known when the Native Americans first began building these boats, but tribes have lived in the region and used the waterways for an estimated 10,000 years. What boat am I?

Voyageur Boat

By the 1600s French Fur traders had begun to use the canoe as a way to explore and expand their trapping and trading business. To adapt to their needs, the voyageurs lengthened and expanded the traditional canoe to increase its capacity and invented this boat. The French fur companies used these great freight canoes in similar ways to today's modern trucks. The largest of these boats was called *canots de maitres*. They ranged from 7 to 11 meters (25 to 36 feet) in length and carried 1,016 to 3,048 kilograms (1 to 3 tons) of cargo and a crew of 4 to 8 people. What boat am I?

Schooner

After the canoe-shaped boats, larger wooden boats and sailing ships became popular. Even in the 1830s, canoes were still in popular use. After 1836, it became clear that Chicago was becoming a port city, where sailing vessels were very useful. Up until the 1880s, these sailing boats transported a great deal of grain and lumber around the Great Lakes. These boats were seldom longer than 260 meters (200 feet). During the winter, as many as 500 of these boats could be found in the Chicago River, in order to be repaired for the next shipping season. What boat am I?

Steamship

By the late 1880s, these boats became popular for several reasons. They were very reliable, able to operate on a tight schedule and did not depend on the wind to function. The first of these boats were paddle wheel vessels, and then in 1841, they were powered by propellers. Eventually, the propeller-driven ships became the most popular boats on the Great Lakes and in the oceans. This style ruled the lakes in the 1900s as passenger ships, package steamers and bulk carriers. These vessels could carry over 12,000 tons each. What boat am I?

Freighter

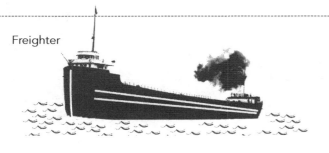

Today, these boats are found most often on the Great Lakes. Originally sailing vessels were largely used, but these have practically disappeared, giving place to steamers, which have grown steadily in size to finally become the boat discussed on this card. These modern vessels are 183 meters (600 feet) long and can carry 14,000 tons. This type of vessel can be loaded in a few minutes, and unloaded in six or eight hours. These ships follow certain well-defined routes and carry things such as: iron ore, coal, wheat, corn and other grains. What boat am I?

6 | Boats of Many Sizes

GRADE LEVEL
3-6

journal pages

FIRST NAME

LAST NAME

Answer these after finding your partner.

[1] Which boat do you have?

[2] How is it useful?

[3] Make a timeline that includes the other boats in the group. Label the timeline and show which boats were most often used during different time periods.

[4] How has shipping helped and caused change in the Great Lakes ecosystem?

[5] Choose one of the boats you have learned about and describe a day or journey on that boat on your Great Lake.

APPROVED BY

EXPLORE

GRADE LEVEL

7 | 200 Years of Change

4-8

90-135 minutes

summary

Students role-play different scenes that characterize the impact of European settlement on the Great Lakes in order to gain an understanding of some interactions that help to define Great Lakes history.

objectives

- Work with others to create and perform a historical skit.
- Describe the relationships between the Native Americans and Europeans in the Great Lakes region between 1600 and 1850.

prerequisite

Who Needs the Lakes?, Seasons Change, Ways of Life

vocabulary

Immunity: bodily power to resist an infectious disease
Reservation: a tract of public land set aside
Sovereign nation: a group or tribe of people with the right to govern themselves

setting

INDOORS

subjects

Social Studies, History, Language Arts

standards

This Great Lakes in My World activity is aligned to the Common Core State Standards and to state learning standards in:

Illinois
Indiana
Michigan
Minnesota
New York
Ohio
Pennsylvania
Wisconsin

This alignment is available on your Great Lakes in My World CD in the "Standards" folder and on-line at http://www.greatlakes.org/ GLiMWstandards.

materials

- Scene cards
- Journals
- Pencils
- Costumes that are made or brought from home

background

A variety of Native American cultures have lived in the Great Lakes region for thousands of years. It is estimated that Ice Age hunters came from Asia, across the Bering Strait, to North America in approximately 14,000 B.C. Over time, there came to be many Native American tribes with both shared and differing beliefs. The tribes sometimes fought with each other, and expanded their territory by conquering one another. Prior to Europeans coming to the area, tribes rose and declined in numbers at different times and under a variety of circumstances.

When the first European settlers arrived in the 1600s, they found a variety of interrelated, but independent tribes existing within North America. Within a span of 200 years (mid 1600-1800), the situation would entirely change as European settlers took over the region and Native Americans, whose numbers were decimated, were forced to leave the lands of their ancestry.

The first Europeans in the region, who were French explorers and fur traders, introduced guns, iron, the wheel and manufactured goods to the Native Americans. They also brought a host of deadly diseases to which the Native Americans had little resistance, including smallpox, measles and cholera. These outbreaks killed one-third to one-half or more of a native population whenever they occurred. The Europeans had a superior advantage over the Native Americans, primarily because of guns, disease and alcohol and used it to conquer the continent of North America. Indeed, there was the rare European leader who was fair, but this was the exception. Although there were many individuals (trappers, settlers) who had good relationships with Native Americans, most did not. This time in North American history is a complicated and painful topic, which can be difficult to address with students and requires discussion and reflection.

History shows the saga of humans conquering new lands, and this usually results in wars. The strongest group, which is frequently the invader, always wins. The weaker group either dies or comes under the rule of the invader. Although it is important not to rationalize this experience of conquering as inevitable or "right," it can bring greater understanding to see it in the larger historical context. The relationship between the Native Americans and the European settlers and their shared dependency on the Great Lakes region is a history from which we have much to learn.

In this activity, students role-play a variety of scenes that characterize the time period of mid 1600-1800. The scenes can be simplified or extended, depending on the students and teacher.

About the skits: There are six skits and each one shares an important piece of the region's history. If there are not enough students to do all the skits, pick the scenes you want to focus on for class knowledge and discussion, or have each student work on two skits. If there are extra students without a group, the groups can be enlarged by adding a narrator or extra characters.

....

procedure

1. Advance preparation: Photocopy the scene cards for each group. Choose a Native American tribe from your region for students to use in their skits.

2. Explain that students will create skits that show some interactions during 200 years of history in the Great Lakes region. The subject of the skits will be the relationship between the Native Americans and the European settlers. Tell students that this relationship was complicated and resulted in extremely difficult times for the Native Americans. Talking about this relationship gives us a chance to learn about history and to think about choices.

3. Divide students into groups of 4-5 people. Give each group a scene card. It is helpful for students to know which European immigrants settled in their region and which Native American group(s) lived in their area, so they can take on roles more specific for the region.

4. Students adopt the roles on the card and work together to create a skit that is 5-10 minutes long. Use dialogue suggestions to determine the script and questions from the scene cards to determine content, or as guides for later discussion. Students may need additional time to conduct research, if necessary. They should rehearse and perform the scene for the class. Students will need time to create the scene, rehearse, and make props and costumes. Have students perform in chronological order.

Stage Tips: Remind students of the following as they create their scenes:
- A narrator may be helpful in providing context or setting the scene for the class.
- Speak in voice that is loud enough for the audience to hear.
- Face the audience when speaking or when doing an action they need to see.
- Really adopt the role you are playing; the skit will be more believable.
- Avoid accents. They can lead to stereotyping and false impressions, and can be difficult to understand.

5. While students are working on their skits, they should complete the appropriate journal pages.

6. Save time for a question-and-answer session after each skit. Ask students for their reflections and questions on the skit contents.

1 | Making Waves

Year: 1620
Roles: Two Native Americans, two European immigrants
Setting: Each pair is out on the Great Lakes in separate boats.
Facts: The Native Americans (choose a tribe from your area) are fishing or traveling in a canoe. The immigrants (choose a group that settled in your region – French, English, Swedish, Dutch, German…) are coming from Europe on a large passenger ship, over the Atlantic Ocean, and through the Great Lakes, to your region. It has been a very long trip, lasting months.
The trip for the Native Americans has not been as long. They are from the Great Lakes region and their ancestors have lived there for over 10,000 years.
Dialogue: Decide what you will talk about. Some ideas: the boat trip, the beauty of the region, when the passenger boat will arrive, what they will be doing later in the day, what they expect will happen in the next few days, where they are from and what is happening there, what type of fish they are catching, what type of bait they use, how they made the fishing gear, how many fish they need to survive.
Questions: Why are the Europeans coming to the Great Lakes region? Will the new place live up to the Europeans' expectations? How are these two cultures similar and different?

2 | Trading Causes Change

Year: 1630
Roles: Two Native Americans, two European settlers
Setting: A Great Lakes community where trading is taking place.
Facts: At first, the trades seem beneficial to all. The Native Americans were able to obtain items they never had before such as guns, metal knives, axes, sewing needles, and brass kettles. In exchange, the Native Americans gave the Europeans furs to send back to their countries for clothing manufacture. In a few cases, where relationships went well, Native Americans showed the Europeans how to survive in the wilderness around the Great Lakes. They introduced them to corn, pumpkins, edible berries and nuts, and showed them how to hunt in the forests and fish in the lake.
Europeans brought more than just trade goods; they brought a host of diseases that Native Americans had never been exposed to before (measles, smallpox, cholera, scarlet fever, yellow fever). Native Americans had no immunity to these diseases. Some epidemics killed entire Native American villages over very short amounts of time.
Dialogue: Decide what you will talk about. Some ideas: what benefits each group gets from this relationship, what both groups get from living in the Great Lakes region, what Europeans and Native Americans think of each other, what works and does not with this new relationship, how the Native Americans try to cope with the new diseases.
Questions: What happened when the Native Americans became dependent on the European goods and lost the skills needed to produce their own traditional goods from wood and stone? What happened when some tribes were given muskets while others were ignored?

3 | Beaver Hats in Fashion

Year: 1660
Roles: voyageurs/fur trappers (in North America), hatters (in Europe), beaver
Setting: This scene could be partially set in Europe where the hats were being made, and partially set in the forests of North America where the beavers and other animals were being hunted for export to Europe.
Facts: Many Europeans came to the Great Lakes region to hunt beavers. Beaver fur was sent to Europe, where it was made into hats. From 1600-1850, no proper European gentleman would be seen in public without a beaver hat. In 1760 alone, enough beaver pelts were sent to England to make 576,000 hats. By 1800, many of the beaver in the Great Lakes region had been wiped out.
Dialogue: Decide what you will talk about. Some ideas: the decreasing number of beaver, new kinds of hats, what to do when the beavers are gone, how the decrease in beaver numbers will impact other species.
Questions: What happened when hunting wiped out most of the beavers in the region?

4 | Whose Land?

Date: 1700 (looking back at 1608 when Champlain sailed on the St. Lawrence River). For historical accuracy, keep in mind that Champlain died in 1635.
Roles: Native Americans, Samuel de Champlain and other Europeans, European king
Setting: On the St. Lawrence River, then on the shores of the Great Lakes; could also be set in Europe to show kings giving away land they had never seen
Facts: In 1608, Champlain and a few men sailed up the St. Lawrence River in search of beaver pelts for the popular European beaver hats. Although thousands of Native Americans lived in the area, Champlain claimed the lands for France and renamed rivers, lakes and geographical features with French names. Europeans wanted land that they could farm, log, mine, own, and pass on to their children. This opportunity was not possible in many of their home countries. Most Native Americans did not believe a person could own land. They commonly believed the spirits of the Earth allowed people to live there and the Earth was to be shared. Meanwhile, European kings gave away huge pieces of Native American land to their business associates. At first, Native Americans did not see a problem, as long as the white men were few in number and did not move into their hunting territory.
Dialogue: Decide what you will talk about. Some ideas: the different beliefs that Europeans and Native Americans had about land, what it means to "own" land.
Questions: What happens as more Europeans come to North America and "own" the land that the Native Americans have been living on? What could the two cultures do to get along? What do you do when someone else wants land you are living on and is willing to fight for it?

5 | Final Removal – Where are they now?

Date: Looking back from either 1920 or the present to 1840
Roles: Native Americans, Europeans
Setting: On a Native American reservation, looking back at what happened since 1835.
Facts: After the Europeans came to North America, they found that their views and the Native Americans' views were very different. European colonialism produced a competitive political climate that drove this expansion into native lands. European individuals seeking a new life also wanted to own the land that the Native Americans were living on. Wars between the French, British and Native Americans, ending with the war of 1812, decided the fate of the people and the land in the Great Lakes region.

Before the Europeans came to the region, Native Americans lived in villages all over the region. After the wars, from 1835 to 1850, the Native Americans were forcibly confined to tiny reservations where there was not enough food to support them. Other Native Americans were sent to harsh, dry areas where farming was extremely difficult for people accustomed to the Great Lakes woodlands. After the United States government sent the Native Americans from the Great Lakes region, it quickly filled up with European farms, factories, roads, towns and cities.

In the 20th century, Native Americans were granted sovereignty by the US government and now rule themselves as sovereign nations within the United State of America. There are currently over 550 sovereign nations or tribes of people that have formed their own governments and now make and enforce their own laws.

Today, Native Americans on reservations do a variety of things such as farm, have gardens, go to college and work. Some Native Americans still live in the Great Lakes region. Some tribes have revived some of their traditions and crafts. Not all Native Americans live on reservations; some live in cities and towns.

Dialogue: Decide what you will talk about. Some ideas: this could be told as a story by someone looking back at the history, the transition to a new place, what is missed about the "old" way of living, what hopes they have for the future, what they do now.
Questions: What might the Native Americans miss most about the way they originally lived near the Great Lakes? What do Native Americans do now on the reservation?

6 | Big Changes – farming, logging, fishing

Date: 1905
Roles: Farmer, logger, fisherman, Great Lakes fish
Setting: Underwater, fish meet to discuss the changes they see happening in the lakes.
Facts: By the mid-1800s, most of the Great Lakes region suitable to farming was settled by Europeans. There were about 400,000 people in Michigan, 300,000 in Wisconsin and about 500,000 in upper Canada. Wheat and corn were some of the first crops grown. As farming grew, crops were exported through the shipping industry. Soon dairy products and meat became strong commodities as well.
Farming: The rapid, large-scale clearing of the land for agriculture brought changes to the region. When land was stripped of vegetation, rich topsoil washed away into the lakes through streams and rivers. This clogged and altered rivers, and ruined fish habitat and spawning areas. Fertilizer run-off in the lakes stimulated algae growth. When algae died, its decomposition took oxygen from the water, which in turn, caused fish to die. When people began to use chemicals to kill crop pests such as insects, fungi and weeds, these chemicals also washed into the rivers and lakes. They continue to cause problems for humans, animals and plants today.
Logging: In the 1830s, people began to cut down trees in the region to sell for construction. Farmers who did not have work in winter generally did the cutting. They felled trees, then floated them down the rivers to the Great Lakes during the spring thaw. Later, specially designed ships transported the logs. Many of these trees were hundreds of years old and could not quickly be replaced. With the trees gone, soil eroded into the rivers and lakes, harming fish habitat and spawning areas.
Commercial Fishing: Catching fish to sell began in 1820 and grew every year. The largest fish harvests were in 1889 and 1899. Catches increased with more efficient equipment and more fishermen. It became too intense for the fish to keep up with. In the early 1900s, the total number of fish began to decrease. Overfishing, combined with pollution and fish habitat destruction, soon caused serious problems for Great Lakes fish populations.
Dialogue: What will be discussed? Ideas include: change over time, the increase in population, how Native American practices were different, the fact that farmers, loggers and fishermen all have families to support, assistance for the Great Lakes. What will the future hold for the Great Lakes? How do these changes impact the Great Lakes wildlife?

wrap-up

Discussion

1. What was similar about the European and the Native American people? *Wanted to live near the Great Lakes, used the area to survive, drank the same water, hunted and fished for the same animals, had families, felt emotions.*

2. What was different between these two groups? *Beliefs about land ownership, tools and weapons they used, diseases their bodies were able to withstand.*

3. How did the two groups treat the land and water differently? *Native Americans did not view land and water as goods to be bought and sold, they did not carry out activities that added chemicals or huge silt loads to the lakes, and there were fewer of them to impact the Great Lakes.*

4. What did you like or dislike about the scenes that were presented?

5. What can we learn from Great Lakes history to help us have a healthy relationship with the Great Lakes' water, land and people? *Every day we help create a new page in Great Lakes history. The choices we make and lifestyles we adopt make a difference.*

sources

Native Americans of the Great Lakes, Stuart A. Kallen, 2000
Great Lakes Country, Russell McKee

assessment

Rubric on page 386

 We value your thoughts and feedback on Great Lakes in My World. Please let us know about any oversights, errors or omissions you find, or if there are things you or your students particularly like.

Send your comments to: education@greatlakes.org

7 | 200 Years of Change

GRADE LEVEL
4-8

journal pages

FIRST NAME

LAST NAME

[1] Answer the following questions while creating and rehearsing your skit

a. What is your role in the skit?

b. Describe what is happening in your skit.

c. What emotions do the characters in your skit feel?

d. Would you make the same decisions as the characters in the skit? Why or why not?

[2] Answer the following questions after seeing the class performances

a. What was similar about the European and the Native American people?

b. What was different about these two groups?

c. How did the two groups treat the land and water differently?

d. What can we learn from Great Lakes history to help us maintain a healthy relationship between the Great Lakes' water, land and people?

APPROVED BY

INVESTIGATE

8 | Something's Fishy

GRADE LEVEL
6-8

90 minutes

summary

Students work in groups to examine a time period's interaction and influence on the Great Lakes fishery. They categorize the events of the time period and then present the information to the class, using discussion and diagrams to synthesize information and come to a historical understanding of the Great Lakes fishery.

objectives

- Discuss what it means to "eat locally."
- Categorize events from a time period.
- Present historical information to the class.
- Discuss the relative impact of events on the Great Lakes fishery.
- Create a diagram that synthesizes historical understanding of the Great Lakes fishery.

prerequisite

Who Needs the Lake?, Ways of Life and 200 Years of Change, Boats of Many Sizes

vocabulary

See next page

setting

INDOORS

subjects

Environmental Science, Social Studies

standards

This Great Lakes in My World activity is aligned to the Common Core State Standards and to state learning standards in:

Illinois
Indiana
Michigan
Minnesota
New York
Ohio
Pennsylvania
Wisconsin

This alignment is available on your Great Lakes in My World CD in the "Standards" folder and on-line at http://www.greatlakes.org/GLiMWstandards.

materials

- Journals
- Pencils
- Note cards, and three colored markers/pens (or different colored paper) for each student group of four
- Creature Cards

background: vocabulary

Bioregion: a region whose limits are naturally defined by topographic and biological features (such as mountains, watersheds and other ecosystems)

Commercial catch: fish that are taken out of the water by people to sell for use as food or other products

Commercial fishing: capture of large quantities of fish using nets, trawlers and/or lines in order to sell to others as a food product

Fishery: the activity or business of fishing; a place or establishment for catching fish; in the Great Lakes, the common resource of naturally reproducing and stocked fish species that moves across state and federal boundaries and supports a large sport fishing industry and a much smaller commercial fishing industry

Invasive species: plant or animal that is not native to an ecosystem and successfully competes against native species for food and shelter

Sport fishing: the pursuit and capture of game fish for the purpose of enjoyment and relaxation; may or may not include eating the fish caught

background

When you sit down at a seaside restaurant in many areas of the world, you are likely to see fresh fish on the menu every day. There's a good chance that the fish was swimming in the ocean within an hour or two of the place where you're ordering dinner. Yet in the Great Lakes region, where states are bounded by enormous lakes that hold 20% of the world's fresh surface water, it's a challenge to find fish that were freshly caught near home. What happened here?

When Europeans first arrived in the Great Lakes region, they were astounded at the variety of fish to be had in the Great Lakes. Giant lake trout and huge schools of yellow perch filled the nets of settlers. These fish were consumed locally as well as shipped out to major population centers for food. Ancient lake sturgeon were so abundant that, in the early 19th century, they were derided as "trash fish," burned as fuel, or simply allowed to rot on the shore. It was said that Atlantic salmon were so plentiful in Lake Ontario that they could be removed by hand.

In the mid-19th century, the Great Lakes states, which were undergoing a rapid transformation from prairie and forest to productive farmland, were a source of wood for construction. The abundant fisheries became the target of serious overfishing by commercial fishermen. Timber cutting devastated fish populations with a one-two punch of changes caused by floating logs in lakes, as well as through habitat alterations along streams that native fishes depend on. And the agriculture industry followed the deforestation with cultivation of newly open land for food, bringing with it the problem of eroding soil and contaminated runoff entering streams that supported native fish.

By the early 20th century, it was clear that something was very wrong in the Great Lakes. Catches of sturgeon, now commercially valuable, had plummeted. Atlantic salmon had been completely removed from Lake Ontario. States began to try their hand at fish stocking (adding fish to the lakes) with little success. As if the damage wrought by the 19th century wasn't enough, Great Lakes fish faced a host of new problems. Sea lamprey had reached the upper Great Lakes in large numbers due to the opening of the Welland Canal, and populations of this parasite were booming. Lampreys attach themselves to top predator fish like lake trout and whitefish, and cause damage to these fish that often results in death. Industrial chemicals such as dioxin were entering the Great Lakes from paper mills and other sources, making it difficult for lake trout to reproduce successfully. The flesh of many commercially important fish was contaminated with polychlorinated biphenyls, or PCBs. These byproducts of some of the manufacturing facilities located along the coast take many years to naturally degrade in the lakebottom sediments, and cause cancer in humans. To make up for the decline in native predator fish, state fishery managers began stocking Pacific salmon that ate another invasive species, the alewife. By the mid-20th century, the Great Lakes had fewer native fish than they ever had, and many of the fish that were left were unsafe to eat or embattled in a fight with the sea lamprey. The most abundant fish were artificially stocked and invasive species.

Several policies have figured into the stabilization of the problems with the Great Lakes fishery. In 1954, the *Convention on Great Lakes Fisheries* was signed by the United States and Canada. This agreement created the Great Lakes Fishery Commission, which immediately began an aggressive sea lamprey control program and developed shared fishery management goals for each Great Lake across state and international boundaries. The passage of the federal National Environmental Protection Act in 1969 and the Clean Water Act in 1972 granted protections to the Great Lakes from new inputs of chemicals like dioxin and PCBs, among others. The signing of the binational Great Lakes Water Quality Agreement in 1972 between the two Great Lakes countries set the stage for the eventual development of Remedial Action Plans (RAPs) that would help clean up the most contaminated sites in the lakes so they could no longer contribute toxic chemicals to the fish we eat.

Today, the Great Lakes fishery is still embattled, and it is unclear if the balance is shifting towards renewal or continued decline. Over 180 invasive species have established in the lakes, each of them causing distinct problems for one or more native species. While industrial pollution has greatly declined since the mid-20th century, pollution from agricultural sources continues to be a vexing problem in our streams

background continued

that carry water - and pollution - to the Great Lakes. Coastal wetland habitats that many fish rely on for reproduction have been destroyed or compromised by development. On the positive side, the small native populations of lake trout in Lake Superior are on the rebound, and there may be natural reproduction of lake trout occurring in Lake Michigan as well. State managers see an occasional leap in the numbers of yellow perch and walleye, two popular sportfishing species. But the fishery is still largely comprised of the millions of non-native salmonid fish stocked by the states each year, while low numbers of native top predators continue to struggle.

The history of the Great Lakes fishery can be divided into several time periods:

1. Early Times of Abundance:
   15,000 years ago to 1800 A.D. or Common Era (C.E.)
2. Changing Times:
   Exploitation and Degradation – 1800-1870s
3. Early Efforts of Regulations and Stocking: 1870s – 1890
4. Continued Efforts of Regulations and Stocking: 1890-1920
5. Era of New Invaders and Challenges: 1920 – 1930s

6. Continued Era of New Invaders and Challenges: 1930s – 1950s
7. New Problems and Recovery: 1960s - 1980s
8. Continued Time of New Problems and Recovery: 1980s - present

Changes that have affected the fishery can be categorized as social, technological, environmental, or some combination of these three (Suggested answers on p. 360 and 361.) All three of these changes may affect the economy:

S = Social Change: Any change in group behavior, attitude, policy, or politics.

T = Technological Change: Any change that results from a new invention, or which alters the ability of people to use tools.

E = Environmental Change: Any change in the Great Lakes habitat or human/fish populations that affects the health of the ecosystem.

In this activity, students investigate the impact of a specific time period on the Great Lakes fishery and present the information to the class.

procedure

1. Ahead of time, photocopy and cut up the different sections of "fishery time" for the student groups.

2. Ask students what it means to "eat locally." *Eating "bioregionally" means that individuals eat what is living (bio) within a certain area (region). This can be termed "eating locally." Prior to rapid transportation and refrigeration, people only ate what was from their region. In the Great Lakes area, native people and settlers ate a diet that consisted primarily of Great Lakes fish, meat from animals hunted locally, and fruits and vegetables grown in the region.* Ask students to create a list of fish they might eat from the Great Lakes. *They will probably struggle to create this list. Many of the fish we eat are from the ocean, and fish may not be a big part of students' diets.* Familiarize students with some Great Lakes fish by showing them the yellow perch, walleye, lake trout, and whitefish Creature Cards. Discuss the following: Why don't we eat fish from the Great Lakes as much as we used to? Should people be able to eat what grows and lives in the region?

3. Explain that students will do an activity that will show them the changes the Great Lakes have gone though in the past several hundred years that have impacted the fish

in the lakes. Assign students to eight small groups, and give each group a time period card and a stack of note cards. Depending on the size of the group, some time periods can be combined to create fewer stations. Have students write out one timeline event on each note card, then classify each event as positive, negative or having no impact on the health of the fishery. Also classify the events as having to do with technology, the environment, social change, or a combination.

4. Have students develop a creative way to orally present their time period to the class, highlighting what they think are the most important events. They will have 3-5 minutes to present the events during the following class period. Every student should participate in the oral presentation. Have the students post their note cards in chronological order along a class timeline once they have planned their presentation.

5. In the next class, students present their timeline sections to each other. Each presentation should include highlights from the time period, an explanation of which events seem most important to the Great Lakes fishery and a research question each student had after learning about this time period.

wrap-up

1. After listening to each other's presentations, look around the room at the changes that have been posted. How did we know there were problems in the Great Lakes fishery? Think about Lake Erie. Why did Lake Erie get singled out early on for its environmental problems? *Think about the size of Lake Erie as opposed to the other lakes. It is much smaller.* How does Lake Erie serve as a warning signal for the rest of the lakes? Which positive and negative changes seemed to have the biggest impact on the fishery? Have students discuss specific events. The changes were categorized as social, environmental and technological. Which kind of change seemed to have a larger impact than another?

2. Future Wheels: Have each student choose two changes that happened to the fishery. Write the change at the center of the page and draw lines toward words that answer the question: What did this change mean? Remember that changes and their results can be both positive and negative. As an example, choose one change and work through it on the board with the class.

Example:
One example that touches on many categories is an increase in human population.
An increase in human population means: more fishing, more eating of fish, fewer fish, more fish sales, more shipping, more invasive species
Another aspect of a growing human population could be: more farmers – more variety in food types – less fish being eaten

Other ideas might include:
Invasive species mean…
Canals mean….
War means…
Overfishing means…
People who care about the Great Lakes mean…

3. After creating the future wheels, discuss the following questions. What change(s) seems to have the most impact on Great Lakes fish? Discuss what caused the problems in the Great Lakes. *Ultimately, human action.* How did humans go about trying to solve the problems?

4. Have students write an answer for the following: How have humans both hurt and helped the Great Lakes? Give specific examples.

Future Wheels Example

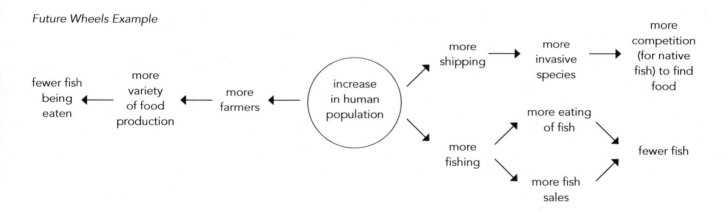

extension

1. Students write three to five questions that will require additional research on the Great Lakes fishery. Some aspect of the question and research must reflect back to impacts on the Great Lakes fishery. These questions can be used for class research projects that result in research papers or educational posters.

sources

Michigan Sea Grant: Life of the Lakes, Great Lakes Fisheries Timeline.

assessment

Rubric on page 386

Fisheries timeline (for teachers): Category answers provided below. For student "Fishery Time" cards, see following section.

S = Social Change: Any change in group behavior, attitude, policy, or politics.

T = Technological Change: Any change that results from a new invention, or which alters the ability of people to use tools.

E = Environmental Change: Any change in the Great Lakes habitat or human/fish populations that affects the health of the ecosystem.

Station #1 | Early Times of Abundance – 15,000 years ago to 1800 A.D. or C.E.

E 15,000 years ago: Glaciers retreat and the Great Lakes begin to take shape.

E/T 8,000-10,000 B.C. (Archaic Period) - Prehistoric people hunt, fish and gather food. Fishing is done with spears and hooks.

T 1,000 B.C. – 1600 A.D. or C.E. (Woodland Period) – Native people add nets and harpoons to fishing gear.

S 1600s: Europeans begin to explore the Great Lakes.

S 1700s: The French and British establish trading posts where fishing gear is traded.

S 1760s: French and Indian War (1754 – 1763) ends and Great Britain takes control of the region.

S 1770s – 1790s – U.S. Revolutionary War takes place. U.S./Canadian border is established.

S Throughout this era – The fishery is thought to be inexhaustible.

Station #2 | Changing Times: Exploitation and Degradation – 1800-1870s

S 1800: European settlement increases.

E 1812: After the War of 1812, the first commercial fisheries are established to serve eastern cities with salted fish.

E 1820s – 1830s: Fur trading begins to decline and fur companies convert to fishing.

T 1825: The Erie Canal opens, connecting Lake Ontario with the Atlantic Ocean.

T 1829: The Welland Canal opens, which allows ships to travel around Niagara Falls.

E/T 1830: The sea lamprey, an invasive species, is first reported. The lake trout population will be greatly reduced by the sea lamprey that feed on them.

S 1836: The Treaty of 1836 (Ottawa-Chippewa Treaty) transfers one of the largest tracts of land in the Great Lakes region from the Native Americans to the United States. Native Americans retain fishing and hunting rights.

E 1830s – 1840s: The Atlantic salmon is overfished in Lake Ontario. This raises great concerns in the region. (This fish was last seen in the Great Lakes in the late 1800s. Current Great Lakes salmon are non-native Pacific salmon).

E 1860s – 1870s: Logging activity peaks in the upper Great Lakes region. Logging waste, dammed streams and soil erosion negatively affect fish habitat.

E 1860s: Fish begin to decline in many areas of the Great Lakes. Fishing is prohibited in some areas.

Station #3 | Early and Continued Efforts of Regulations and Stocking: 1870s – 1918

S Late 1800s: Another wave of settlers arrives in the region. Some bring their fishing cultures and skills with them. Cities grow.

T 1870s: Shipbuilding begins using steel and steam engines in power tugboats. Machine-made nets replace handmade nets.

T 1875: Railroad cars carry frozen fish from the Great Lakes to the east coast.

E 1870 – 1890: Fish are raised in facilities called hatcheries. Fish are stocked (added) to the lakes to reverse declining populations.

E 1880s: Alewives begin to appear in the late 1800s.

E 1889: More than 10,000 people are fishing the lakes; over 146 million pounds (66.4 million kg) of fish are caught.

E Late 1880s – early 1900s: Arctic grayling and Atlantic salmon decline. Fewer blue pike, lake trout, lake whitefish and chubs are being caught in most lakes, particularly in Lake Erie. Lake sturgeon declines in all lakes between 1890 and 1910.

T 1900: Motorized net lifters are able to haul larger nets from the water. The Chicago Sanitary and Ship Canal is constructed, connecting the Great Lakes with the Mississippi watershed.

S Early 1900s: Governments in the Great Lakes region begin to adopt some regulations on fishing by setting limits and quotas on catches, restricting access to certain species, setting constraints on fishing gear and limits on who may fish.

S 1909: The Boundary Waters Treaty between the U.S. and Great Britain (in control of Canada) established the International Joint Commission to study water pollution in the Great Lakes and recommend solutions to the governments.

S 1914: Great Britain (ruling Canada) enters World War I and fishing in Canada is considered an essential service.

E 1915: The fish catch from the Great Lakes reaches an all-time high of 151 million pounds (68.6 million kilograms).

E 1918: Fish catches decline.

Station #4 | Era of New Invaders and Challenges: 1920s – 1950s

S 1920s and 1930s: Tourism and commercial fishing grow.

E 1920s – 1930s: Total fish catch levels off to less than 120 million pounds (54.5 million kilograms) per year until World War II. The Lake Erie lake herring population crashes.

S/E 1929: The U.S. stock market crashes and many fish wholesalers go broke (along with many other people in the U.S.).

S 1930: A Michigan court case rules that Native Americans have no special fishing and hunting rights under state regulations. Native American commercial fishermen have to purchase commercial state licenses.

T/S Mid 1930s: The unusually efficient bull-net is banned in most areas of the U.S. Great Lakes.

S Mid 1930s: There is wide spread acknowledgement that the fishery is in trouble. Lake Superior seems to have been spared.

E 1930s – 1940s: The non-native alewife and sea lamprey make their way in to the upper Great Lakes through the Welland Canal.

S 1939 – 1942: The US and Canada enter World War II. Fish demand is great. People fish more, but catch less.

E Late 1940s: The fishery is in bad shape and getting worse. By the 1950s the Lake Superior lake trout population is fed on by the sea lamprey and begins to collapse.

S 1954: The Convention on Great Lakes Fisheries was signed by the U.S. and Canada. This agreement created the Great Lakes Fishery Commission.

S/E 1955: The Great Lakes Fishery Commission, a partnership between the U.S. and Canada, is established. Initially, they cooperate to control the sea lamprey. Shared fishery management goals are developed for each Great Lake across state and international boundaries.

E Late 1950s: A chemical is applied to some Great Lakes streams to control the sea lamprey.

T 1959: The Saint Lawrence Seaway opens, allowing medium-sized international ocean-going vessels to travel to the Great Lakes.

Station #5| Time of New Problems and Recovery: 1960s - 1980s

E Early 1960s: The lake trout is lost, causing alewife populations to increase (normally eaten by the lake trout). Alewife die-offs (piles of dead alewives) litter beaches in the 1960s. This occasionally continues to happen in modern times.

E 1966: Pacific salmon are introduced into Lake Michigan to provide fishing opportunities and prey on the alewife.

Late 1960s: Mercury is acknowledged to be contaminating walleye in Lake Erie.

E 1969: The Cuyahoga River emptying into Lake Erie is so contaminated that it catches fire. Lake Erie is so polluted with sewage, agricultural and industrial pollution that it contains very little oxygen. The media proclaims Lake Erie "dead."

E 1969: The National Environmental Protection Act is passed, granting federal protections to the Great Lakes.

E 1970: The entire sport and commercial fisheries of Lake Erie are temporarily closed.

E 1970s: The U.S. and Canada ban the sale of DDT (an insecticide) and PCBs (chemicals which contaminate the Great Lakes).

S 1972: The U.S. and Canada sign the first Great Lakes Water Quality Agreement to protect and improve Great Lakes water quality by controlling sewage, industrial pollution and phosphorus. This sets the stage for the development of Remedial Action Plans (RAPs) that would help clean up the most contaminated sites in the lakes so they could no longer contribute toxic chemicals to the fish we eat.

E 1972: The Clean Water Act is passed protecting the Great Lakes from new chemicals inputs like dioxin and PCBs.

S Late 1970s and 1980s: Walleye rebound in Lake Erie. As other fish begin to make a comeback, the Great Lakes system is seen as resilient, able to "bounce back."

Station #6 | Continued Time of New Problems and Recovery: 1980s - present

S/E 1980: The Great Lakes Fishery Commission and several other groups implement a Joint Strategic Management Plan for the Great Lakes fishery.

S 1980s: The total economic impact of the Great Lakes sport fishery is estimated between $2-4 billion per year, and the recreational fishery supports over 60,000 jobs in the region.

S/E 1981: The Chippewa-Ottawa Treaty Fishery Management Authority is established to stabilize and enforce fishing regulations for tribal fishermen.

E 1981: Native American tribes and the U.S. government negotiate a settlement called the Entry of Consent Order, which grants tribes exclusive fishing rights in certain treaty waters. In exchange, the tribes agree not to fish commercially in certain areas important for sport fishing or for re-establishing lake trout populations.

E Mid 1980s: Invasive species alert! The zebra mussel arrives via a ship from the ocean. It is native to the Baltic Sea. Zebra mussels proceed to eat a great deal of plankton (plankton is the base of the food chain, upon which many other fish depend), affecting yellow perch populations. In addition, mussels clog water intake pipes, causing expensive maintenance issues. Also, a new exotic species, the spiny water flea (a type of zooplankton) arrives in Lake Huron and spreads throughout the Great Lakes.

E 1989: More invasive species?! The quagga mussel is spotted in the Great Lakes. At first sight it seemed a larger zebra mussel, however, by 1991 it was verified to be a quagga mussel (a new invader).

E 1990: Licensed commercial catch in the Great Lakes is 105 million pounds (47.7 million kilograms) of mostly lake whitefish, yellow perch and alewife. The catch is largest in Canada.

E 1990s: Concentrations of PCBs, DDT and other contaminants in fish decline over 90% from the levels recorded in 1970.

S/E 2008: The ballast water treatment standards bill passes through the House and Senate, helping to eliminate the transportation of invasive species.

E 2010: Asian carp finally make their first appearance within the Great Lakes, (bighead carp) and the region braces for more to come.

Student Page

Station #1 | Early Times of Abundance – 15,000 years ago to 1800 A.D. or C.E.

15,000 years ago: Glaciers retreat and the Great Lakes begin to take shape.

8,000-10,000 B.C .(Archaic Period) - Prehistoric people hunt, fish and gather food. Fishing is done with spears and hooks.

1,000 BC – 1600 A.D. or C.E. (Woodland Period) – Native people add nets and harpoons to fishing gear.

1600s: Europeans begin to explore the Great Lakes.

1700s: The French and British establish trading posts where fishing gear is traded.

1760s: French and Indian War (1754 – 1763) ends and Great Britain takes control of the region.

1770s – 1790s – U.S. Revolutionary War takes place. U.S./Canadian border is established.

Throughout this era – The fishery is thought to be inexhaustible.

Station #2 | Changing Times: Exploitation and Degradation – 1800-1870s

1800: European settlement increases.

1812: After the War of 1812, the first commercial fisheries are established to serve eastern cities with salted fish.

1820s – 1830s: Fur trading begins to decline and fur companies convert to fishing.

1825: The Erie Canal opens, connecting Lake Ontario with the Atlantic Ocean.

1829: The Welland Canal opens, which allows ships to travel around Niagara Falls.

1830: The sea lamprey, an invasive species, is first reported. The lake trout population will be greatly reduced by the sea lamprey that feed on them.

1836: The Treaty of 1836 (Ottawa-Chippewa Treaty) transfers one of the largest tracts of land in the Great Lakes region from the Native Americans to the United States. Native Americans retain fishing and hunting rights.

1830s – 1840s: The Atlantic salmon is overfished in Lake Ontario. This raises great concerns in the region. (This fish was last seen in the Great Lakes in the late 1800s. Current Great Lakes salmon are non-native Pacific salmon).

1860s – 1870s: Logging activity peaks in the upper Great Lakes region. Logging waste, dammed streams and soil erosion negatively affect fish habitat.

1860s: Fish begin to decline in many areas of the Great Lakes. Fishing is prohibited in some areas.

Station #3 | Early and Continued Efforts of Regulations and Stocking: 1870s – 1918

Late 1800s: Another wave of settlers arrives in the region. Some bring their fishing cultures and skills with them. Cities grow.

1870s: Shipbuilding begins using steel and steam engines in power tugboats. Machine-made nets replace handmade nets.

1875: Railroad cars carry frozen fish from the Great Lakes to the east coast.

1870 – 1890: Fish are raised in facilities called hatcheries. Fish are stocked (added) to the lakes to reverse declining populations.

1880s: Alewives begin to appear in the late 1800s.

1889: More than 10,000 people are fishing the lakes; over 146 million pounds (66.4 million kg) of fish are caught.

Late 1880s – early 1900s: Arctic grayling and Atlantic salmon decline. Fewer blue pike, lake trout, lake whitefish and chubs are being caught in most lakes, particularly in Lake Erie. Lake sturgeon declines in all lakes between 1890 and 1910.

1900: Motorized net lifters are able to haul larger nets from the water. The Chicago Sanitary and Ship Canal is constructed, connecting the Great Lakes with the Mississippi watershed.

Early 1900s: Governments in the Great Lakes region begin to adopt some regulations on fishing by setting limits and quotas on catches, restricting access to certain species, setting constraints on fishing gear, and limits on who may fish.

1909: The Boundary Waters Treaty between the U.S. and Great Britain (in control of Canada) established the International Joint Commission to study water pollution in the Great Lakes and recommend solutions to the governments.

1914: Great Britain (ruling Canada) enters World War I and fishing in Canada is considered an essential service.

1915: The fish catch from the Great Lakes reaches an all-time high of 151 million pounds (68.6 million kilograms).

1918: Fish catches decline.

Station #4 | Era of New Invaders and Challenges: 1920s – 1950s

1920s and 1930s: Tourism and commercial fishing grow.

1920s – 1930s: Total fish catch levels off to less than 120 million pounds (54.5 million kilograms) per year until World War II. The Lake Erie lake herring population crashes.

1929: The U.S. stock market crashes and many fish wholesalers go broke (along with many other people in the U.S.).

1930: A Michigan court case rules that Native Americans have no special fishing and hunting rights under state regulations. Native American commercial fishermen have to purchase commercial state licenses.

Mid 1930s: The unusually efficient bull-net is banned in most areas of the U.S. Great Lakes.

Mid 1930s: There is wide spread acknowledgement that the fishery is in trouble. Lake Superior seems to have been spared.

1930s – 1940s: The non-native alewife and sea lamprey make their way in to the upper Great Lakes through the Welland Canal.

Student Page

1939 – 1942: The U.S. and Canada enter World War II. Fish demand is great. People fish more, but catch less.

Late 1940s: The fishery is in bad shape and getting worse. By the 1950s the Lake Superior lake trout population is fed on by the sea lamprey and begins to collapse.

1954: The Convention on Great Lakes Fisheries was signed by the U.S. and Canada. This agreement created the Great Lakes Fishery Commission.

1955: The Great Lakes Fishery Commission, a partnership between the U.S. and Canada, is established. Initially, they cooperate to control the sea lamprey. Shared fishery management goals are developed for each Great Lake across state and international boundaries.

Late 1950s: A chemical is applied to some Great Lakes streams to control the sea lamprey.

1959: The Saint Lawrence Seaway opens, allowing medium-sized international ocean-going vessels to travel to the Great Lakes.

Station #5 | Time of New Problems and Recovery: 1960s - 1980s

Early 1960s: The lake trout is lost, causing alewife populations to increase (normally eaten by the lake trout). Alewife die-offs (piles of dead alewives) litter beaches in the 1960s. This occasionally continues to happen in modern times.

1966: Pacific salmon are introduced into Lake Michigan to provide fishing opportunities and prey on the alewife.

Late 1960s: Mercury is acknowledged to be contaminating walleye in Lake Erie.

1969: The Cuyahoga River emptying into Lake Erie is so contaminated that it catches fire. Lake Erie is so polluted with sewage, agricultural and industrial pollution that it contains very little oxygen. The media proclaims Lake Erie "dead."

1969: The National Environmental Protection Act is passed, granting federal protections to the Great Lakes.

1970: The entire sport and commercial fisheries of Lake Erie are temporarily closed.

1970s: The U.S. and Canada ban the sale of DDT (an insecticide) and PCBs (chemicals which contaminate the Great Lakes).

1972: The U.S. and Canada sign the first Great Lakes Water Quality Agreement to protect and improve Great Lakes water quality by controlling sewage, industrial pollution and phosphorus. This sets the stage for the development of Remedial Action Plans (RAPs) that would help clean up the most contaminated sites in the lakes so they could no longer contribute toxic chemicals to the fish we eat.

1972: The Clean Water Act is passed protecting the Great Lakes from new chemicals inputs like dioxin and PCBs.

Late 1970s and 1980s: Walleye rebound in Lake Erie. As other fish begin to make a comeback, the Great Lakes system is seen as resilient, able to "bounce back."

Station #6 | Continued Time of New Problems and Recovery: 1980s - present

1980: The Great Lakes Fishery Commission and several other groups implement a Joint Strategic Management Plan for the Great Lakes fishery.

1980s: The total economic impact of the Great Lakes sport fishery is estimated between $2-4 billion per year, and the recreational fishery supports over 60,000 jobs in the region.

1981: The Chippewa-Ottawa Treaty Fishery Management Authority is established to stabilize and enforce fishing regulations for tribal fishermen.

1981: Native American tribes and the U.S. government negotiate a settlement called the Entry of Consent Order, which grants tribes exclusive fishing rights in certain treaty waters. In exchange, the tribes agree not to fish commercially in certain areas important for sport fishing or for re-establishing lake trout populations.

Mid 1980s: Invasive species alert! The zebra mussel arrives via a ship from the ocean. It is native to the Baltic Sea. Zebra mussels proceed to eat a great deal of plankton (plankton is the base of the food chain, upon which many other fish depend), affecting yellow perch populations. In addition, mussels clog water intake pipes, causing expensive maintenance issues. Also, a new exotic species, the spiny water flea (a type of zooplankton) arrives in Lake Huron and spreads throughout the Great Lakes.

1989: More invasive species?! The quagga mussel is spotted in the Great Lakes. At first sight it seemed a larger zebra mussel, however, by 1991 it was verified to be a quagga mussel (a new invader).

1990: Licensed commercial catch in the Great Lakes is 105 million pounds (47.7 million kilograms) of mostly lake whitefish, yellow perch and alewife. The catch is largest in Canada.

1990s: Concentrations of PCBs, DDT and other contaminants in fish decline over 90% from the levels recorded in 1970.

2008: The ballast water treatment standards bill passes through the House and Senate, helping to eliminate the transportation of invasive species.

2010: Asian carp finally make their first appearance within the Great Lakes, (bighead carp) and the region braces for more to come.

8 | Something's Fishy

GRADE LEVEL
6-8

FIRST NAME																				
LAST NAME																				

[1] Which time period are you working on?

....

[2] Read the events and make decisions about each one. Abbreviate and record each event
on a separate note card. If you abbreviate, make sure it is understandable to all.
- If it is related to technology, write it in black.
- If it is related to the environment, write it in green.
- If it is a social change, write it in red.
- On each note card, mark a '+' if it is positive for the health of the fishery,
a '-' if it is negative for the health of the fishery, and a '0' if it does not
cause a change for the fishery.
- Post the note cards in chronological order on the class timeline.

[3] How many of each kind of change do you have in your time period?

....

....

[4] What do these changes mean overall for the Great Lakes fishery?

....

....

[5] Which events had the greatest impact on the health of the Great Lakes fishery?

....

....

[6] How will you creatively present the fishery information from your timeline to the
class? Everyone in the group must participate in the presentation. Decide on roles
for each person.

....

....

....

Future Wheels
[7] Choose 1 or 2 changes that happened to the Great Lakes fishery and
create Future Wheels for each. Use separate paper if needed.

APPROVED BY	

INVESTIGATE

9 | Water Quality Over Time

GRADE LEVEL
6-8

90 minutes

summary

Students circulate through stations to answer questions, learn about the history of water quality in the Great Lakes watershed and discuss their conclusions with the class.

objectives

- Discuss the importance and role of water in students' lives.
- List reasons the Great Lakes have been important to people in the region over time.
- Identify ways humans have degraded and improved Great Lakes water quality.
- Demonstrate an understanding of the factors, including population, that have had a major impact on Great Lakes water quality.

prerequisite

Who Needs the Lakes?, 200 Years of Change

vocabulary

Areas of Concern: Seriously contaminated sites in the Great Lakes. These toxic hotspots impair beneficial uses of the Great Lakes by causing harm to wildlife, habitat and drinking water
Biomagnification: Concentrations of chemicals become magnified and more powerful as larger animals eat them

setting

INDOORS

subjects

Environmental Science, History

standards

This Great Lakes in My World activity is aligned to the Common Core State Standards and to state learning standards in:

Illinois
Indiana
Michigan
Minnesota
New York
Ohio
Pennsylvania
Wisconsin

This alignment is available on your Great Lakes in My World CD in the "Standards" folder and on-line at http://www.greatlakes.org/GLiMWstandards.

materials

- Journals
- Pencils
- Art supplies
- Graph paper

background

The abundance of clean water in the Great Lakes is a major reason that humans have settled here over time. However, maintaining water quality has proven a challenge for humans. Prior to 1600, the Great Lakes Basin population is estimated at 250,000 Native American people (although some estimates are higher). As Europeans began to settle in the area, the population grew and industry intensified, which caused the water quality to decline for several reasons. The exploding population challenged communities' and the lakes' abilities to handle sewage. The fertile farming land of the region was treated with chemical fertilizers and pesticides that carried chemicals to streams, groundwater, and the lakes. The rich forests around the lakes supplied the wood for the paper and pulp industry, which discharged chlorine compounds and other waste into the air and lakes. Eventually, positive actions began to counteract the damage done to the Great Lakes water quality.

In this activity, important Great Lakes events and people are mentioned very briefly, due to the nature of a timeline. Consider having students research some of these events and people and report to the class on them.

procedure

1. Advanced preparation: Photocopy the timeline information in this activity, and cut it into the eight sections. Put the information for each section at a different spot in the classroom in a chronological order.
2. Have students create a list of the first five things they did this morning after getting out of bed. *Possible lists might include: brushing teeth, taking a shower/washing up, eating breakfast and getting dressed.* Ask students to raise their hands if their list included the use of water. Discuss the importance of water. How else do we depend on it? Where does this water come for students living in the Great Lakes watershed? *The Great Lakes or connected aquifers and groundwater.*
3. Read the following description of the condition of Lake Erie in the 1970s:
   "In the 1970s, it was reported that 'Lake Erie is dead.' In fact, the opposite was true. Lake Erie was clogged with algae due to the abnormally high amount of phosphorous put into the lake by human activities. Phosphorus is a common nutrient found in nature. Unfortunately, it's also found in sewage, fertilizers and detergent – and when an excessive amount enters a lake, the growth of algae and other aquatic plants can explode. This becomes a problem when those plants die, because their decay consumes huge amounts of oxygen. Very little oxygen – if any – remains for the lake's fish. Thus, the fish populations decline, with some species disappearing altogether."
4. Ask students how they think the water quality of Lake Erie is today. *Much improved, but still needs more help.* Tell students they will be finding out about what caused the decline and improvement in Lake Erie and the other Great Lakes.
5. Assign students to small groups and have each group stand at one of the eight stations around the room. Tell them to find the corresponding station number in the journal pages. Give the students about 5-10 minutes at each station to answer the questions, depending on the groups and the amount of time available. Rotate clockwise until each group has visited each station. Because students will be starting at various places in the timeline, make sure they are moving chronologically forward to minimize confusion.

wrap-up

1. Have students complete the journal pages. Graph the population over time using the numbers the students have recorded. Talk about what the graph reveals. Discuss: How did population impact the Great Lakes over time?
2. Think about the timeline: How did we know there were problems in the Great Lakes? What were the signs or indicators? Discuss what caused the problems in the Great Lakes. *Ultimately, human action.* How did humans go about trying to solve the problems?
3. Have students answer the following in writing: How have humans both hurt and helped the Great Lakes? Give specific examples.

assessment

Rubric on page 386

sources

International Joint Commission, Twenty-fifth Anniversary of the Great Lakes Water Quality Agreement publication, 1997.

resources

For additional information, see the International Joint Commission's web site at: www.ijc.org/en/summit

For information on the Chicago River: Chicago Public Library http://www.chipublib.org/cplbooksmovies/cplarchive/timeline/index.php

Friends of the Chicago River http://chicagoriver.org/education/curricula/lesson_plans/

Timeline

#1 | 1600s and before

Note: Native Americans have been living in the region since the ending of the last Ice Age, about 10,000 years ago.

Before 1600: estimated at 250,000 Native American people, (although some estimates are considerably higher)

1612-1615: French explorer Etienne Brulé reaches Lake Huron and Lake Ontario.

1622: Etienne Brulé reaches Lake Superior.

1634: French explorer Jean Nicolet reaches Lake Michigan.

1669: French explorer Louis Joliet reaches Lake Erie.

#2 | 1800s

1825: The Erie Canal, which stretches from Albany to Buffalo, New York (363 miles/584 kilometers), opens, which brings large numbers of settlers west to the Great Lakes.

1829: The Welland Canal (27 miles and 44 km) opens, connecting Lake Erie and Ontario and bypassing Niagara Falls.

1850: Population: 1.2 million

1854: Chicago, Illinois experiences a cholera epidemic because of sewage contamination in the drinking water.

1870: Hamilton, Ontario has a water contamination problem and can no longer draw drinking water from Hamilton Harbor on Lake Ontario.

1891: Chicago experiences a typhoid epidemic because of drinking water contamination.

#3 | 1900 - 1950

1900: Population: 11.5 million

1900: The Chicago River is reversed. It once flowed into Lake Michigan. Early sewerage systems dumped waste into Lake Michigan or into the Chicago River, which flowed into the lake, the drinking water supply. People got sick and were dying as a result of this contamination. Engineers then reversed the river to flow into the Mississippi River as it does today. Sewage continues to be dumped into the Chicago River, but the river no longer flows into Lake Michigan, the present day source of the region's drinking water.

1909: Boundary Water Treaty signed to prevent and resolve disputes over water quality and water levels in the rivers and lakes along the U.S./Canada border.

1910: Population: 12.5 million

1911: First meeting of the International Joint Commission, a group of U.S. and Canadian Commissioners in charge of addressing water quality issues. This group came together as a result of the Boundary Waters Treaty.

1930: Population 17.4 million

#4 | What problems were developing in the Great Lakes?

As Europeans began to settle in the Great Lakes area in the 1800s and 1900s, the population grew and industry intensified. This caused the water quality to decline for several reasons. The exploding population challenged communities' and the lakes' abilities to handle sewage. The fertile farming land of the region was treated with fertilizers and pesticides that washed into streams, the groundwater and lakes. The rich forests around the lakes supplied wood for the paper and pulp industry, which discharged chlorine compounds and other waste into the air and lakes.

#5 | 1950-1970

1950: Population 22.7 million

1950 – 1960: Bald eagle and double-crested cormorant populations decrease due to eggshells becoming thin. Why did this happen? When the chemical DDT was sprayed on crops to control insect damage, it washed into rivers, lakes and streams, where it entered the food chain. There it was absorbed by plants and small animals that were consumed by fish. Eagles, cormorants and other large birds of prey ate the contaminated fish. The main effect of DDT poisoning on birds was that it interfered with eggshell production, and the resulting shells were not strong enough to be incubated.

1959: St. Lawrence Seaway opens.

1962: Rachel Carson writes Silent Spring, a book warning that insecticides/pesticides are toxic to humans and animals.

1969: Cuyahoga River (which flows into Lake Erie) near Cleveland catches fire due to the oil and debris floating on top of the river. During the welding of a bridge, a spark from a welder's torch causes the fire.

#6 | 1970-1980
1970: Population 30.8 million
1971: Deformities such as crossed bills, club feet, and missing eyes are observed in common tern chicks in Hamilton Bay, Lake Ontario.
1972: On December 31, it becomes illegal to use DDT.
1972: Canada and the United States sign the Great Lakes Water Quality Agreement and the United States passes the Clean Water Act.
1977: Breeding success of bald eagles and double-crested cormorants begins to improve.
1978: Great Lakes Water Quality Agreement is renewed and strengthened, with the U.S. and Canada agreeing to "virtually eliminate" the discharge of toxic substances to the Great Lakes.

#7 | 1980-1990
1980: Negative physical and behavior differences are found in Michigan infants whose mothers ate Great Lakes fish.
1986: Great Lakes governors sign the Great Lakes Toxic Substance Control Agreement to try and reduce the amount of dangerous chemicals entering the lake.
1987: Canada and the U.S. create list of Areas of Concern (42 originally) and agree to develop plans to help communities clean up areas that are especially contaminated.
1988: Canada develops a new Environmental Protection Plan.
1990: Population 33 million
1990: Negative behavior differences found in New York infants whose mothers ate Great Lakes fish.

#8 | 1990 – 2000
1990: Report states that exposure to toxic substances is a threat to children's health.
1991: U.S.-Canada Air Quality Agreement calls for a reduction in acid rain.
1994: Collingwood Harbour, Ontario on Lake Huron is cleaned up. It is the first site on the list of "Areas of Concern" to be cleaned up. This cleanup involved dredging (digging) out the contaminants from the bottom of the lakes.
  Area of Concern: Seriously contaminated sites in the Great Lakes. These toxic hotspots impair beneficial uses of the Great Lakes by causing harm to wildlife, habitat and drinking water.
1995: The U.S. Environmental Protection Agency made a plan to restore the health of the Great Lakes. This plan is called the Great Lakes Initiative and was agreed to by the Great Lakes states.
1997: The Great Lakes Water Quality Initiative is implemented in all states and regulation of water quality begins.
2000 Population: 34 million (based on 2000 census information)

#9 | 2000 – 2010*
2004: Great Lakes Water Quality Agreement (which began in 1972) is reviewed and updated.
2005: Senate Bill 332 requires ocean ships to kill ballast water invasive species using environmentally sound technology.
2006: Great Lakes Regional Collaboration issued the GLRC Implementation Framework to describe how the GLRC will be organized to ensure that the shared commitment to protect and restore the Great Lakes is met in an ongoing manner.
2008: The Great Lakes – St. Lawrence River Basin Water Resources Compact receives its final revisions and signatures. The Compact seeks to ban the diversion of Great Lakes water, with some limited exceptions, and set responsible standards for water use and conservation within the basin.
2010: Great Lakes Restoration Initiative (GLRI) made restoring the Great Lakes a national priority when President Obama allocated $475 million to the nation's largest fresh surface water ecosystem. The initiative, led by the EPA, seeks to stop invasive species from entering the lakes, clean up beaches, remove toxic pollution and restore fish and wildlife habitat.

*At time of printing the Census data for 2010 had not yet been published

9 | Water Quality Over Time

GRADE LEVEL
6-8

journal   pages

FIRST NAME																	
LAST NAME																	

#1 | 1600s and before

[1] Record the population:

[2] Before 1600, only Native American people lived in the Great Lakes region. Why do you think Native Americans chose to live near the Great Lakes? How are these reasons different from or similar to the reasons we live here today?

[3] Write a sentence about how your life would have been if you were the explorer that discovered one of the Great Lakes.

#2 | 1800s

[1] Record the population:

[2] What do canals have to do with the change in population?

[3] People who live near the Great Lakes have always counted on them for drinking water. What do you think happened to contaminate the drinking water during the disease epidemics during this time? (Hint: What happens to your water when you flush the toilet? What do you think happened in the late 1800s?)

#3 | 1900 - 1950

[1] Record the population in 1900, 1910 and 1930:

[2] Name one good thing and one bad thing about the reversal of the Chicago River.

[3] In your opinion, what is the most positive event that happens during this time period? Why?

APPROVED BY	

9 | Water Quality Over Time

GRADE LEVEL
6-8

FIRST NAME																			
LAST NAME																			

#4 | What problems were developing in the Great Lakes?
[1] What were two jobs people were doing during this time, based on the paragraph
      provided?
....

....

[2] What problems were industries causing?
....

....

....

[3] In what ways was population growth affecting the Great Lakes?
....

....

....

#5 | 1950-1970
[1] Record the population:
....

[2] Some facts:
      a. Bald eagles and mink eat fish, small mammals and frogs.
      b. Fish, small mammals and frogs eat plants, insects and small fish.
      c. Plants, insects and small fish eat or absorb chemicals in the Great Lakes.
      d. Concentrations of chemicals become magnified and more powerful
         (biomagnification) as larger animals eat them.

Use the facts to explain why you think bald eagle, double crested cormorant and mink
populations were declining.
....

....

....

....

....

[3] How is <u>Silent Spring</u> related to question #2?
....

....

....

APPROVED BY	

9 | Water Quality Over Time

GRADE LEVEL
6-8

journal pages

FIRST NAME

LAST NAME

#6 | 1970-1980
[1] Record the population:

....

[2] There is good and bad news for wildlife during this time. How do you explain this?

....

[3] Why do you think Canada and the United States worked together to improve water quality?

....

#7 | 1980-1990
[1] Record the population:

....

[2] When certain chemicals are released into the environment, they can make their way
into the food chain and accumulate to dangerous levels. This begins on the bottom
level of the food chain, with numerous small, contaminated organisms being eaten by
a group of animals. When a predator feeds upon that group of animals, all those
chemicals enter its body – and may remain. After a period of time, a dangerous
amount of chemicals can build up, and this may affect offspring. The effects depend
upon the type of chemical involved, the predator involved and the amount consumed.
How do you think this affected the infants whose mothers ate Great Lakes fish?

....

....

....

[3] List the ways humans tried to solve the problems in the Great Lakes during this
time period.

....

#8 | 1990 - 2000
[1] Record the population:

....

[2] Why do you think we needed the Great Lakes Water Quality Initiative?

....

[3] List three ways that poor water quality would affect you and your family or friends.

....

APPROVED BY

9 | Water Quality Over Time

GRADE LEVEL
6-8

FIRST NAME																				
LAST NAME																				

#9 | 2000-2010

[1] Record the population (research online):

....

[2] How was the Great Lakes Restoration Initiative (GLRI) beneficial to the region?

....

....

....

....

[3] The Great Lakes Restoration Initiative brought groups throughout the region together. What restoration projects do you think will be undertaken by groups in your state?

....

....

....

....

....

PART TWO

[1] Graph the population over time using the numbers you have recorded. (use graph paper)

[2] On a separate sheet of paper describe how humans have both helped and hurt the Great Lakes. Give specific examples.

APPROVED BY	

INVESTIGATE: FINAL PROJECT

10 | A Day in the Life

GRADE LEVEL

K-3

several days

summary

Students create a poster that reflects a different cultural time period within the Great Lakes region. They draw pictures and write about the daily life of the people and how that population viewed and used the lakes.

objectives

- Discuss the importance of learning historical information.
- Describe a culture that lived in the Great Lakes region.
- Describe how a long-ago culture depended on the Great Lakes.

prerequisite

Age appropriate activities in this unit will give students necessary background.

vocabulary

None

setting

INDOORS

subjects

Social Studies, History

standards

This Great Lakes in My World activity is aligned to the Common Core State Standards and to state learning standards in:

Illinois
Indiana
Michigan
Minnesota
New York
Ohio
Pennsylvania
Wisconsin

This alignment is available on your Great Lakes in My World CD in the "Standards" folder and on-line at http://www.greatlakes.org/GLiMWstandards.

materials

- Pencils, pens, markers, colored pencils
- Poster board
- Books on Great Lakes history (see resource list for suggestions)

background

Communicating information is an essential part of being human. Over time, humans learn, remember and grow by telling and comparing stories. In this project, students focus on the Native American lifestyle for their poster. Choose a Native American group from your region for students to learn about. Read them stories about the time period in order for them to gain information for their posters. They will complete a poster that conveys information about a culture of people. Students can work in teams or individually.

procedure

1. Ask students to think about a first or very early memory and share it with a partner. Have students explain why they think this memory has stayed with them. Discuss the importance of memory with the class. Why is important to remember things? *To learn, to improve upon what we do, to not repeat mistakes, to laugh, to reflect on how we became who we are, to celebrate accomplishments.*

2. Ask students to think about someone in their lives who has lived longer and seen more of life. How might their memories be different from students' memories? What kinds of things might they have experienced? When an event is older than our memory, how do we learn about the past? *Diaries, photographs, newspapers, letters, people that are still living, encyclopedias, books, magazine articles, internet.* Ask students to think about the different ways that people learn about what is happening in the world. *TV, internet, radio, word of mouth, newspaper.*

3. Tell students they will learn about some people who lived near the Great Lakes long ago and they will make a poster that tells about them. If they are unclear on how posters can be used to convey knowledge, discuss movie posters and how they give information to people. Choose a Native American group that was living in your area to focus on.

4. Read stories to the students about the tribe you have selected. Use your school or local library to find books, including those listed in the history section of the resource list for this curriculum. For K-1, discuss the items on the journal pages. For 2-3, have each students complete the journal pages.

5. Based on the research done to complete the journal pages, students (individually or in groups) create a poster, incorporating the items discussed, with older students responsible for more detail. Tell students they will evaluate each other's work. Use the activity rubric to discuss criteria.

wrap-up

1. Students can rotate stations to look at each other's posters or they can present them to each other. Students should be extremely careful if they are handling each other's work.

2. At each station they will view each other's posters. Older students should complete the final questions in the Journal Pages.

3. Discuss the ways Native American groups depend on the Great Lakes and compare this with the students' current relationship with the Great Lakes.

4. Have the students discuss what they learned from their own and other students' posters.

assessment

Rubric on page 387

! We value your thoughts and feedback on Great Lakes in My World. Please let us know about any oversights, errors or omissions you find, or if there are things you or your students particularly like.

Send your comments to: education@greatlakes.org

10 | A Day in the Life

GRADE LEVEL
K-3

journal pages

FIRST NAME																			
LAST NAME																			

Write down what you find out.
[1] Group of people you are learning about:

....

Food
[2] What food did these people eat?

....

....

....

....

[3] Where did their food come from?

....

....

....

....

Housing
[4] On separate paper, draw a picture of what the houses looked like.

[5] What were the houses made of?

....

....

....

Transportation
[6] How did people get around?

....

....

....

Clothing
[7] What did people wear?

....

....

....

APPROVED BY	

10 | A Day in the Life

GRADE LEVEL
K-3

journal pages

FIRST NAME																		
LAST NAME																		

Lake

[8] How did they depend on the lake?

....

....

....

....

Fun

[9] What did they do for fun?

....

....

....

....

Beliefs

[10] What were important beliefs to these people?

....

....

....

....

[11] What are two things you like about another poster?

Who made this poster? ....

a. ....

....

b. ....

....

[12] What are two things you would improve about another poster?

a. ....

....

b. ....

....

APPROVED BY	

INVESTIGATE

11 | Sign of the Times

GRADE LEVEL

4-8

Several days

summary

Students create newspapers that reflect different time periods within the Great Lakes region. They research and write articles that show how different populations viewed the lakes and how their lifestyles affected the health of the lake system.

objectives

- Discuss the importance of conveying historical information.
- Research a time period in the Great Lakes.
- Write articles that pertain to a historical time period.
- Reflect on people's relationships with the Great Lakes over time.
- Evaluate others' work.

prerequisite

Age appropriate activities in this unit will give students necessary background.

vocabulary

None

setting

INDOORS

subjects

Social Studies, History, Environmental Science

standards

This Great Lakes in My World activity is aligned to the Common Core State Standards and to state learning standards in:

Illinois
Indiana
Michigan
Minnesota
New York
Ohio
Pennsylvania
Wisconsin

This alignment is available on your Great Lakes in My World CD in the "Standards" folder and on-line at http://www.greatlakes.org/ GLiMWstandards.

materials

- Research materials (see resource list for suggestions, "Where Have We Been?" handout on p. 380)
- Computers to type stories and internet access for research
- Pencils, pens, markers, colored pencils
- Poster board or large paper for newspaper

background

Communicating and learning from information is an essential part of being human. Over time, humans learn, remember, and grow by telling and comparing stories. In this project, students compare several time periods by creating a newspaper that reflects a specific time in Great Lakes history. Students will compare time periods in the region by reading each other's newspaper articles. This can be done by assigning each group of four students a time period (six time periods provided on the Where Have We Been? handout), or by having the class as a whole work on one or two time periods that are currently being studied, to create newspapers. The latter approach works well if there is a particular time period that is part of the curriculum. Great Lakes history can be divided up into the categories on the Where Have We Been? handout in the Journal Pages. Another option for grouping students is to use the groups and background information from Who Needs the Lakes?

procedure

1. Ask students to think about their first, or a very early memory. Students share this memory with a partner. Have students offer an explanation for why they think this particular memory has stayed with them. Discuss the importance of memory with the class. Why is it important to remember things? *To learn, to improve upon what we do, to not repeat mistakes, to laugh, to reflect on how we became who we are, to celebrate accomplishments.* Ask students to think about someone in their lives who has lived longer and seen more of life. How are their memories different from students' memories? What kinds of things might they have experienced?

2. When an event is older than our memory, how do we preserve it or find out about it? Have students list possible ways: *diaries, photographs, newspapers, letters, people that are still living.* Ask students to list sources that report information but do not come from the time period they address: *encyclopedias, books, magazine articles, internet.* Ask students to think about the different ways that people learn about what is happening in the world today: *TV, the internet, radio, word of mouth, newspaper.*

3. Tell students they will be taking on the role of a person from a certain time period in order to share Great Lakes news about what was happening at that time. Although many cultures would not have used a newspaper, that is the format all groups will be using for this project. The newspaper can be completed on paper or as a web site, depending on capabilities and resources. Each person in the group will write at least two articles for the newspaper. In addition, they will take on one of the additional roles listed below.

4. Give students the Where Have We Been? background information handout. Assign each group a time period or let them choose.

5. In small groups, have students make and record decisions.

6. Peer editing: As students write their articles, they can pair up and read each other's article to help with the process. They answer the questions:

- What spelling and grammar changes do you recommend?
- What are two pieces of advice you can give to your partner to improve his or her article?
- What are two pieces of advice your partner can give you to improve your article?

wrap-up

1. Students assemble in their small groups with their completed newspapers at pre-determined stations in the room. Tell students they will be investigating each other's newspapers, looking for clues about the culture of the time period. Students should be extremely careful in handling each other's work!

2. Reflection and Evaluation: Students complete questions 1-9 for their own newspaper and another group's newspaper. Make two or more copies of these pages per student.

3. Discuss the final four journal questions as a class.

assessment

Rubric on page 387

11 | Sign of the Times

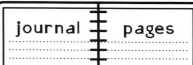

journal pages

FIRST NAME																		
LAST NAME																		

Newspaper Decisions

Everyone will be a newspaper writer AND have one of the roles below.

Decision #1 | Newspaper Role: Which will you be? Record names below.

Editor
Makes sure there is no duplication of article information.
Makes sure articles are relevant.
Chooses pictures that strengthen articles.
Works with writer to help them design or choose a picture for their articles.

Manager
Ensures that assignments are turned in on time.
Reminds group of rubric guidelines.
Hands in group information on due date.

Layout Designer
Coordinates what articles go where in the newspaper.
Makes detailed decisions about article and picture placement.

Communications Coordinator
Reports orally to class on updates.
Records group information.
Keeps track of information.

Decision #2 | Newspaper Articles: What will you write?

Each group member picks two topics to research and writes two newspaper articles. The Communications Coordinator within each group records this information. Writers must also draw or find pictures to accompany articles. Relate each story to the lake.

Topic choices include:

- Great Lakes News (national/international news, can be about any Great Lake)
- Regional News (local lake-related discoveries, inventions, or news)
- Environmental Health (state of the lake)
- Cultural Happenings (community and recreation activities on or near the lake)
- Intercultural Reports (looks at different cultures)
- Food (fishing, crops, irrigation)
- Transportation (modes of getting around, styles of boats)
- Trading (with whom, what, how?)
- Surrounding Ecosystems (explores the surrounding sand dunes, wetlands, forests)
- Additions to the newspaper might include: weather, comics, crossword puzzles

APPROVED BY	

11 | Sign of the Times

| FIRST NAME | | | | | | | | | | | | | | | | | | | |
| LAST NAME | | | | | | | | | | | | | | | | | | | |

Where Have We Been?

Although you will need to do additional research, this page gives you basic historical information.
Note: there is overlap in these time periods. The date is an estimate of when they began.

Paleo-Indians

1. 6,000 years ago: Descendents from the first inhabitants (who arrived at the Great Lakes about 10,000 years ago) were using copper from the south shore of Lake Superior and had established hunting and fishing communities throughout the Great Lakes Basin.

Prehistoric Tribes

2. 1500s: Native people of the Great Lakes have been estimated at a population of 250,000 and greater. They occupied widely scattered villages and grew crops including corn, squash, beans and tobacco. European explorers were just beginning to come through the region.

European Explorers/Voyageurs

3. 1600s: The French were exploring the forests around the St. Lawrence Valley and beginning to trap animals in the area for the European fur trade. Samuel de Champlain and Etienne Brulé, the first Europeans to see the Great Lakes, explore Lake Huron and Lake Ontario in 1615. Throughout the 1600s, the European settlers and explorers built forts and transported furs, but the only permanent settlements were Forts Frontenac, Michilimackinac and Niagara.

Settlers/Farmers

4. 1700s: The immigrant population increased. Settlers came to find farmland in order to make a living. As populations grew, dairying and meat production for local consumption began to dominate agriculture in the Great Lakes Basin. Specialty crops, such as fruit, vegetables and tobacco, grown for the burgeoning urban population, claimed an increasingly important share of the lands suitable for them.

Other events: Fort Oswego was established on the south shore of Lake Ontario by the British in 1727 and European settlement began in earnest in the valleys near the Great Lakes. In 1759, the British captured Quebec (formerly maintained by the French). The British maintained control of the Great Lakes region during the American Revolution in the late 1700s.

Early Industrialists

5. 1800s: Nearly all the settlements that grew into cities in the Great Lakes region were established on the waterways that transported people, raw materials and goods. The largest urban areas developed at the mouths of tributaries because of transportation advantages and the supply of fresh water for domestic and industrial use. Historically, the major industries in the Great Lakes region have produced steel, paper, chemicals, automobiles and other manufactured goods.

Other events: The Great Lakes area was divided between the Americans and the British (controlling Canada) after the War of 1812. Native people, who had become involved in the war in order to secure their homeland, did not get to share in the victory and were forced out of the region by the government. By the mid 1800s, most of the Great Lakes region where farming was possible was settled. Commercial logging began in the 1830s in upper Canada, Michigan, Minnesota and Wisconsin. Commercial fishing began in the 1820s and quickly expanded. Paper-making also began and over time the United States and Canada grew to be the world's leading producers of pulp and paper processing. Canals and shipping also expanded during this time. The population dramatically increased.

Industrialists and Caretakers of the Lakes

6. 1900s: More people had more free time and the Great Lakes began to see the effects of recreation. Extensive development took place during this time, including homes, marinas and the establishment of public beaches. This resulted in the loss of dunes, forests and wetlands around the lakes. The fisheries were seeing the effects of overfishing. By the mid-1950s, average annual catches were declining. Recreational fishing became more and more popular, leading people to be take an active role in helping the fishery to recover. Also, non-native fish, such as salmon, were being stocked for sport fishers. By the mid-1900s, the water quality of the Great Lakes had declined due to certain ways humans were using the lakes. In order to address this, legislation such as the Clean Water Act (1972) and the Great Lakes Water Quality Agreement (1972) were passed and continue to be upheld.

| APPROVED BY | |

11 | Sign of the Times

GRADE LEVEL
4-8

journal ≡ pages

FIRST NAME

LAST NAME

[1] Date of your newspaper:

....

[2] What is your role on the newspaper team?

....

[3] Which two articles will you be writing?

....

....

[4] List your research sources

....

....

....

....

Reflection and Evaluation

[5] Record the title and time period of the newspaper article you are reviewing.
     If it is your own, indicate this.

....

....

[6] In what ways does this historical group depend on the Great Lakes?

....

....

....

....

[7] Describe this culture's relationship with the Great Lakes. Is the relationship
     respectful? Is there disregard, dislike, affection for, or dependency on the lake?

....

....

....

....

APPROVED BY

11 | Sign of the Times

GRADE LEVEL
4-8

journal pages

FIRST NAME

LAST NAME

[8] Describe the state of the lake's health during this time.

[9] What are some of the cultural/social events that this newspaper reports on?

[10] Give an example of how this society meets its basic needs for food, clothing and shelter.

[11] If this is not your own paper, what makes this time period different from yours? If this is for your own paper, indicate this and proceed to question number [12].

[12] What are two things you like about this newspaper?

[13] What are two things you would improve?

APPROVED BY

11 | Sign of the Times

GRADE LEVEL
4-8

journal pages

FIRST NAME

LAST NAME

After reading other newspapers:

[14] How have people's relationships with the Great Lakes changed over time?

[15] How has the health of the Great Lakes (or your local lake) changed over time?

[16] What is something you can do to help the Great Lakes stay healthy?

[17] Out of all of the time periods you have read about, which is the one you would most like to visit and why?

APPROVED BY

CONNECT   1 | Who Needs the Lakes?

ELEMENTS	★★★★	★★★☆	★★☆☆	★☆☆☆
GROUP WORK: Student takes on a historical role and works with others to discuss the significance of the cultural group they are in, and records the characters.	Addresses all of the components	Missing one component	Missing two components	Missing three or more components
ROLE-PLAY: Student introduces him/herself in character to others and records at least 4 others s/he comes in contact with, including role, time period and connection to the lake.	Addresses all of the components	Missing one component	Missing two components	Missing three or more components
DISCUSSION and JOURNAL: Student participates in large group discussion, sharing who s/he met, his/her own group's role in history and the significance of Great Lakes caretakers. Student answers journal questions reflectively.	Addresses all of the components	Missing one component	Missing two components	Missing three or more components

CONNECT   2 | Now and Then

ELEMENTS	★★★★	★★★☆	★★☆☆	★☆☆☆
GROUP WORK: Student works with a partner to create a list of the ways the Great Lakes play a role in their lives, in their communities, and in the lives of past people and cultures.	Addresses all of the components	Missing one component	Missing two components	Missing three or more components
DISCUSSION: Student participates in discussions both before and after creating lists of the importance of the Great Lakes, and uses active listening skills.	Addresses all of the components	Missing one component	Missing two components	Missing three or more components

CONNECT   3 | Beaches Over Time

ELEMENTS	★★★★	★★★☆	★★☆☆	★☆☆☆
LISTENING: Student listens quietly to the sounds of a Great Lakes beach. S/he uses words and/or images to reflect what is heard and felt.	Addresses all of the components	Missing one component	Missing two components	Missing three or more components
DISCUSSION: Student participates in class discussion about the poem Beaches Over Time, and how the Great Lake beaches may have changed throughout history.	Addresses all of the components	Missing one component	Missing two components	Missing three or more components
OBSERVATION: Student walks around the beach alone or with a partner and makes a written/mental list of what they observe. Student distinguishes between natural and human-made, and between objects from the present and past.	Addresses all of the components	Missing one component	Missing two components	Missing three or more components

EXPLORE   **4 | Seasons Change**

ELEMENTS	☆☆☆☆	☆☆☆	☆☆	☆
DISCUSSION: Student participates in the class discussions both before and after drawing the season s/he chooses. Student uses active listening skills during the discussions.	Addresses all of the components	Missing one component	Missing two components	Missing three or more components
LISTENING: Student listens attentively to the story and does not talk inappropriately or distract other students.	Addresses all of the components	Missing one component	Missing two components	Missing three or more components
DRAWING: Student draws her/his interpretation of a Native American child's life during a particular season. Drawing reflects an understanding of the differences between lifestyles and times.	Addresses all of the components	Missing one component	Missing two components	Missing three or more components

EXPLORE   **5 | Ways of Life**

ELEMENTS	☆☆☆☆	☆☆☆	☆☆	☆
DISCUSSION: Student participates in class discussion about Native Americans in the Great Lakes region both before and after completing the Venn Diagram. Student reads journal information and demonstrates an understanding of the similarities and differences between groups.	Addresses all of the components	Missing one component	Missing two components	Missing three or more components
VENN DIAGRAM: Student constructs an accurate Venn Diagram, comparing and contrasting the cultures of both Native American tribes and European settlers.	Addresses all of the components	Missing one component	Missing two components	Missing three or more components

EXPLORE   **6 | Boats of Many Sizes**

ELEMENTS	☆☆☆☆	☆☆☆	☆☆	☆
BOAT EXPLORATION: Student finds the appropriate match for his/her boat. Student works cooperatively with her/his group to produce a boat timeline.	Addresses all of the components	Missing one component	Missing two components	Missing three or more components
DISCUSSION: Student helps create the class timeline for the boats, discusses the significance of shipping now and in the past and changes that are related to the Great Lakes shipping.	Addresses all of the components	Missing one component	Missing two components	Missing three or more components
WRITING: Student writes about a day onboard a Great Lakes boat or ship and shares it with a partner. Writing is the appropriate length and sentence structure.	Addresses all of the components	Missing one component	Missing two components	Missing three or more components

EXPLORE   7 | 200 Years of Change

ELEMENTS	★★★★	★★★☆	★★☆☆	★☆☆☆
HISTORICAL SKIT: Student works cooperatively with her/his group to produce a creative, historical scene from the Great Lakes region. Skit accurately portrays the chosen scene, and the student clearly demonstrates a personal investment in the skit.	Addresses all of the components	Missing one component	Missing two components	Missing three or more components
PERFORMANCE: Student follows activity guidelines to perform skit in a manner that conveys the intended information.	Addresses all of the components	Missing one component	Missing two components	Missing three or more components
DISCUSSION: Student actively participates in the wrap-up discussion. Student demonstrates an understanding of the historical relationship between the Native Americans and Europeans.	Addresses all of the components	Missing one component	Missing two components	Missing three or more components

INVESTIGATE   8 | Something's Fishy

ELEMENTS	★★★★	★★★☆	★★☆☆	★☆☆☆
DISCUSSION: Student actively participates in the class discussion and demonstrates an understanding of "eating locally".	Addresses all of the components	Missing one component	Missing two components	Missing three or more components
TIME PERIOD CARDS: Student works cooperatively in her/his group on the time period cards. Cards are complete and student offers sound reasoning for classifications.	Addresses all of the components	Missing one component	Missing two components	Missing three or more components
PRESENTATION: Student works cooperatively with her/his group to creatively present their time period to the class. Presentation is 3-5 minutes long, and every student participates in the oral presentation.	Addresses all of the components	Missing one component	Missing two components	Missing three or more components
FUTURE WHEEL: Student completes future wheels that accurately portray two changes, and the effects of these changes.	Addresses all of the components	Missing one component	Missing two components	Missing three or more components

INVESTIGATE   9 | Water Quality Over Time

ELEMENTS	★★★★	★★★☆	★★☆☆	★☆☆☆
DISCUSSION: Student actively participates in class discussion both before and after the activities. Student demonstrates a clear understanding of the importance of water in their lives, and the effects humans have had on Great Lakes water quality.	Addresses all of the components	Missing one component	Missing two components	Missing three or more components
STATIONS: Student visits all stations in chronological order, and answers all questions completely.	Addresses all of the components	Missing one component	Missing two components	Missing three or more components
GRAPH: Student actively participates in creating a class graph of population over time. Student demonstrates an understanding of the impact human population had on the Great Lakes.	Addresses all of the components	Missing one component	Missing two components	Missing three or more components
WRITING: Student answers wrap-up questions in a complete and well-constructed piece of writing.	Addresses all of the components	Missing one component	Missing two components	Missing three or more components

INVESTIGATE 10 | A Day In The Life

	★★★★	★★★	★★	☆
DISCUSSION: Student participates in the class discussion about memories and demonstrates active listening skills. Student demonstrates a clear understanding of the importance of conveying historical information.	Addresses all of the components	Missing one component	Missing two components	Missing three or more components
POSTER: Student creates a poster that addresses the aspects of food, housing, transportation, appearance, beliefs, and the lake of a Native American tribe. All aspects are addressed and the information is organized and clearly presented.	Addresses all of the components	Missing one component	Missing two components	Missing three or more components
PEER EVALUATION/QUESTIONS: Student completes an evaluation of her/his peers' work and answers all journal questions completely.	Addresses all of the components	Missing one component	Missing two components	Missing three or more components

INVESTIGATE 11 | Sign of the Times

	★★★★	★★★	★★	☆
DISCUSSION: Student actively participates in the class discussion about memories, and the wrap-up discussion about the unit. Student demonstrates a clear understanding of the importance of conveying historical information, and peoples' relationships with the Great Lakes over time.	Addresses all of the components	Missing one component	Missing two components	Missing three or more components
GROUP WORK: Student works cooperatively with classmates to complete a newspaper. Student selects a role and assumes all duties of that role.	Addresses all of the components	Missing one component	Missing two components	Missing three or more components
NEWSPAPER: Student works effectively in her/his role to contribute to the completion of the newspaper. Student contributes at least two articles to the newspaper and cites sources. Articles contain accurate information, are related to the lake, and have an illustration/photo as appropriate.	Addresses all of the components	Missing one component	Missing two components	Missing three or more components
PEER EVALUATION: Student completes an evaluation of her/his own newspaper by thoroughly responding to the reflection/evaluation questions. Student completes the final 4 journal questions. Student reads her/his peers' newspapers and answers the Reflection and Evaluation questions completely.	Addresses all of the components	Missing one component	Missing two components	Missing three or more components

Unit 6

Geology and Water Flow

essential questions

- **How were the Great Lakes formed?**
- **How does water flow throughout the Great Lakes system?**
- **What is the significance of Great Lakes geology and water flow?**

The dragonfly (Aeschna constricta) lives near the Great Lakes. Dragonflies are living fossils, as they have not changed in over 300 million years and would have witnessed the formation of the Great Lakes.

unit overview

Concepts are explored through the geologic timeline in comparison to the student's personal timeline, as well as direct observation of the local landscape. Students create a model of a glacier and its impact on the Great Lakes. Students gain an understanding of the Great Lakes system we have today, how it functions, and its importance. The final project synthesizes the unit information in the creation of an educational communication piece that conveys the knowledge learned. Related issues that are addressed include Great Lakes climate change and water exportation and withdrawals.

concepts

⊙ Geologic time is on a scale so large that it can exceed our comprehension. Yet, geologic events in history shape the human culture today.

⊙ Glaciers advancing and retreating formed the five Great Lakes, which are all connected in one water flow system that reaches the ocean.

⊙ The Great Lakes are a national resource of global importance, which have shaped the history of the region and are affected by past and present human actions.

unit activities

CONNECT

1 | Timelines

GRADE LEVEL
4-8

45 minutes

Developmental Modifications: For younger students: Use the K-3 journal pages. Ask for three instead of five important events on the personal timelines. Have students draw representative images for their time period signs, instead of using only words. During the class discussion focus on wrap-up questions: a, b, c, f and g.

summary

Students create a geologic timeline that includes the formation of the Great Lakes along a 100-meter space. Students compare this to timelines of their own lives.

objectives

- Explain a timeline.
- Describe how human lives fit into the relative scale of geologic history and the formation of the Great Lakes.
- Discuss the importance of the Great Lakes.

prerequisite

None

vocabulary

Timeline: representation of key events within a particular historical period
Geology: scientific study of the origin and structure of the earth
Epoch: geological subunit of a period
Period: geological subunit of an era
Era: geological subunit of an eon
Eon: longest division of geologic time, made up of eras
Great Lakes basin: the area that drains into the Great Lakes; also known as the Great Lakes watershed

setting

INDOORS   OUTDOORS

100-meter space (track, hallway or 100-yard football field will work)

subjects

Geology, Social Studies

standards

This Great Lakes in My World activity is aligned to the Common Core State Standards and to state learning standards in:

Illinois
Indiana
Michigan
Minnesota
New York
Ohio
Pennsylvania
Wisconsin

This alignment is available on your Great Lakes in My World CD in the "Standards" folder and on-line at http://www.greatlakes.org/GLiMWstandards.

materials

- 100-meter length (such as a track with a 100-meter straightaway or a hallway)
- 6 poster boards
- Markers
- Journals
- Pencils

Optional:
- Illustrated timeline
- Image of the Sears Tower on Chicago landscape
- 100 meter rope with every 10 meters marked

background

Geologic time is viewed on an extremely large scale compared to the timelines of our own lives. This is important to understand when studying the formation of the Great Lakes, as geologic events shape the world we live in today. Geologic time is divided into units. Epochs make up periods. Several periods make up an era, and several eras makeup an eon. The number of units varies, depending on events. However, the Precambrian does not have many subdivisions because there is not as much data available during this time due to a lack of fossils. The Precambrian was rich in an abundance of soft-bodied organisms, lacking hard parts necessary for fossils. The timeline provided here focuses on significant events in relation to the formation of the Great Lakes. These events are italicized in the chart.

Additional Information

Canadian Shield: A u-shaped region of ancient rock, stretching north from the Great Lakes to the Arctic Ocean. It covers most of Canada and Greenland. Its granite rocks formed during the Precambrian, a time of volcanic activity and mountain building. The southern and eastern portions of the shield are covered with sedimentary rocks formed during the Paleozoic Era.

Glaciation

During the Pleistocene Epoch, glaciers advanced and retreated from the north four times, forming the landscape we see today. River valleys from the previous era were deepened and widened by the glaciers, hills were scraped flat, large basins were scooped out, and piles of rocks were deposited in various formations. As the climate warmed, the glaciers melted, filling in a large basin and forming the Great Lakes. A glacier can be 3.2 km (two miles) thick (equal to seven Sears Towers!) and is made of ice, snow and rocks. A glacier occurs when ice and snow build up over a long period in which precipitation is greater than melting, due to constant cold temperatures. Interglacial periods are times of climate warming between glaciers, when plants and animals return. We are currently living in an interglacial period.

sources

Great Lakes Atlas, http://www.epa.gov/glnpo/atlas/index.html
Kenosha Public Museum, Kenosha, WI

....

procedure

1. Introduce the Geology and Water Flow unit by asking if students know how the Great Lakes formed. Ask them what the area might have been like when the Earth first formed. Explain the word "geology" and its value.

2. Before going to the track or hallway, discuss how timelines can be used to understand the past, present and future. *Timelines chart events and processes that happen over time and can use whatever time is best suited for its purpose, e.g., the hours preceding a crime or the years that chronicle a 50-year marriage.* Draw a simple example on the board.

3. Have students create timelines of their lives in their journals. The timelines should start with the date of their birth, and include five significant events.

4. Break students into six groups. Have groups create signs to place as markers large enough to read from far away. Four groups should make signs for the four eras (Precambrian, Paleozoic, Mesozoic, Cenozoic), using similar colors and copying key points from the chart provided. The fifth should use different colors to create a Pleistocene Epoch sign. The sixth group makes a sign that reads: 20,000 years ago, Great Lakes begin to form. Students may decorate their signs with sample species or other relevant pictures if time permits. For younger students, choose one or two events from each time period to put on each sign.

5. Go out to the 100-meter space and explain that you will be making a timeline (to scale) of the life of the Earth. You will be highlighting six points on the timeline. Ask students to guess the location of each event.

6. One student (or more) stands at the beginning of the area. This point (sign #1) is 4.6 billion years ago, the beginning of the Precambrian Era when the rocks and atmosphere were formed.

7. Take the rest of the class 87 meters down the space, and have one student stand there. This is (sign #2) the beginning of the Paleozoic Era, when organisms such as fish, insects, and vascular plants began to evolve.

8. Take the rest of the class 95 meters down the space (5 meters from the end) and have one student stand here. This is (sign #3) the beginning of the Mesozoic Era, when dinosaurs roamed the earth. *This is not closely related to the formation of the Great Lakes, but is a good reference point for students, who are generally familiar with dinosaurs.*

9. Take the rest of the students 97 meters down (3 meters from the end). This is (sign #4) the Cenozoic Era when humans first began to appear.

10. Now take the students to the very end of the space. Show them that the last centimeter is (sign #5) the most recent glacial period, the Pleistocene Epoch, when the Great Lakes were formed, 20,000 years ago. During this time, humans were populating the Earth. Next to the Pleistocene sign, place the (sign #6) Great Lakes sign.

11. Ask the students take a look at where the "marker" students are standing. Bring the whole class back together to respond to journal questions and discuss the timelines.

Era	Epoch Years Ago	Key Characteristics
Precambrian Era	4.6 billion – 600 million years ago	• The origin of life; characterized by soft bodies lacking shells (very few fossils due to a lack of hard parts) • Time of volcanic activity, and mountain and atmospheric building
Paleozoic Era	600 million – 230 million years ago	• Pangea forms-all continents are connected • Two ice ages occur • Life-forms with hard parts appear • Life moves onto land • Fish, insect, invertebrate, reptile and vascular plants evolve
Mesozoic Era	230 million – 63 million years ago	• Pangea divides • Tropical climate worldwide • Ferns and gymnosperms dominant plants • Dinosaurs dominant animals
Cenozoic Era	63 million years ago – present	• Mammals dominant • Continental fragmentation continues • Reptiles, fish, and invertebrates take on present form • Evolution of flowering plants • Humans began to appear (Homo erectus) (in the Quaternary Period, about two million years ago)
	Pleistocene Epoch 2 million – 11, 000 years ago	• Many modern life forms appear 2 million – 11, 000 years ago • Large land mammals dominate (mammoth, saber-toothed tiger) • Modern humans (Homo sapiens) appear and expand their numbers (beginning about 120,000 years ago) • The most recent glaciers advance • Great Lakes begin to form 20,000 years ago as the glaciers melted

wrap-up

1. Use the following questions to discuss the timeline as a class:

a. What surprised students about the Earth's timeline? How did this activity change students' view of the timeline of the earth?

b. How do their personal timelines fit into this picture? *They are a VERY small part of the whole earth's long timeline.*

c. Compare the Earth's timeline to students' personal timelines and discuss examples of short-term vs. long-term changes.

d. How do other forces (besides glaciation) change and shape the Earth? *Wind and precipitation can cause change to the Earth's surface.*

e. Precambrian times started over 4.5 billion years ago. How big is 1 billion? Have you been alive for 1 billion seconds? *You will not have been alive for 1 billion seconds until you are 32 years old.*

f. Can you imagine the landscape before the Great Lakes were formed? *20,000 years ago, the Laurentide glacier was at its peak. Ice 3.2 km (2 miles) thick covered Canada and the entire Great Lakes basin and temperatures averaged 9 degrees Celsius (15 degrees F) lower than they are today. Glaciers were as tall as 7 Willis Towers (formerly Sears Tower) !*

g. Glaciers created the Great Lakes. How did the process of glaciation change the availability of resources in the region today to make this the amazing place that it is now? *Because of the Great Lakes plants, animals, and humans are able to live here easily. They are able to get freshwater, which we all need to survive and the Great Lakes provide a habitat for many organisms to survive. Humans also rely on the Great Lakes for transportation, recreation, beauty and shipping.*

extension

Students write essays that tell the history of the Earth and Great Lakes based on timelines.

1. Discuss: How did the landscape come to be what it is today? How did the Great Lakes form?

assessment

Rubric on page 462

1 | Timelines

FIRST NAME																						
LAST NAME																						

[1] YOUR Timeline: Mark five important events in your life on the timeline below. Write your age at each event.

```
|------|------|------|------|------|------|------|------|------|------|------|------|------|------|------|
0
years
```

[2] HISTORY'S Timeline: Make a timeline for the points you put on the geologic timeline you made with the class. Indicate where your life timeline would fit.

[3] Explain how you think the Great Lakes formed.

....

....

....

....

....

[4] Why are the Great Lakes important to you?

....

....

....

....

[5] What questions do you have about the formation of the Great Lakes?

....

....

....

....

APPROVED BY	

1 | Timelines

GRADE LEVEL
K-3

journal pages

FIRST NAME																	
LAST NAME																	

[1] My Timeline

|----------|----------|----------|----------|----------|----------|----------|----------|----------|----------|

0   1   2   3   4   5   6   7   8   9   10

years   years

[2] I am _____ years old. Circle the number

[3] I was born on: _____

[4] The Great Lakes are _____ years old.

[5] DRAW a plant or animal that lived long ago.

APPROVED BY	

CONNECT

2 | Looking at Landscape

GRADE LEVEL
K-8

45 minutes

Developmental Modifications: Follow K-3 or 4-8 procedure and Journal Pages.

summary

Students observe the local landscape then use journaling and discussion to explore its impact on their lives.

objectives

- Discuss the importance of observation and using senses to collect information. (K-3)
- Describe the local landscape and explain its influence on human lives.
- Reflect on the impact of the Great Lakes landscape on the lives of people who settled in the region.
- List reasons the Great Lakes are important.

prerequisite

Timelines, Watershed Orientation (Lakes Unit) recommended

vocabulary

Landscape: the land that can be seen
Observation: the gathering of information by noting facts or occurrences

setting

OUTDOORS

subjects

Geology, Social Studies

standards

This Great Lakes in My World activity is aligned to the Common Core State Standards and to state learning standards in:

Illinois
Indiana
Michigan
Minnesota
New York
Ohio
Pennsylvania
Wisconsin

This alignment is available on your Great Lakes in My World CD in the "Standards" folder and on-line at http://www.greatlakes.org/ GLiMWstandards.

materials

- Journals
- Pencils
- Crayons or Markers

background

On a daily basis, our landscape influences the actions we are able to take, the modes of transportation we use, and our access to resources. Historically, the presence of the Great Lakes influenced people's decisions to settle in the area.

Today, the lakes and their surrounding landscapes are still essential to the people who live around them. The Great Lakes are necessary for drinking water, recreation, shipping and other water uses that impact the people of the region.

procedure

1. (K-3) Ask students to list the different ways people learn. *Watching, listening, asking questions, reading, doing an activity, using their senses.*
2. (K-3) Ask for examples of how they use each sense to learn.
3. (K-3) Tell students that they will be using their eyes, or sense of sight, to learn about where they live.
4. (All) Take students outside (the schoolyard will work, but someplace where they can see a lake, wetland or river is preferable). If you cannot see a Great Lake, ask students to talk about how Great Lakes are part of our landscape, even if we cannot see them.
5. (K-3) Have students look around them and draw a picture of everything they can see, as far as they can see.
(4-8) Have students look around and record the landscape features they see, as far as they can see; then sketch the landscape.
6. (All) Share journal drawings with the large group—are there any parts of the landscape some students noticed and others did not?
7. (All) Discuss as a class:
What is the general shape of the landscape?
What are the major landforms or features? *For example, hills, ridges, water bodies, plains.*

What do you think is the shape of the land under your nearest Great Lake? *Bowl-shaped depression to hold the water?* What do you do with the features you see from day to day? For example, do you swim in the lake, ride your bike over the hill, walk along the stream, etc?
(4-8) Additional questions: How have these features influenced your life? How do your interactions with the landscape compare with people's experiences in other parts of the world? What are some of the forces that are constantly changing the Earth? Which forces create change more quickly? *Examples include: wind, sunlight, storms, plate tectonics, rivers, wave action.* Why do you think many cities and towns are located near bodies of water? *Using the Great Lakes as an example, it was a draw for many Native American communities and European settlers - it offered drinking water, food and transportation to other places. Today, it might influence people's decisions to move to the area because of recreation, beauty, or drinking water.*

8. As students discuss the reasons the Great Lakes are important, create an ongoing list that can be added to throughout the time the class studies the Great Lakes.

wrap-up

1. Let the students use their imaginations. They may draw or write in their journals as you give them the following scenario based on Timelines: Think back to the timeline, to the space between the end of the Precambrian Era (at 87 meters down the track straightaway or hallway) and the dinosaurs (at 95 meters). Can you imagine this landscape during this time? *It looked much different then. In fact, the Great Lakes were not here, and marine seas often flooded the land.* How would your life be different if the landscape had not changed since then?
2. How did the landscape come to be what it is today? How did the Great Lakes form? Use this question to gain a sense of students' previous knowledge of this topic.

extension

Students locate the landforms they have drawn on local maps or geologic contour maps, available at: www.topozone.com.

Discuss:
• How did the landscape come to be what it is today?
• How did the Great Lakes form?

assessment

Rubric on page 462

2 | Looking at Landscape

GRADE LEVEL
K-3

| FIRST NAME | | | | | | | | | | | | | | | | | | | |
| LAST NAME | | | | | | | | | | | | | | | | | | | |

[1] Draw the landscape as far as you can see.

[2] How do you think the Great Lakes were formed?

APPROVED BY

2 | Looking at Landscape

GRADE LEVEL
K-3

FIRST NAME																				
LAST NAME																				

[3] Draw a picture of yourself doing an activity outside on the land or in the water.

[4] Why are the Great Lakes important?

....

....

....

....

....

APPROVED BY	

2 | Looking at Landscape

GRADE LEVEL
4-8

journal pages

FIRST NAME

LAST NAME

[1] MaKe a list of all of the geologic features you can see, as far as you can see.

[2] SKetch the landscape.

APPROVED BY

2 | Looking at Landscape

GRADE LEVEL
4-8

FIRST NAME																			
LAST NAME																			

[3] How do you interact with these features day to day? For example, do you swim in the lake, ride your bike over the hill, walk along the stream, etc?

....

....

....

[4] How have these geologic features influenced your life?

....

....

....

....

[5] How do your interactions with your local landscape compare with people's experiences in other parts of the world?

....

....

....

....

[6] What are some of the forces that are constantly changing the Earth? Which forces create change quickly? Which forces create change slowly?

....

....

....

....

[7] Why are cities/town located near bodies of water?

....

....

....

[8] List 2 reasons the Great Lakes are important.

....

....

....

APPROVED BY	

EXPLORE

3 | Water, Water Everywhere

GRADE LEVEL

4-8

45 minutes

Developmental Modifications: For younger students (grades 4 and 5), do the demonstration so they can see the limited amount of freshwater on Earth. Because the Annex article in this activity may be too advanced, teachers can incorporate some of the information into the discussion by using the article as background information.

summary

Students participate in a demonstration of the types of water on Earth and reflect on their own water use through reading, discussion and graphing.

objectives

- Explain how much freshwater on the Earth is available for human consumption.
- Describe how much water Americans use, and for what purposes.
- List ways to conserve water.

prerequisite

Timelines, Looking at Landscape

vocabulary

Great Lakes basin: The land where water from the ground, rivers and streams flow into the Great Lakes, also known as Great Lakes watershed

setting

INDOORS

subjects

Geology, Hydrology, Social Studies

standards

This Great Lakes in My World activity is aligned to the Common Core State Standards and to state learning standards in:

Illinois
Indiana
Michigan
Minnesota
New York
Ohio
Pennsylvania
Wisconsin

This alignment is available on your Great Lakes in My World CD in the "Standards" folder and on-line at http://www.greatlakes.org/ GLiMWstandards.

materials

- 1 liter container with milliliters marked
- 1 liter of water in a bucket
- Map of the world
- Annex 2001 article (in activity)
- Copies of Personal Water Log (several per student)

background

About three-quarters of the Earth is covered with water. Of this, 97% is saltwater, which humans cannot drink. 2% of the water on Earth is frozen in glaciers. This leaves only one percent of the water on Earth available for human use. On average, Americans have a use of over 100 gallons of water daily for household use. Examples of household use are drinking and washing. Examples of indirect water uses of water include water used to grow the food we eat and manufacture products we buy. The biggest use of water is cooling water for power plants and agriculture, but each has instituted conservation measures in recent years. For example, power plants reuse cooling water several times and some are turning to air cooling, while irrigation methods have become much more efficient in recent years. The United States uses 25 trillion gallons of freshwater each year.

According to the U.S. Environmental Protection Agency, we are using our freshwater faster than we can recharge the groundwater. In the United States, 50% of the wetlands, which recharge and filter freshwater, have been destroyed. The Great Lakes provide 20% of the world's fresh surface water and 95% of the United States' fresh surface water. They contain six quadrillion gallons of freshwater; only the polar ice caps and Lake Baikal in Siberia contain more. Spread evenly across the continental U.S., the Great Lakes would submerge the country under about 9.5 feet of water. If spread it across the North American continent, the Great Lakes would cover the entire land mass with about two feet of water. While this is certainly a lot of water, freshwater is a precious resource that must be conserved. The Great Lakes are not bottomless, nor is any freshwater resource.

procedure

1. Show students the map of the world. Ask them how much of the Earth they think is covered by water. *About three-quarters. This is a lot of water!* Ask students what makes water in the ocean different from water in the Great Lakes. *The oceans are made of saltwater, the lakes of freshwater, different species live in each place.* Ask students if they think the ocean water is okay for humans to drink. *Why not? Humans cannot drink salt water because the salt dehydrates us. As of now, the process of desalination (taking the salt out of the water) is very expensive and uses high amounts of energy.* Given that we cannot drink from the oceans, ask students how much of the water on Earth they think is available for humans to drink. *Only 1%.* Ask students if they can think of any other water on Earth (besides the oceans) that is not available for drinking. *The water that is frozen in the ice caps, about 2%.*

Demonstrate

2. Show students the liter container. It is made up of 1000 ml, which are marked on the side.
3. Have a student fill the container with water. This represents all of the water on Earth. Of this water, 97% is in the oceans. Have a student carefully pour out 970 ml of the water.
4. Two percent of the total water on Earth is frozen in the ice caps. This is 20 ml. Ask a student to pour out this water.

5. One percent, or 10 ml, of the total water on Earth is left in the container. This is all of the water that is available for humans to drink and use for watering crops. The Great Lakes contain 20% of that water.

Discuss

6. What are the implications of such a small percentage of the water on Earth being available for human use? What if this water is polluted? *Currently, the world population has an annual growth rate of 1.4%, or 80 million new people each year. Unlike population, the water supply is not growing—water is not gained or lost from the Earth's hydrological cycle. At the current rate in the U.S., we are using water faster than it can be cleaned and replenished.* How should this knowledge impact our water use? Should we be more careful with the amount of water we use and how it is treated?
7. Of the available freshwater on Earth, 20% is found in the Great Lakes. How much of the one liter of water is this? (two ml) What does this mean? *This gives the people of the Great Lakes watershed a large responsibility for managing and caring for this water.*
8. Complete and discuss the journal pages. This includes reading the Annex 2001 article provided in this activity.

wrap-up

1. Ask students how much water they use in 24 hours. Ask students to design a method to monitor their water use and use the accompanying journal pages to do so.
2. What conclusions can students draw from their own water use charts? From other students' water use charts? Are there ways in which the students could reduce the number of liters they each consume each day?
3. Students complete the last column in the chart by including conservation options they could use, then recalculate their total liters per day. Which options do they really think they will use? To make this exercise worthwhile, students

will have to follow through at home by conserving water in the ways they suggested. Even by adjusting one habit and getting their family to do the same can make a big difference over time.
4. Have students graph the amounts of water they use in one week without water conservation methods and with water conservation methods. Have students compare the amounts. Now that students have this information, what can they do with it? Discuss ways to educate others or implement the water conservation methods suggested.

extension

Students can creatively display their water use data conservation options and ideas and use it to educate others in the school or community.

....

sources

U.S. Department of Agriculture, Natural Resources Conservation Service, http://www.nrcs.usda.gov/

Great Lakes basin brochure, 1990, Michigan Sea Grant

EPA: Kid's Stuff, http://www.epa.gov/ow/kids.html

....

resources

Environment Canada, http://www.ec.gc.ca/water/en/e_quickfacts.htm

Alliance for the Great Lakes, Visit http://www.greatlakes.org/healthybeachesactionguide/

U.S. Department of Agriculture, Natural Resources Conservation Service, http://www.nrcs.usda.gov/

U.S. Geological Survey, http://ga.water.usgs.gov/edu

The Thirsty Lizard Project

H2ouse: Water Saver Home, http://www.h2ouse.net

....

assessment

Rubric on page 462

We value your thoughts and feedback on Great Lakes in My World. Please let us know about any oversights, errors or omissions you find, or if there are things you or your students particularly like.

Send your comments to: education@greatlakes.org

Our lakes, our future, our responsibility

The Great Lakes are a unique and precious resource. They are a natural wonder of the world. The Great Lakes provide freshwater for the 44 million people who live within the Basin. They support the region's ecosystem and economy. The Great Lakes watershed contains nearly 20 percent of the Earth's fresh surface water. It is the only freshwater system of its kind in size and ecological diversity and is essential to humans and wildlife alike; providing homes, food, recreation, and economic sustainability.

The Great Lakes are vulnerable to depletion and degradation. The Great Lakes are a vast resource, but each year rainfall and snowmelt replenish only about one percent of the water in the basin. The other 99 percent is finite and nonrenewable. That fact coupled with a growing demand for water by domestic users - including utilities, agriculture, manufacturers, and housing- and proposals to export water to other parts of the U.S. and to foreign countries, is cause for concerns regarding keeping the region's freshwater resources safe for future generations.

In 2005, after nearly five years of negotiations, the Great Lakes Governors and Premiers endorsed a precedent-setting agreement to protect and conserve the Great Lakes. In 2008, a companion compact became effective in the eight Great Lake states, following approval by the Great Lake legislatures, the U.S. Congress and President. The Great Lakes - St. Lawrence River Basin Water Resources Compact and Agreement implement the Great Lakes Charter Annex signed by the parties in 2001. The Compact and Agreement provide for comprehensive water use protections throughout the Great Lakes Basin. The agreements protect the Great Lakes from harm by implementing strong and effective water management and conservation programs. These agreements close the door on diversions to places like the Middle East, and arid Southwest U.S., but they also put our own house in order by protecting us from unwise water use in the face of growing demand from across the nation and the world. The Compact and Agreement provide a foundation for the long-term protection and sound management of Great Lakes water, ensuring that they are protected today and for generations to come.

Excerpted from a National Wildlife Federation fact sheet.

3 | Water, Water Everywhere

GRADE LEVEL
4-8

FIRST NAME																		
LAST NAME																		

[1] Personal Water Log: 24 hours

Date _____

USE	AMOUNT (Liters)	CONSERVATION USE (Liters)
Total Amount Used		

Here are some amounts for typical personal water use, according to the U.S. Environmental Protection Agency.

What methods could you use to reduce your water use? Use this information to fill the last column in the water use table (above).

Calculate how much water you would use and save by using these new methods.

Use	Liters / Gallons	Conservation Options
Flushing	19-26 / 5-7	Displace water in tank: 15 liters / 4 gallons
Showering	94.5 / 25	Reduce shower time: 57 liters /15 gallons
Bathing	151 / 40	Reduce water level: 38 liters / 10 gallons
Brushing Teeth	19 / 5	Turn off tap: 2 liters / ½ gallon
Washing Hands or Face	7.5 / 2	Plug and fill basin: 4 liters / 1 gallon
Dishwasher	60.5 / 16	Use the dishwasher when it's full
Dish Washing by Hand	113 / 30	Plug and fill basin: 19 liters / 5 gallons
Washing Clothes	227 / 60	Use the washing machine when it's full

APPROVED BY	

3 | Water, Water Everywhere

GRADE LEVEL
4-8

journal pages

FIRST NAME

LAST NAME

[2] What is the importance of clean freshwater?

....
....
....
....

[3] What do you think is the responsibility of the people who live near the Great Lakes, with regard to taking care of the water?

....
....
....
....

[4] Read the article "Annex 2001". What do the governors and premiers think their responsibility should be with regard to caring for the Great Lakes basin or watershed?

....
....
....
....

[5] Examine your personal water consumption log. What trends and/or patterns do you notice? Did anything surprise you?

....
....
....
....

[6] What do you think you could do to help preserve the Great Lakes?

....
....
....
....

APPROVED BY

3 | Water, Water Everywhere

GRADE LEVEL
4-8

| FIRST NAME | | | | | | | | | | | | | | | | | |
| LAST NAME | | | | | | | | | | | | | | | | | |

[7] What ways do you use water at home?

....

....

....

[8] Graph your water use BEFORE using water conservation strategies.

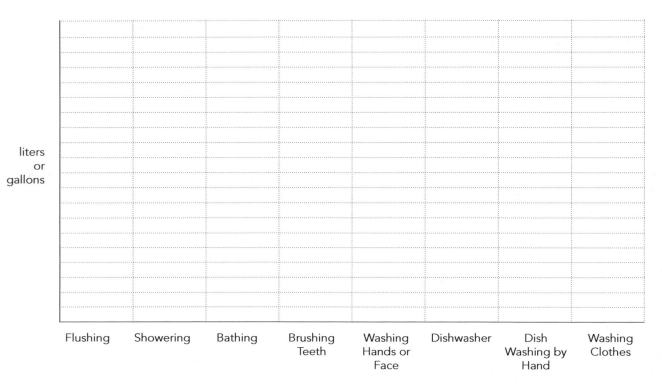

liters
or
gallons

Flushing   Showering   Bathing   Brushing   Washing   Dishwasher   Dish   Washing
                                      Teeth   Hands or   Washing by   Clothes
                                                 Face   Hand

[9] This is for one day. Multiply to find the results for one week. One month?

[10] BONUS: Can you figure out the water use for the whole class for one day
      or one week?

| APPROVED BY | |

3 | Water, Water Everywhere

GRADE LEVEL
4-8

FIRST NAME																						
LAST NAME																						

[11] What ways can you conserve water at home?

....

....

....

[12] Graph your water use AFTER using water conservation strategies.

liters
or
gallons

Flushing   Showering   Bathing   Brushing   Washing   Dishwasher   Dish   Washing
Teeth   Hands or   Washing by   Clothes
Face   Hand

[13] Describe how much water you saved for one day. Describe the methods you used.

....

....

....

....

[14] This is for one day. Do the math to find the water saved for one day, one week and one month.

APPROVED BY	

4 | Follow the Water

Developmental Modifications: For younger students, have them fill in the Journal Page labels as a class.

summary

Students act out the Great Lakes water cycle, read a water flow poem, sing a water cycle song and label the water movements on a map.

objectives

- Describe the Great Lakes water cycle.
- List at least 3 parts of the Great Lakes water cycle.
- Show the movement of water through the Great Lakes.

prerequisite

Some knowledge of the water cycle is helpful.

vocabulary

Water cycle: also known as the hydrologic cycle; the series of conditions through which water naturally passes from water vapor in the atmosphere through precipitation upon land or water surfaces and finally back into the atmosphere as a result of evaporation and transpiration

Watershed: the area that drains into a river or lake; the Great Lakes watershed is also known as the Great Lakes basin

Condensation: change from a less dense to a denser, or more compact form

Evaporation: pass off into vapor from a liquid state

Precipitation: to change from a vapor to a liquid or solid and fall as rain or snow

setting

INDOORS

subjects

Geography, Geology, Hydrology, Language Arts

standards

This Great Lakes in My World activity is aligned to the Common Core State Standards and to state learning standards in:

Illinois
Indiana
Michigan
Minnesota
New York
Ohio
Pennsylvania
Wisconsin

This alignment is available on your Great Lakes in My World CD in the "Standards" folder and on-line at http://www.greatlakes.org/ GLiMWstandards.

materials

- Map of the Great Lakes watershed (p. 418)
- String or rope for lake outline
- Water cycle cards
- Signs for water cycle stations
- Poem "Drip Drop" (p. 420)

background

The Great Lakes...

- And their connecting channels are the largest group of freshwater lakes on Earth.
- Cover 94,000 square miles, and hold 6 quadrillion gallons of water.
- Drain 200,000 square miles of land. (All runoff water in the 200,000 square mile watershed of the Great Lakes flows into one of the lakes.)
- Make up one-fifth of the world's fresh surface water supply and nine-tenths of the United States' supply.
- Watershed includes eight states and one province: Minnesota, Wisconsin, Illinois, Indiana, Michigan, Ohio, Pennsylvania, New York, and Ontario.
- Watershed is home to (as of 2002), over 33 million people, including one-tenth of the U.S. population and one-quarter of Canada's population.

The Water Cycle

The water levels in the Great Lakes vary on short time scales, by season and year to year, but remain steady over a long time period. The water levels can fluctuate 30cm-60cm per year (12in-24in). They are influenced by precipitation, upstream flows, groundwater, surface water runoff, evaporation, diversions, and human regulations. Westerly winds carry moisture into the Great Lakes basin in air masses from other parts of North America. An approximately equal amount of water leaves the basin through evaporated moisture in departing air masses and the outflow into the ocean. Of the total volume of water in the Great Lakes, only 1% enters the Great Lakes each year.

The Channels

- The St. Marys River is a 60-mile waterway connecting Lake Superior and Lake Huron. The Soo locks bypass the St. Marys rapids.
- The Straits of Mackinac connect Lake Michigan and Lake Huron.
- The St. Clair River, Lake St. Clair, and Detroit River are an 89-mile channel connecting Lake Huron and Lake Erie.
- The Niagara River is 35 miles long, connecting Lake Erie and Lake Ontario. The Niagara Falls spills 50,000-100,000 cubic feet of water per second. The falls are bypassed by the Welland Canal.
- The St. Lawrence River is 1,000 miles long, flowing from Lake Ontario to the Atlantic Ocean.

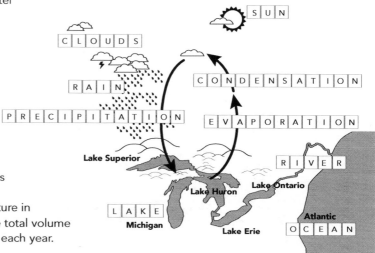

procedure

1. In small groups, have students look at maps of the Great Lakes watershed (p. 418). Help them find where they live in the watershed on the map. Students decide whether the lakes are all connected or separate: Can they trace the water clear through between each lake or is there land in the way? *Students should find that the lakes are all connected.*

2. Ask students if they think that the water moves between the lakes, or is still. *The water flows between the lakes: From Superior to Michigan and Huron, to Erie, Ontario, then out to the Atlantic.* Read the poem Drip Drop and discuss the path that the water drop takes.

3. On their journal page maps, have students draw arrows through all of the lakes, showing how the water moves throughout the system. Use either p. 413 or p. 418 map. Draw an example on the board or overhead so that students can see what they are trying to draw.

4. Ask students to guess where else water might come from or go to (think about the water cycle). *Streams, rivers,*

groundwater, plants, animals, clouds, etc. If students are unfamiliar with the water cycle, draw a picture that shows how evaporation, precipitation, and condensation happen in the Great Lakes watershed.

5. To teach or review the water cycle, try singing the following song with students that uses the tune of "Found a Peanut" or "Oh My Darling Clementine" (same tune): *"Evaporation, Condensation, Precipitation all day long. These are the steps of the water cycle, and they continue on and on."* Hand motions should be included to indicate evaporation as an upward motion, condensation as a fluffy, cloud-like motion, and precipitation as a downward motion, using the fingers to indicate raindrops or snowflakes.

Hydrological Cycle Game

Students will act out a simple Great Lakes water cycle.

6. In an open space, use string to make an outline on the ground of the Great Lakes. Call this station: Great Lake. Set up stations for Cloud (evaporation), Groundwater, River, Precipitation and Ocean, according to the cards.

procedure

1 CLOUD

The sun comes out, causing the drops of water to evaporate. They become water vapor. The water vapor condenses into clouds.

→ CHOOSE **2**

2 PRECIPITATION

Tiny drops of water in the clouds fall down as rain/snow.

→ CHOOSE **3**, **4** OR **5**

3 GROUNDWATER

The water seeps into the ground, to an underground river.

→ CHOOSE **4** OR **6**

4 RIVER

The water goes into a river above ground that flows into your Great Lake.

→ CHOOSE **1** OR **3**

5 GREAT LAKE

The rainwater falls into your Great Lake.

→ CHOOSE **1** OR **6**

6 OCEAN

The water flows into the St. Lawrence River and into the Atlantic Ocean.

→ CHOOSE **1**

Follow the directions to vary the order of these cards and show students that stages of the water cycle are not linear, but happen according to different circumstances. Make sure they make sense as they are being read.

7. Have some or all of the students stand next to a station that you choose, and tell them to pretend to be drops of water. If they stand next to multiple stations, you will need to read directions for each station each time.

8. Choose a card from the stack, or have a student choose a card from the stack, and read aloud to the class. The cards may be rearranged, and cards will be repeated. (For example, evaporation will need to be done more than once.) Students should act out the instructions on the card, pretending to be water drops in the Great Lakes.

wrap-up

1. Have a short discussion with the class about the water cycle, and the places where water can be found in the Great Lakes watershed. Ask students if they can think of any other places water can be found that were not a part of the game. *Plants and animals.*

2. Have students label the water cycle elements on the Great Lakes map in their journals, using the words provided. See map on page 411 for an example.

3. If you have not yet sung the Water Cycle Song, it is a good concluding activity (see #5).

assessment

Rubric on page 463

4 | Follow the Water

GRADE LEVEL
K-3

journal   pages

FIRST NAME

LAST NAME

[1] Use these words to label the picture below.

- SUN
- LAKE
- RIVER
- CLOUDS
- RAIN
- OCEAN
- EVAPORATION
- CONDENSATION
- PRECIPITATION

[2] What is the name of the water that helps the Great Lakes stay full, but can't be seen in this picture? Hint: It is found underground!

The water is called: G | | | | | | W | A | T | E | R |

| U |

| L | | | | |

| R | | | |

| C | | | D | | | S | | I | | |

P | | C | | | I | | | T | | | |

| E | | | P | | R | | T | | |

Lake Superior

| | | V | | |

Lake Huron

Lake Ontario

| A | | |

Michigan

Atlantic

| O | | | | |

Lake Erie

APPROVED BY

EXPLORE

5 | Water Flow

GRADE LEVEL
4-8

45 minutes

summary

Students act out the Great Lakes water cycle and flow in a game, read a water flow poem and label the water movements on a map.

objectives

- List at least five components of the Great Lakes water cycle and flow.
- Describe the Great Lakes water cycle, including water flow and turnover.

prerequisite

Timeline and Landscape Observation

vocabulary

Aquifer: a water-bearing layer of rock, sand, or gravel that holds water and may allow it to pass through to the surface or other aquifers
Groundwater: water within the earth that supplies wells and springs
Tributary: a stream flowing into a larger stream or lake
Impervious: not letting something enter or pass through
Watershed: the area that drains into a river or lake; the Great Lakes watershed is also known as the Great Lakes basin
Retention rate: approximate length of time a water drop stays in a body of water.

setting

OUTDOORS

subjects

Geology, Hydrology, Geography, Language Arts

standards

This Great Lakes in My World activity is aligned to the Common Core State Standards and to state learning standards in:

Illinois
Indiana
Michigan
Minnesota
New York
Ohio
Pennsylvania
Wisconsin

This alignment is available on your Great Lakes in My World CD in the "Standards" folder and on-line at http://www.greatlakes.org/ GLiMWstandards.

materials

- Maps of the Great Lakes watershed (p. 419)
- Optional: Poem: "Drip Drop" (p. 418)
- 24 dice
- Pencils
- Journal pages
- 24 pieces of blank paper

background

The waters of the Great Lakes are, for the most part, a nonrenewable resource. They are composed of numerous aquifers (groundwater) that have filled with water over the centuries, waters that flow in tributaries of the Great Lakes, and waters that fill the lakes themselves. Although the total volume in the lakes is vast, on average less then one percent of the Great Lakes water is renewed annually by precipitation, surface water runoff (includes tributaries), and inflow from groundwater sources. Of this one percent, groundwater contributes 42 percent, precipitation is 35 percent, and surface water (includes tributaries) is 23 percent. Because glaciers formed the Great Lakes, tributary inflow is limited. More than 1,000 miles cubed of groundwater are stored in the Great Lakes basin, a volume of water approximately equal to that of Lake Michigan.

The Great Lakes...

- And their connecting channels are the largest surface freshwater system on Earth.
- Cover 94,000 square miles, and hold six quadrillion gallons of water.
- Drain 200,000 square miles of land. (All runoff water in the 200,000 square mile watershed of the Great Lakes flows into one of the lakes.)
- Make up one-fifth of the world's fresh surface water supply and nine-tenths of the United States' supply.
- Watershed includes eight states and one province: Minnesota, Wisconsin, Illinois, Indiana, Michigan, Ohio, Pennsylvania, New York and Ontario.
- Watershed is home to (as of 2002), over 33 million people, including one-tenth of the U.S. population and one-quarter of Canada's population.

The Channels

- The St. Mary's River is a 60-mile waterway connecting Lake Superior and Lake Huron. The Soo locks bypass the St. Marys' rapids.
- The Straits of Mackinac connect Lake Michigan and Lake Huron.
- The St. Clair River, Lake St. Clair, and Detroit River make up an 89-mile channel connecting Lake Huron and Lake Erie.
- The Niagara River is 35 miles long, connecting Lake Erie and Lake Ontario. The Niagara Falls spills 50,000-100,000 cubic feet of water per second. The Welland Canal bypasses the falls.
- The St. Lawrence River is 1,000 miles long, flowing from Lake Ontario to the Atlantic Ocean.

Groundwater

Because groundwater is not necessarily a visible part of the water cycle, students may not be familiar with its importance. Groundwater is essential to ecosystems in the Great Lakes region because it is a large, below surface reservoir from which water is released slowly to provide a reliable minimum level of water flow to streams, lakes and wetlands connected to the Great Lakes and other water bodies Groundwater discharge to streams generally provides good quality water that can promote habitat for aquatic animals and sustain aquatic plants during periods of low precipitation. In the Great Lakes region, groundwater indirectly contributes more than 50 percent of the stream discharge to the lakes. Also, groundwater is the source of drinking water for millions of people in the region, is an important water supply for agriculture and many industries, and provides a fairly uniform supply of water in some ecologically sensitive areas to sustain plant and animal species.

Urban development may reduce the amount of water going back into (or recharging) groundwater because impervious surfaces (such as roads, buildings, and paved areas) often drain to storm sewers, a situation that increases surface runoff and reduces infiltration into the ground. These processes may significantly alter groundwater conditions in many urban settings by "short-circuiting" to streams and lakes water that would have infiltrated to the water table.

The Great Lakes Water Cycle

The water levels in the Great Lakes vary from season to season and year to year, but remain relatively steady over a long time period. The water levels can change 30cm-60cm per year (12in-24in). They are influenced by precipitation, upstream flows, groundwater, surface water runoff, evaporation, diversions, and human regulations. Westerly winds carry moisture into the Great Lakes basin in air masses from other parts of North America. An approximately equal amount of water leaves the basin through evaporated moisture in departing air masses and the outflow into the ocean. Of the total volume of water in the Great Lakes, only one percent is renewed within the lakes each year through surface water (tributaries), groundwater and precipitation.

procedure

Part One: Looking at Maps

Students will look at a map of the Great Lakes watershed to determine that the lakes are one water flow system, then will play a game to demonstrate the Great Lakes hydrological cycle.

1. In small groups, have students look at maps of the Great Lakes watershed or basin. Students should decide whether the lakes are all connected or separate. Can they trace the water clear through between each lake or is there land in the way? *Students should find that the lakes are all connected.*

2. If time, read the poem Drip Drop and discuss the path a water drop would take within the Great Lakes watershed. This can also be read with the activity "Water in Motion"

3. Have student groups take turns announcing the names of the waterways connecting each of the Great Lakes.

4. On their journal maps, have students indicate the water flow through the lakes. *The water flows between the lakes: From Superior to Michigan and Huron, to Erie, Ontario, then out to the Atlantic.* Ask students to guess where else water might come from or go to (think about the water cycle). *Streams, rivers, groundwater, plants, animals, clouds, etc.* Infiltration cleans the water, and without this step, surface water carries pollutants directly to the lake.

Part Two: Hydrologic Cycle Game

5. Assign each student to one of the underlined words on the list in the journal pages for this activity. Add your local waterway and appropriate options, if not listed. If there are more students than words (24), some students may pair up. With less than 24 participants, students should just circulate between stations. Each student folds a piece of paper in half. On one half, they write the underlined word in clear, large letters. On the other half, they write the sentences that follow the underlined word, including the numbers beside them. Have the students stand up

the folded paper on their desks so that the large word is visible. Ask students if they all understand the meaning of the sentences and words they have just written down. Take time for clarification if necessary.

6. Pass out one die to each student. The die should be left on the desks. Explain to students that they are each a drop of water on a path through the hydrological cycle in the Great Lakes watershed. Ask students to share with the class what they already know about the water cycle. Ask them what states water can take. *Solid, gas, liquid.*

7. For the game, students should all roll their dice, then look at the sentences on their papers to determine their fate. For example, if the student with the word Irrigation rolls a three (ODD), then s/he would be absorbed by plant roots.

8. Students follow the directions according to the number they roll. For instance, the above student would then move to the station with the sign that says *Absorbed by Plant Roots*. Students indicate where they go on the map and record each station s/he goes to in their journal, then repeat the steps of rolling the die and moving to the next appropriate station. The students will move through the stations in a random order, according to the numbers they role. More than one student may be at a station at the same time. Continue play until students have been to approximately five stations each. Then have students return to their original seats.

9. Have each student label their "journey" on the blank map in the appropriate place. Students may look at the map of the Great Lakes watershed for reference. Have students add labels, arrows and drawings for evaporation, precipitation, condensation, moving air mass, groundwater, animals, plants and humans. See sample on next page.

10. Have students draw lines on the map outlining the paths that they took during the game. If room, have them also record another student's water "journey" on the map. The result should be a web-like criss-crossing of lines.

wrap-up

1. Ask students if they think there was a pattern to the paths they each took as drops of water. *No, their paths should be random. Why is this the case? Pictures tend to show the water cycle as a neat circle. However, depending on circumstances, water can go in many directions.*

2. Ask students to raise their hands if their drop of water at some point entered the Great Lakes. Then have students raise their hands if their drops of water at some point left the watershed. *There should be a relatively low number of these compared with the rest of the moves students made.* Have students tell the class the ways in which the water came into or out of the Great Lakes watershed.

3. Ask students if they think that in real life much water enters or leaves the Great Lakes. *Explain that only one percent of the total volume of water is renewed (or re-enters the Great Lakes system) each year.*

4. How does groundwater play a part in the Great Lakes system? *See background information. Groundwater has an important role in recharging the water in the Great Lakes. Approximately the same amount of water that is in Lake Michigan is stored underground as groundwater near the lake!*

5. A drop of water stays in each of the Great Lakes for different lengths of time. Ask the students to try and explain this, knowing that the water is constantly moving. *Each lake has a different volume and flow rate.* Have students try to figure out in which lake a drop of water would spend the longest and shortest amounts of time. This is called the "retention rate." You can also provide the students with the number of years and have them try to figure it out. The water retention rates for the Great Lakes are included in this activity.

wrap-up continued

6. What if the water in one of the lakes is polluted? Discuss what would happen, based on the retention rates. *The lakes would recover slower or faster, depending on their retention rates. In Lake Erie, for example, pollution would be most quickly noticed, and most quickly cleaned, as water leaves quicker than in the other lakes due to the smaller water volume.*

7. Have students write a story in their journals about their journey as a water droplet. These stories can be creative, as long as they include the stations visited by the student during the activity, and incorporate the idea of the water retention rates.

resources

United States Geological Survey
http://water.usgs.gov/ogw/pubs/WRI004008/contents.htm

International Joint Commission : "Protection of the Waters of the Great Lakes" Final Report to the Governments of Canada and the United States. February 22, 2000.

David J. Holtschlag and James R. Nicholas (1998), *Indirect Groundwater Discharge to the Great Lakes*, USGS Open File Report 98-57

assessment

Rubric on page 463

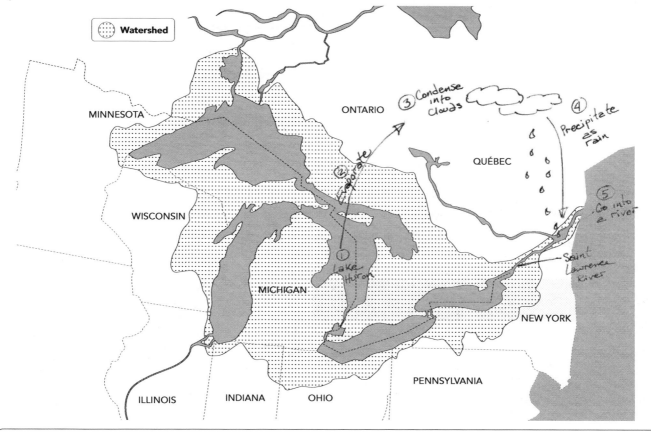

Lake	Retention Rate	Volume			
Lake Superior	191 years	12,100 km3	or	12,100,000,000,000,000 liters	(2,900 mi³)
Lake Michigan	99 years	4,920 km3	or	4,920,000,000,000,000 liters	(1,180 mi³)
Lake Huron	22 years	3,540 km3	or	3,540,000,000,000,000 liters	(850 mi³)
Lake Ontario	6 years	1,640 km3	or	1,640,000,000,000,000 liters	(393 mi³)
Lake Erie	2.6 years	484 km3	or	484,000,000, 000,000 liters	(116 mi³)

Drip Drop

If you were a drop, just a tiny young drip,
And felt it was time that you'd taken a trip,
Why, you could just head out Lake Superior way.
Just roll through the lake and start on your way.

Superior's highest,
the Great Lake's high peak.
The truth is Superior has a small leak.
It spills down to Huron
by day and by night,
and also Lake Michigan, both the same height.

These two lakes are huge, and the water is rough.
You'd float and you'd surge,
swim through all kinds of stuff.
You'd come to the point where Lake Huron drops down,
and flow down to Erie, and spin round and round.

But gravity pushes and jostles and calls,
till you'd find your way over Niagara Falls!
Just roaring and churning, so 3-D and stereo,
five hundred feet down to the quiet Ontario.

Then over the currents you'd glide, oh so fast,
a roller-coaster ride, you'd be having a blast!
The Saint Lawrence River will give you the notion
that soon you'll be part of the Atlantic Ocean.

From there, head to Europe and don't ever stop.
The world is wide open for one little drop.

Author: Denise Rodgers
From: Great Lakes Rhythm and Rhyme, available through River
Road Publications: www.riverroadpublications.com/

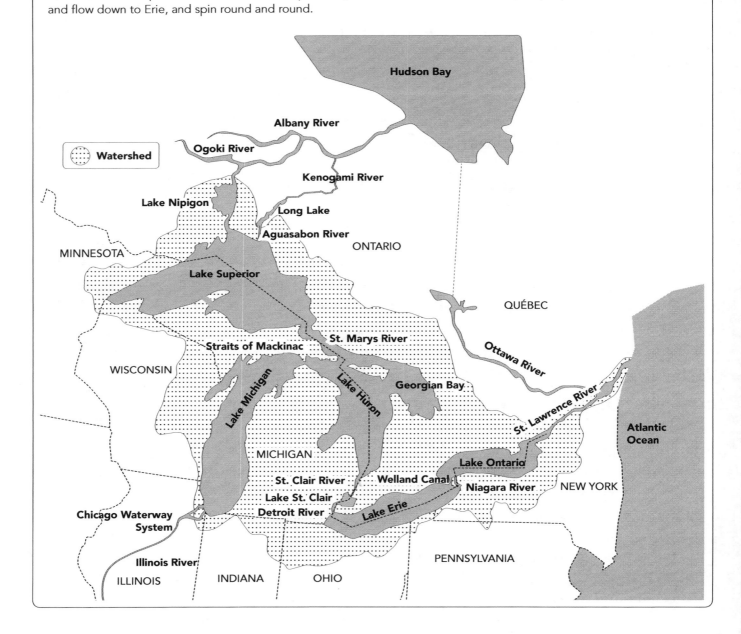

5 | Water Flow

FIRST NAME

LAST NAME

[1] Label the map below to show your "water journey." Add labels, arrows and drawings for evaporation, precipitation, condensation, moving air mass, groundwater, animals, plants and humans.

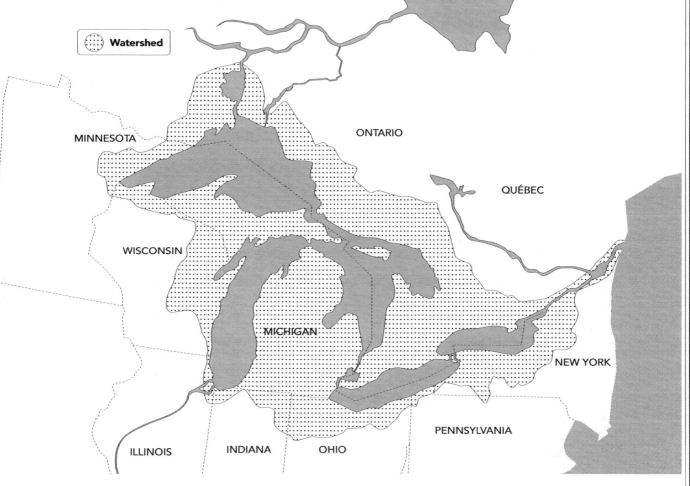

[2] Use the volume to determine how many years a drop of water would stay in each Great Lake (retention rate). Place the correct number in the spaces below: 6 years, 22 years, 191 years, 2.6 years, 99 years.

Lake	Retention Rate	Volume		
Lake Superior	_____years	12,100 km³ or	12,100,000,000,000,000 liters	(2,900 mi³)
Lake Michigan	_____years	4,920 km³ or	4,920,000,000,000,000 liters	(1,180 mi³)
Lake Huron	_____years	3,540 km³ or	3,540,000,000,000,000 liters	(850 mi³)
Lake Ontario	_____years	1,640 km³ or	1,640,000,000,000,000 liters	(393 mi³)
Lake Erie	_____years	484 km³ or	484,000,000, 000,000 liters	(116 mi³)

APPROVED BY

5 | Water Flow

GRADE LEVEL
4-8

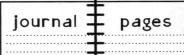

FIRST NAME

LAST NAME

Evaporate

EVEN	Become a part of a moving air mass.
ODD	Condense into clouds.

Condense into Clouds

EVEN	Precipitate as rain.
ODD	Become a part of a moving air mass.

Precipitate

1,2	Go into the ground water.
3,4	Become surface water runoff.
5,6	Go into one of the Great Lakes or rivers.

Moving Air Mass

EVEN	Leave/Enter the Great Lakes watershed (to or from the ocean).
ODD	Condense into clouds.

Groundwater

1,2	Be absorbed by plant roots.
3,4	Be extracted by a well.
5,6	Flow into one of the Great Lakes.

Surface Water Runoff

1,2	Flow into one of the Great Lakes.
3,4	Be consumed by an animal.
5,6	Evaporate.

Well Water

EVEN	Be consumed by a person/animal.
ODD	Washed down the drain, treated, then back into the groundwater.

Welland Canal Diversion Around Niagara Falls

1,2	Flow into Lake Ontario.
3,4	Evaporate.
5,6	Be consumed by an animal.

Chicago Water System

1	Move out of the Great Lakes basin (to the ocean).
2,3	Be consumed by an animal.
4,5	Evaporate.
6	Be absorbed by plant roots.

Lake Superior

1,2	Evaporate.
3	Be consumed by an animal.
4	Be absorbed by plant roots.
5,6	Flow into the St. Marys River.

Lake Michigan

1,2	Evaporate.
3	Be consumed by an animal.
4	Be absorbed by plant roots.
5,6	Flow through the Straits of Mackinac.

Lake Huron

1	Evaporate.
2,3	Be consumed by an animal.
4,5	Be absorbed by plant roots.
6	Flow into the St. Clair and Detroit Rivers

Lake Erie

1	Evaporate.
2,3	Be consumed by an animal.
4,5	Be absorbed by plant roots.
6	Flow into the Niagara River.

Lake Ontario

1,2	Evaporate.
3	Be consumed by an animal.
4	Be absorbed by plant roots.
5,6	Flow into the St. Lawrence River.

Transpirate (water is given off by plants)

EVEN	Become a part of a moving air mass.
ODD	Condense into clouds.

Consumed by a Person/Animal

EVEN	Be excreted into the ground water.
ODD	Be excreted into a body of water or river.

Absorbed by Plant Roots

EVEN	Be consumed by an animal.
ODD	Transpire into the air.

Irrigation

EVEN	Become part of the ground water.
ODD	Be absorbed by plant roots.

St. Marys River

1	Flow into Lake Michigan or Lake Huron.
2,3	Be consumed by an animal.
4,5	Be absorbed by plant roots.
6	Evaporate.

Straits of Mackinac

1,2	Flow into Lake Michigan or Lake Huron.
3	Be consumed by an animal.
4	Be absorbed by plant roots.
5,6	Evaporate.

St. Clair & Detroit Rivers

1	Flow into Lake Erie.
2,3	Be consumed by an animal.
4,5	Be absorbed by plant roots.
6	Evaporate.

Niagara River

1,2	Flow into Lake Ontario.
3	Be consumed by an animal.
4	Be absorbed by plant roots.
5,6	Evaporate.

St. Lawrence River

1	Flow into the Atlantic Ocean.
2,3	Be consumed by an animal.
4,5	Be absorbed by plant roots.
6	Evaporate.

Atlantic Ocean

1,2	Be consumed by an animal.
3,4	Be absorbed by plant roots.
5,6	Evaporate.

APPROVED BY

5 | Water Flow

GRADE LEVEL
4-8

FIRST NAME

LAST NAME

[1] In the space below, record each of the water (hydrological) cycle stations that you visit.

a.

b.

c.

d.

e.

[2] Why do you think it is significant that such a small amount of water (one percent) moves in and out of the lakes?

[3] What questions do you have about Great Lakes water flow?

APPROVED BY

5 | Water Flow

GRADE LEVEL
4-8

| FIRST NAME | | | | | | | | | | | | | | | | | | | | | | | |
| LAST NAME | | | | | | | | | | | | | | | | | | | | | | | |

[4] Explain why groundwater is important to the Great Lakes.

....

....

[5] Look at retention rate and water volume in the journal pages. Explain the relationship between them.

....

....

....

....

....

[6] Explain what would happen to the other Great Lakes if one lake was polluted. Include the concepts of retention rate and water volume in your answer.

....

....

....

....

....

[7] Write a story about your journey as a water droplet. Include the stations you visited during the activity in your story. Be creative and use extra paper!

....

....

....

....

....

....

....

....

....

....

....

| APPROVED BY | |

6 | Landscape Changes

GRADE LEVEL

4-8

90 minutes

Developmental Modifications: Follow procedure and directions for K-3 and 4-8. For the younger students, consider creating the model ahead of time. Use appropriate Journal Pages. Use separate assessment rubrics for K-3 and 4-8. Use Journal Page number 430 for K-3.

summary

Students create a model of a glacier and simulate the formation of the Great Lakes landscape.

objectives

- Describe a glacier.
- Compare and contrast glacial impact.
- Explain how the Great Lakes were formed.

prerequisite

Timelines and Landscape Observation

vocabulary

Glacier: a large body of ice moving slowly down a slope or valley, or spreading outward on a land surface
Moraine: a pile of earth and stones carried and deposited by a glacier
Drumlin: a long oval hill of material left by a glacier
Kame: a short ridge or mound of material deposited by water from a melting glacier

setting

INDOORS

subjects

Geology, History

standards

This Great Lakes in My World activity is aligned to the Common Core State Standards and to state learning standards in:

Illinois
Indiana
Michigan
Minnesota
New York
Ohio
Pennsylvania
Wisconsin

This alignment is available on your Great Lakes in My World CD in the "Standards" folder and on-line at http://www.greatlakes.org/GLiMWstandards.

materials

- Journals
- Pencils
- World map
- Rocks, Sand, Clay, Gravel
- Half-gallon milk containers (one per student group)
- Large plastic tubs (one per student group)
  (wider than the milk containers and with room for the glacier to move)
- Container to catch the run-off water

background

During the Precambrian Era, the geologic setting was established bedrock and mountains that later contributed to the formation of Lake Superior during the glacial advances of the Ice Age. At that time, there was a fracture in the Earth running from Oklahoma to Lake Superior. Mountains were created that covered Wisconsin and Minnesota, and the Laurentian Mountains appeared in eastern Canada. Molten magma below the area of Lake Superior spewed out to the sides, causing the Earth to sink and form a large rock basin, which now holds the lake. Inland seas covered the area, depositing sand and silt that were compressed into a soft substrate of sandstone, shale and limestone. The seas retreated before the end of the Precambrian Era.

Over the last million years, glaciers advanced and retreated over the Great Lakes area several times. The most recent glaciers occurred during the Pleistocene Epoch (2 million-11,000 years ago). The ice leveled mountains and carved out shallow valleys. River valleys from the previous era were widened and deepened. The hard bedrock in the north was not as heavily eroded as the softer sandstones and shales in the south. As the glaciers melted and retreated, the valleys filled with the freshwater that is now the Great Lakes. The lakes continued to change over time as the land rebounded from the release of the weight of the glaciers. The land still rises today at a rate of a few centimeters each century. To see a flash video of the formation of the lakes, go to Environment Canada Great Lakes Kids: http://www.on.ec.gc.ca/greatlakeskids/GreatLakesMovie5.html.

procedure

Advance Preparation

1. Prior to class, remove one side of the milk containers. Fill one-third of the container with water, sand, gravel, and rocks. Place the containers in the freezer. Once the water freezes, remove the containers from the freezer and add another one-third mixture of water, sand, gravel, and rocks. Return the containers to the freezer. Repeat this step a final time.

2. Before class, fill the bottom of a large plastic tub (the tub should be a bit wider than the milk carton) with sand and clay. Fill the tub only about two inches so it doesn't overflow with water later.

Part One

1. (K-3) Shape the sand and clay into a pre-Great Lakes landscape prior to student's involvement. There should be extra space at both ends for the glacier to begin and end. Poke one or two holes in the tub at the level of the sand/clay landscape to drain excess water. You may wish to place the tub in a sink or larger basin to catch the runoff water. (This can represent the ocean.) The landscape you create should use the clay to resemble areas where there is land today and sand to resemble areas where there is water today. The landscape should look something like the illustration provided (p. 425).

   (4-8) Refer back to the personal timelines students created. Students should each choose two points on their timelines and think about how they had changed from one point to the other. Have students write or draw in their journals about how they changed between those two events. The changes may be emotional or physical, any type of change the student can think of. Discuss how the students have changed over time.

2. (All) Ask students if they think that like people, the Earth can change over time. Respond in journals. What about landscapes, can they change over time? *Yes, the Earth*

and its landscapes can change over time. Some changes happen over a shorter period of time (like floods or storms) some changes happen over a very long period of time (like mountain building or erosion). Ask students for examples of landscape changes.

3. (All) Look at a map of the world. Have students point out the largest bodies of freshwater that they can find. *They should find that the Great Lakes are the largest bodies of freshwater in the world. They make up 20 percent of all drinkable water on earth.*

4. (All) Ask students if the Great Lakes landscape has changed (or was always as it is now), and if so, when and how? *See the background information.*

5. (4-8) Ask students to help plan the demonstration. Ask them to brainstorm in response to the question: How can we create a model that shows what the Great Lakes looked like before and after glaciers came through the area? Take students' ideas and incorporate them into the demonstration when possible.

Part Two

Students will create a model of a glacier and carve out a landscape.

1. (All) Briefly explain glacier formation and movement.

   (All) A glacier occurs when, over time, the rate of precipitation accumulation is greater than the rate of melting. Ice and snow build up and move forward with gravity. Glaciers recede when temperatures rise enough to cause the ice and snow to melt. The formation, as well as the melting and receding, of glaciers takes hundreds of years. The model students will create does not reflect the formation of a glacier, only the impact a glacier has on the landscape.

procedure continued

(K-3) To make this idea clearer for students, ask them what happens in the winter when it snows and snows. *The snow gets deeper.* What keeps the snow from getting infinitely deeper and deeper? *When it gets warmer, the snow melts.* If it didn't get warmer, the snow would just pile up instead of melting. This is what causes a glacier to form.

Procedure for K-3

2. Show the students the model created ahead of time and explain that the sand represents the softer rocks and the clay represents harder rock. Place the ice at the top (or north) end of the tub. Allow students to push the "glacier" across the landscape. Ask students what their *pushing represents. The pushing represents the glacier moving across the landscape.*

3. Allow the glacier to melt. As it melts, tip the southern end of the tub up slightly (representing the land rebounding) to allow the water to fill up the holes that the glacier has created. In the end, the new landscape should have some lake formations filled with water. It is fine if the landscape doesn't look just like the Great Lakes, as long as there are some lake-like formations.

4. Explain to students that this is similar to what happened when the glaciers were here. The ice and rock carved out gentle valleys, then melted to form the freshwater lakes. Without this change, the Great Lakes would not exist.

Procedure for 4-8

2. This can be done ahead of time, if desired. Fill the bottom of a large plastic tub (the tub should be about as wide (6 inches) as the half-gallon milk container) with sand and clay about two inches deep. Explain to the students that the sand represents soft sandstone and shale, and the clay represents hard bedrock, such as volcanic deposits (including the Lake Superior basin).

3. Allow students to shape the sand and clay into the landscape they imagine the Great Lakes area looked like before the glaciers. There should be extra space at the top and bottom of the landscape for the glacier to begin and end. Poke one or two holes in the tub at the level of the sand/clay landscape to drain excess water. The holes go at the height of the sand/clay. It would be most accurate to have the holes where the Chicago River and St. Lawrence Seaway would be. The holes are just meant to drain off excess water that would go into the ocean in real life so that the entire landscape isn't flooded, only the lakes.

4. The tub should be tilted approximately 20 degrees, or one inch, so that the water can flow slightly back to simulate the glaciers receding. You may wish to place the tub in a sink or larger basin to catch the runoff water. (This can represent the ocean.) The landscape they create should use the clay to resemble areas where there is land today and sand to resemble areas where there is water today

(keeping in mind that the Lake Superior basin was already formed). The landscape should look something like the illustration below.

5. Instruct the students to remove the "glacier" from the milk container. Place the "glacier" at the top (or north) end of the tub. In journals, diagram the landscape before the "glacier" advances.

6. Allow students to push the "glacier" across the landscape. Ask students what their pushing represents. *The pushing represents the accumulation of ice and snow moving across the landscape.*

7. Provide time for the glacier to melt. During this time, students can work on the journal drawings, scale calculations and discussion questions. As it melts, tip the southern end of the tub up slightly (representing the land rebounding from the weight of the glacier lifting) to allow the water to fill up the holes that the glacier has created. In the end, the new landscape should have some lake formations filled with water.

8. Explain to students that this is similar to what happened when the glaciers were here. *The ice and rock carved out low spots, then melted to form the freshwater lakes. In other places around the Great Lakes, the glacier scraped the Earth fairly flat. The only hills are generally the piles of rock and sand dumped during melt periods; e.g. moraines, drumlins and kames. Without glaciation, the Great Lakes and the surrounding land would not exist in its current state.*

9. Ask students to explain why this model is not like the actual glaciation that occurred. *Not the actual landscape, students do not see how the glacier was formed, happens in a much shorter amount of time, much smaller scale.* Ask students why they think the Great Lakes are sometimes called a "gift of the glaciers?"

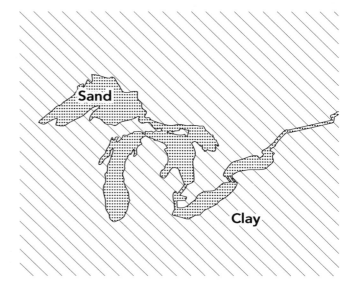

wrap-up

1. Ask students how long it took to change a "landscape" in the classroom. Ask students how long they think it took to form the Great Lakes. *About one billion years, beginning with the formation of the Lake Superior basin.*

2. Ask students how thick they think a glacier is. The last Great Lakes glacier was about 3.2 kilometers (two miles) thick. Think of a spot 2 miles from the classroom to indicate this distance. Ask students whether they think it would be easy or difficult to create another large source of freshwater like the Great Lakes. *Difficult.*

3. (K-3) Have students explain to a partner how the Great Lakes were formed.

4. Have students answer remaining journal questions. In their journals, have students diagram the formation of the Great Lakes. They draw what they saw happen in the tub: the landscape before and after the glacier. Students should include descriptions to explain the ideas represented in the drawings.

5. In their journals, have students record questions they have about glaciers and the Great Lakes geologic history. Use these questions for future research in Rock Songs and Shaped by Geology.

extension

For another example of how the Great Lakes were formed, show the video: The Rise and Fall of the Great Lakes. Have students conduct further research on glaciers through Rock Songs.

assessment

Rubric (K-3) on page 463
Rubric (4-8) on page 464

 We value your thoughts and feedback on Great Lakes in My World. Please let us know about any oversights, errors or omissions you find, or if there are things you or your students particularly like.

Send your comments to: education@greatlakes.org

6 | Landscape Changes

GRADE LEVEL
4-8

journal pages

FIRST NAME																		
LAST NAME																		

Before demonstration

[1] Look back at your personal timeline. Choose two points on the timeline and write or draw about how you changed between those two points in time.

[2] Do you think that like people, landscapes can change over time? If so, give an example.

[3] How you think the Great Lakes landscape has changed over time?

APPROVED BY	

6 | Landscape Changes

FIRST NAME																				
LAST NAME																				

Draw "before" and "after" diagrams of the formation of the Great Lakes.
Provide a written description for each diagram.

Before

After

APPROVED BY	

6 | Landscape Changes

GRADE LEVEL
4-8

journal pages

FIRST NAME																		
LAST NAME																		

FIGURE IT OUT!

[1] If a person is approximately 2 meters (6 feet) tall, how many people does it take to equal the height of a 4 Kilometer glacier? Use this number to help you draw your picture to scale. To find out the answer, solve the equations below and use the information.

one Kilometer = 1000 meters

[2] Determine the height of the glacier in meters using the following equation:

1000 meters × 4 Kilometers = _____ meters

[3] Determine the number of people to equal the height of the glacier using the following equation:

$$\frac{\text{Height of glacier}}{\text{Height of a person}} = \text{_____ number of people}$$

[4] Describe how the model of classroom glacier is different and similar to an actual glacier.

....
....
....
....
....
....
....
....
....
....
....
....
....

APPROVED BY	

6 | Landscape Changes

GRADE LEVEL
4-8

journal   pages

FIRST NAME																				
LAST NAME																				

[5] Give two examples of how landscapes can change over short and long time periods.

....

....

....

....

....

....

....

....

[6] Why do you think the Great Lakes are sometimes called "a gift of the glaciers"?

....

....

....

....

....

....

....

....

[7] What questions do you have about the Great Lakes geology, including glaciation
     and water flow?

....

....

....

....

....

....

....

....

....

APPROVED BY	

INVESTIGATE

7 | Rock Songs

GRADE LEVEL

3-6

45 minutes

summary

Students conduct geology research and re-write the lyrics to songs to convey knowledge based on self-generated Great Lakes geology questions.

objectives

- Research and synthesize information learned.
- Create a song based on scientific information.
- Present information learned in the unit through performance.

prerequisite

Landscape Observation, Water Flow, Landscape Changes

vocabulary

None

setting

INDOORS   OUTDOORS

subjects

Geology, Hydrology, Language Arts

standards

This Great Lakes in My World activity is aligned to the Common Core State Standards and to state learning standards in:

Illinois
Indiana
Michigan
Minnesota
New York
Ohio
Pennsylvania
Wisconsin

This alignment is available on your Great Lakes in My World CD in the "Standards" folder and on-line at http://www.greatlakes.org/GLiMWstandards.

materials

- Journals
- Pencils
- Internet access
- Music compact discs and a way to play them (optional)

background

Incorporating sound, music and performance into learning can offer an alternative way for students to creatively take ownership of knowledge. It enables students to weave an interest in music, popular or other, into their learning.

Howard Gardner's theory on Multiple Intelligences states that there are seven different ways to demonstrate intellectual ability. He includes Musical/Rhythmic Intelligence as the ability to produce and appreciate music. Musically inclined learners think in sounds, rhythms and patterns and immediately respond to music either appreciating or criticizing what they hear. Many of these learners are extremely sensitive to environmental sounds (e.g. crickets, bells, dripping taps).

People with Musical/Rhythmic Intelligence may have skills that include: singing, whistling, playing musical instruments, recognizing tonal patterns, composing music, remembering melodies and understanding the structure and rhythm of music.

Source

LdPride.net, http://www.ldpride.net/learningstyles.MI.htm

procedure

1. Discuss the qualities of good research questions. *They require looking up information to answer them, do not have a yes/no answer and should be something students really want to know about.* In this case, students will write questions about Great Lakes geology and water flow.

2. Have students brainstorm questions. Some examples might be: *How do we know that glaciers formed the Great Lakes? Why does the water flow into the Atlantic Ocean and not the other way? How can we know if we are using too much Great Lakes water? Why are some lakes deeper than others? How long does a drop of water stay in the Great Lakes?* Another option is to take an activity in the geology unit and turn what they learned into the lyrics of a song. Students should turn the concept into a question to practice creating research questions, and add additional researched information, if they choose this option.

3. Break students into small groups. Have the group choose questions or concepts and give them access to resources. Each group should choose a song they all like and know.

4. Students re-write the words to their chosen song, using information from the previous activities and their research. Students should refer to their journal pages for ideas and details. Songs should be accurate, detailed, make sense and address at least one concept and three to five facts learned in the unit. Students may choose to leave in some of the original lines of the song if they make sense in their new song. This tactic may help students to remember their songs.

Examples
Students can use current, popular songs or "older" songs, such as those listed below:
Goodness, Gracious, Great Balls of Fire! - rewritten as: Goodness, Gracious, Great Walls of Ice!
You've Lost That Lovin' Feeling - rewritten as: You've Lost That Cenozoic Landscape
In the Jungle, the Mighty Jungle - rewritten as: In the Watershed, the Mighty Watershed

5. Have students move into break-out spaces to develop and practice their songs.

wrap-up

1. Have student groups sing their songs for the class. Students may choose to combine their singing with a dance performance or movements to go with the song.

2. Students answer questions from other classmates on the song content.

assessment

Rubric on page 464

 We value your thoughts and feedback on Great Lakes in My World. Please let us know about any oversights, errors or omissions you find, or if there are things you or your students particularly like.

Send your comments to: education@greatlakes.org

7 | Rock Songs

GRADE LEVEL
3-6

journal ☰ pages

FIRST NAME																				
LAST NAME																				

[1] Question or concept you will be researching:

....

....

[2] Sources used (at least one per group member):

a. ....

b. ....

c. ....

[3] Song Name: _____

Words for the chorus:

....

....

....

....

....

....

....

....

Words for the verses:

....

....

....

....

....

....

....

....

....

....

APPROVED BY	

8 | Water in Motion

90 minutes

summary

Students build a model and design an experiment that explores renewal rates of the Great Lakes and related pollution issues.

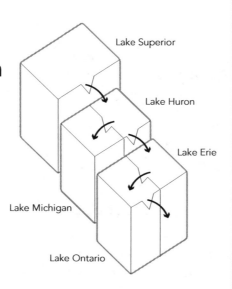

Lake Superior

Lake Huron

Lake Erie

Lake Michigan

Lake Ontario

objectives

- Demonstrate water flow in the Great Lakes.
- List the ways water is replenished in the Great Lakes.
- Explain retention rate and its impact on the Great Lakes and pollution.
- Design an experiment that tests a theory about pollution in the Great Lakes.

prerequisite

Water, Water Everywhere, Water Flow

vocabulary

Contaminant: substance that is not naturally present in the environment, or that is present in environmentally harmful concentrations

Retention rate: the time span for water to move through the system: this measure is based on the volume of water in the lake and the average rate of outflow

setting

INDOORS

subjects

Geology, Hydrology, Geography

standards

This Great Lakes in My World activity is aligned to the Common Core State Standards and to state learning standards in:

Illinois
Indiana
Michigan
Minnesota
New York
Ohio
Pennsylvania
Wisconsin

This alignment is available on your Great Lakes in My World CD in the "Standards" folder and on-line at http://www.greatlakes.org/ GLiMWstandards.

materials

- Milk, cream, soy milk or egg substitute cartons (half gallon carton for Superior, quart for Michigan and Huron, 8 ounce for Erie and Ontario)

  OR

  clear plastic soda bottles (two liter for Lake Superior, 24 oz bottles for Michigan and Huron, 12 oz for Erie and Ontario)
- 4-5 straws
- Duct tape
- Scissors
- CD photographs of models
- Journal pages
- Optional: Poem "Drip Drop" pg. 418
- Optional: Hot glue gun

background

The Great Lakes are among the largest bodies of surface freshwater on Earth. Despite their size, the lakes are still susceptible to the effects of contaminants. Any substance that is not naturally present in the environment, or that is present in environmentally harmful concentrations, is considered a contaminant. Contaminants are washed into the lakes via rivers and streams, or through pipes and discharge outlets. The lakes are also exposed to contaminants through atmospheric deposition.

The Great Lakes contain 20 percent of the world's surface freshwater. Less than one percent of the water is renewed each year through precipitation, groundwater and surface water. The lakes have relatively long water retention times - the time span for water to move through the system - that make them nearly closed systems. Due to a relatively low outflow rate, contaminants don't leave the lakes quickly. A fraction of some contaminants can be "removed" from the system by volatilization, which is a form of evaporation. A fraction can be broken down in the water and another fraction buried in bottom sediments. The rest can be removed by the slow flushing of the system.

While some lake contaminants break down quickly, others are long-lasting, or "persistent." Persistent contaminants generally bioaccumulate, reaching higher levels in organisms than in the surrounding water. In open water, contaminant levels are often difficult to detect. Persistence of contaminants can lead to contaminant levels harmful to the ecosystem. Several factors make the Great Lakes particularly susceptible to the effects of persistent contaminants:

- nearly closed system;
- long water retention time;
- low biological productivity;
- low suspended solids concentrations;
- the presence of a largely self-contained fish and wildlife population dependent on the lakes for food and water;
- heavy concentration of industries and large population centers surrounding the lakes; and
- huge surface areas susceptible to airborne contaminants.

The Great Lakes food chain's lowest level is occupied by phytoplankton -- microscopic plants that absorb their necessary nutrients from the water. As phytoplankton absorb nitrogen and phosphorus, they also collect contaminants and are eaten by zooplankton, which, in turn, are eaten by progressively larger fish. Phytoplankton probably get most of their contaminants from the dissolved fraction of contaminants in the water column.

Although pollutants may be excreted by a fish, most of the persistent contaminants are stored in the soft, fatty tissue and gradually build up, or bioaccumulate. Persistent contaminant concentrations in older, larger lake fish such as lake trout and salmon may be more than a million times higher per unit weight than concentrations in the surrounding lake water. The process by which a contaminant increases in concentration as it rises in the food chain is called biomagnification.

Further studies and cleanup activities are planned for the Great Lakes. Although some contaminant inputs are decreasing, decades-old contaminated sediments continue to be a costly problem.

....

procedure

Part One

1. If time, have students take turns reading the poem Drip Drop on page 418 (if they did not read it during Water Flow) to understand the direction of water flow in the Great Lakes. Students can also look at their maps from Water Flow that show the direction of water flow in the Great Lakes. Discuss the direction of the water flow. Where does the water in the Great Lakes come from? *Originally, from glaciers.* If all the water flows toward the Saint Lawrence Seaway, why is there always water in the Great Lakes? *There is water continually being added to the system through surface water (tributaries), groundwater and precipitation. In this way the water is replenished. Water is also constantly evaporating and being used by humans.*

2. Ask students to explain why the water moves from Superior, to Huron/Michigan, to Erie, to Ontario. *This is due to the different elevations of the Great Lakes, with Superior being at the highest elevation (183 meters) and Ontario being at the lowest (74 meters). Gravity is the force moving the water to lower levels.* Why do we care about water flow in the Great Lakes? *We rely on this water for drinking, irrigation, swimming, and shipping. Because the system is interconnected, when something happens to one lake, it can affect the rest of the system.*

3. How long does water stay in the each of the Great Lakes? *This is called the retention rate and is different for each lake, longer for the larger lakes and shorter for the smaller ones.*

4. Tell students they will be making a model of the way water flows in the Great Lakes. Note: If there is enough time, students can work in small groups and use materials to create their own models and demonstrate them for the class. If doing this, they should be given lake elevations, retention times and volumes to work with.

5. Brainstorm a list of what a model would need to have to show what happens to the water flow in the Great Lakes. *Water, lakes at different elevations and with different volumes, groundwater, precipitation, evaporation.* Some of the models may not have all of these details, but students should know what their model is missing that makes it different from the actual Great Lakes system.

procedure continued

6. Work with student ideas to create a model of the Great Lakes by connecting (duct tape will work) different sized containers together to represent each lake. The containers should have a notch cut on the side adjoining another "lake" container to allow the water to flow through. The size of the notch will determine the flow between the "lakes." Make a larger notch between Lakes Superior and Huron. The notch from Huron to Michigan can be smaller. A big notch between Huron and Erie mimics the low retention rate of Lake Huron; a long notch between Lakes Erie and Ontario simulates shallow Lake Erie. If you make the model out of plastic containers, cut holes in the plastic between the "lakes" and use cut pieces of straws to guide the water between them. Use duct tape or hot glue to create a seal around the straw's entry holes on Lakes Michigan and Ontario to ensure their water levels will be higher than Lakes Huron and Erie. Have students predict and record what happens when water is poured through the model. After placing the model in a basin, pour some water into each "lake" so students understand that the lakes always have water in them. Put a half-gallon of water into the Lake Superior half-gallon "lake." *Remind students that this represents initial glacial melt, 191 years of precipitation, surface water inflow, and groundwater replenishment, as well as evaporation and water withdrawals.* Then pour additional water into "Lake Superior." This will cause water to flow throughout the model. What does this mean for the actual Great Lakes? How do lake levels in one lake effect another lake?

7. Students create a diagram that shows what happened.

Part Two

1. Pollution Experiment: Tell students they will be working in small groups to create an experiment that uses the model.

2. Have a "Questions Only" brainstorm about what happens to pollution in the Great Lakes. Do not take answers, but have the students generate additional questions about pollution in the Great Lakes. *Questions might include: Will some lakes stay polluted longer than others? If one lake is polluted, will others become polluted as well? Which ones?*

3. In small groups, have the students choose one of the questions on the list and design an experiment around that question. Remind them that not all questions are possible to answer in an experiment. Put the scientific method on the board so that students can refer to it:

   a. Observe an aspect of the universe.
   b. Hypothesize an explanation of your observation.
   c. Make predictions and decide on a procedure.
   d. Test the predictions by experimentation and further observation and then modify hypothesis.
   e. Repeat steps c and d.

4. Give the students the elevation list, retention rates, and lake volume. Circulate to help students and ask guiding questions as students are creating experiments.

5. Get an idea of what students will need for their experiments and have them bring it from home if you do not have it in the classroom.

Part Three

1. Have the students conduct their experiment for the class, stating their hypothesis beforehand.

2. Students write up their experiment in a lab report and create charts to display their data.

wrap-up

1. Explain that in the past, Lake Erie has had major problems with pollution. Put drops of dark food coloring into the Lake Erie container in the model (1/2 pint works) so that the water darkens. Pour another ½ pint of clean water into "Lake Erie," explaining that it takes 2.5 years for water in Lake Erie to be replaced (retention time). Is the water clean? *No, the water is not clean as only half of the food coloring will be gone.*

2. Count how many 2.5 flushing cycles it takes to make Lake Erie look clean. How many years is this? *Answers will vary. Explain that it took Lake Erie about 15 years to become significantly cleaner after the pollution was better managed.*

3. How would the situation be different if it was Lake Superior that was polluted? *Pollution would eventually get into all the other lakes. When water leaves the Great Lakes, where does it go? The Gulf of Saint Lawrence, and then into the Atlantic Ocean.*

4. Have students create a list of the ways they can help keep the Great Lakes clean.

sources

This activity has been adapted with permission from ES-EAGLS, Great Lakes Climate and Water Movement, Ohio Sea Grant.

Wisconsin Sea Grant
http://www.seagrant.wisc.edu/education/

The Great Lakes: An Environmental Atlas and Resource Book
http://www.epa.gov/glnpo/atlas/intro.html

assessment

Rubric on page 464

8 | Water in Motion

GRADE LEVEL
4-8

FIRST NAME

LAST NAME

Lake	Retention rate	Volume			
Lake Superior	191 years	12,100 km^3	or	12,100,000,000,000,000 liters	(2,900 mi^3)
Lake Michigan	99 years	4,920 km^3	or	4,920,000,000,000,000 liters	(1,180 mi^3)
Lake Huron	22 years	3,540 km^3	or	3,540,000,000,000,000 liters	(850 mi^3)
Lake Ontario	6 years	1,640 km^3	or	1,640,000,000,000,000 liters	(393 mi^3)
Lake Erie	2.6 years	484 km^3	or	484,000,000,000,000 liters	(116 mi^3)

[1] a. What does "retention rate" mean?

....

....

....

b. Using the table, determine which lakes have the shortest and longest retention rate.

....

....

....

c. Why does each lake have a different retention rate?

....

....

....

[2] What components would a model need in order to show what happens to water flow
in the Great Lakes?

....

....

....

....

....

....

....

....

....

....

....

APPROVED BY

8 | Water in Motion

GRADE LEVEL
4-8

FIRST NAME																						
LAST NAME																						

[3] Predict what happens when water is poured through the model.

....

....

....

....

....

....

[4] Diagram what happens when water is poured through the model.

[5] Why do we care about water flow in the Great Lakes?

....

....

....

....

[6] Brainstorm 3 questions to investigate in your experiment.

....

....

....

....

....

....

APPROVED BY	

8 | Water in Motion

FIRST NAME																					
LAST NAME																					

[7] Design your experiment.

a. What question are you trying to test?

....
....
....

b. What predictions do you have?

....
....
....
....

c. What will your procedure be?

....
....
....
....
....
....

d. What are your results and conclusions?

....
....
....
....
....
....
....
....
....
....
....
....

APPROVED BY	

9 | Whose Water?

summary

Students research, discuss and debate views on Great Lakes water withdrawals and exportation by taking different roles in the issue.

objectives

- Research varying views on the export of Great Lakes water.
- Defend one view on the export of Great Lakes water.
- Evaluate a debate.
- Articulate his or her personal belief regarding the export of Great Lakes water.

prerequisite

Water, Water Everywhere and Water Flow

vocabulary

Diversion: The transfer of water from one watershed to another
Great Lakes watershed: The lands where water from the ground, rivers and streams flow into the Great Lakes
Great Lakes basin: Great Lakes watershed

setting

INDOORS

subjects

Social Studies, Language Arts, Environmental Science, Hydrology

standards

This Great Lakes in My World activity is aligned to the Common Core State Standards and to state learning standards in:

Illinois
Indiana
Michigan
Minnesota
New York
Ohio
Pennsylvania
Wisconsin

This alignment is available on your Great Lakes in My World CD in the "Standards" folder and on-line at http://www.greatlakes.org/GLiMWstandards.

materials

- Fact sheet (p. 441)
- Related news articles (on cd)
- Role cards
- Journal pages
- Pencils
- Clear plastic bag with holes in it

background

Water exportation information for students:

Fishbowl Debate

The style of debate the students will be using is called a fishbowl. Half of the class will debate while the other half, in a circle around the debaters, observes. The students switch between debaters and observers half-way through the time period. The observers may not speak during the debate. Their job is to take notes on the behavior of the debaters. Before students trade roles, the observers will report on their observations. The class may discuss ways to make the next round of debate more successful.

Export of Great Lakes Water

Are the waters of the Great Lakes at risk from being diverted to too many places around the United States and the world? In the next 25 years, at least 55 percent more freshwater than is now available will be needed to satisfy the growing global population. Communities in the United States and around the world are outgrowing their water supply.

The Great Lakes states and provinces depend on the Great Lakes for their drinking water and economy. Great Lakes water helps produce 60 percent of North America's steel and cars. The overall production in the Great Lakes states and provinces is about $2 trillion annually, which is more than any other country in the world except Japan and the economy of the United States as a whole. The sport fishing industry is worth $7 billion annually. Great Lakes waters provide drinking water for over 33 million people living in the watershed (Great Lakes basin).

The Great Lakes contain 20 percent of the world's fresh surface water, but only one percent of it is renewed through precipitation, groundwater and surface water (tributaries, snowmelt). This means that if the Great Lakes are too heavily used as a water source we could start to deplete the lakes themselves. There are already water shortages in many parts of the Great Lakes basin including Green Bay, Wisconsin, Chicago, Illinois, Saginaw, Monroe and Oakland counties in Michigan, areas in northwestern Ohio, Rochester, New York and Waterloo, Ontario. For an example of what has happened to the Aral Sea, another freshwater "inland sea," like the Great Lakes, see: http://nailaokda.8m.com/aral.html

The eight states and two provinces within the Great Lakes basin are working together to find a way to manage and protect the Great Lakes from overuse. It is important that this be done together because the largest negative impacts to the Great Lakes are from the combined effect of the many withdrawals and uses within each of the states and provinces, not from one use alone.

The Great Lakes governors and premiers signed a non-binding agreement called the Great Lakes St. Lawrence Basin Water Resources Agreement in December 2005. In December 2008 a binding companion agreement known as the Great Lakes St. Lawrence Basin Water Resources Compact went into effect in the eight Great Lake states following the approval of the Great Lake state legislatures, the U.S. Congress and the President. The Compact and Agreement prohibit diversions from the Great Lakes except for certain public water supplies who meet the following conditions:

1. There are no alternative water supplies, including conservation of existing water supplies.
2. Water that is used must be returned (minus what was consumed).
3. The water withdrawal does not hurt the Great Lakes, including inland lakes, rivers, stream, wetland, fish and wildlife habitat.
4. Water uses must include conservation planning and implementation.
5. Water uses comply with all municipal, state, federal and tribal laws.
6. Water use must be efficient, supportive of balanced development, and avoid or decrease negative impacts.

The Compact and Agreement also include provisions establishing basin-wide water management and water conservation programs. Each state or province creates their own program following the regulations and suggestions of the Compact and Agreement.

There was much debate over the Compact and Agreement and what they should look like. The debate was between groups that include: industrial users, agriculturalists, municipalities and environmentalists. Generally, the industrial users were concerned that regulations will negatively affect the economy. Because agriculturalists produce food we eat, many do not feel they should be part of any water use regulations and their uses should be exempt. Municipal water suppliers that give water to many of our homes are generally supportive but do not always want to return the water after it is used because it is expensive to build the pipelines to do so. Environmentalists are supportive of the new Compact and Agreement as they believe such measures are necessary to protect the Great Lakes for future generations.

For current updates on this issue,
see: www.greatlakes.org

procedure

Part One: Large group discussion

1. Introduce the topic of diversions and exportation of Great Lakes water and give a flavor for how controversial the issue is. Tell students they will study the issue and participate in a debate about it. Fill a clear plastic bag with water and poke several holes in it, while holding it over a sink or a bucket. Ask students to explain how this is similar to water withdrawals and diversions in the Great Lakes. How is it different? *In the Great Lakes, water diversions can be very large, like for the City of Chicago, or smaller. They can be ongoing for companies or for communities. In any case, they involve taking water from the Great Lakes. Keep in mind that the Great Lakes are glacial deposits that are, for the most part, non-renewable. Each year only one percent of the waters in the Great Lakes are renewable through precipitation, tributaries and groundwater.*

2. Discuss what makes a good debate. Have students brainstorm a list of ideas for ways to make the debate successful. *List might include: Listening to each other, talking loudly enough for others to hear, being polite, choosing a moderator to facilitate.*

3. Students review the information about Great Lakes water exportation. They should read the information on page 441 and/or the additional news articles on the compact disc. If they do not individually read all the articles, they can then break into small groups to teach each other about the one article they have read. Students should summarize their article to share with the other students.

4. As a class, brainstorm a list of relevant characters involved in water diversions, which can be gleaned from the fact sheet or articles the students read. Another option is to give students the included "role cards."

5. As a class, decide on the roles needed for the debate or have students work in teams to create solid arguments for the roles provided on the "role cards." For example, there could be a group of residents or a water company group that work together on preparing their role for the debate.

6. Once roles have been chosen, students should review their own roles, as well as the roles of others within the community for best preparation. Students create a written summary of the statements they would like to contribute to the debate. In addition students should write a three-five sentence summary of their personal beliefs on the water export issue.

Part Two

1. Review the elements of a successful debate and the guidelines for the fishbowl method. Divide the class into observers and debaters.

2. The moderator (educator, or can be another student) calls the class to order.

3. Each character group will have two minutes to make an initial statement. Once this is complete, each will have two minutes to make counter arguments.

4. Observers should report on their observations. Discuss as a class: What was positive about the debate and how could the debate have been more effective?

5. Trade fishbowl positions and repeat for the second group.

wrap-up

1. Students use their observations of the debate and their written summaries to answer the journal questions and discuss them as a class.

extension

1. Student can write an essay summarizing the Great Lakes water diversion issue and explaining his/her stance on the issue. Opinions should be backed up by facts found either in independent research or the news articles provided.

2. If the class is so inclined, students can write a letter to their senator or representative expressing their views on Great Lakes protections. A list of senators and their addresses can be found at the U.S. Senate's homepage.

assessment

Rubric on page 465

resources

Alliance for the Great Lakes
http://www.greatlakes.org/waterconservation

Roll cards

A

You are the mayor of a large city on the Great Lakes. You want your constituents to enjoy their community, drink clean water from the city's waterworks and have access to the lake. But you also want more manufacturing, which might use more water, in your city so there are more jobs for people. And good that are manufactured will be transported through the local port. It will cost your constituents and employers less money if they use less water. Discuss your views and ideas for getting an entire city to conserve water. Consider the affect that lake water levels have on transporting goods to market.

B

You are the chief executive officer of a water bottling plant. Why are you concerned about Great Lakes water exports? You know that your water diversion from a Great Lakes stream has caused it to run dry, but do not plans to change to a new business. You want your business to be as profitable as possible. Many local people are employed at your plant. Develop your character and opinion.

C

You are a third generation farmer in a place where freshwater is becoming increasingly unavailable for you to use to water your crops. As a farmer, you do not feel that you should have to be concerned with new water use laws. After all, you are growing food for people in the region. Develop your character and opinion.

D

You are a resident in a community just outside of the Great Lakes watershed. Because you are outside of the watershed, your community cannot access Great Lakes water. The water you drink has some pollutants in it that could make you sick. What are your options? If Great Lakes water isn't available to you, what will you drink? If water is made available to you, how do you argue that thirsty states in the southeast shouldn't get Great Lakes water also? How do you draw the line?

E

You own a coal-fired power plant that uses water in order to run your plant. Your plant supplies electricity to customers inside and outside of the watershed. You think the new law might put too many restrictions on this use and affect the cost of electricity that is used by manufacturers in your community. If a requirement is to return the water you use back to the lake, can you afford to build the pipeline to do this if it's cheaper to discharge the water to a stream that runs the other way? You have a family and are concerned about the future and enjoy fishing on the Great Lakes.

F

You manage a local marina and you like to sail. Your customers are already having trouble getting their boats to open water because of low lake levels. Consider how a new law that prohibits diversions will affect boaters. When you are not at the marina, you like going to the beach with our family. Because of low lake levels, the beach is bigger than it was last year and you enjoy having a bigger beach. However, you are concerned about the future of the Great lakes for your children. Consider how the new law will impact your children.

9 | Whose Water?

GRADE LEVEL
6-8

journal pages

FIRST NAME																						
LAST NAME																						

[1] List the elements of a good debate.

....

....

....

....

....

[2] Write three sentences summarizing the fact sheet or your article on water
exportation/diversions.

a. ....

....

....

....

b. ....

....

....

c. ....

....

....

....

[3] List possible characters that would be involved in a debate on water diversions and
exportation. Circle the characters the class chooses for the classroom debate.

....

....

....

....

....

....

....

APPROVED BY	

9 | Whose Water?

GRADE LEVEL
6-8

journal pages

FIRST NAME																					
LAST NAME																					

[4] My character in the water diversions debate: _____

[5] Brainstorm a list of water diversion/exportation issues that are relevant to your character.

....

....

....

....

[6] Write three-five sentences summarizing how you/your group will contribute to the debate on behalf of your character.

....

....

....

....

....

....

[7] Write three-five sentences summarizing your personal beliefs on the water diversion issue. Explain if they are similar or different to your character in the debate.

....

....

....

....

....

....

....

....

APPROVED BY	

9 | Whose Water?

GRADE LEVEL
6-8

journal   pages

FIRST NAME																				
LAST NAME																				

[8] Write your opening statement here: (you will have 2 minutes to present this statement)

....

....

....

....

....

....

[9] MaKe notes here during the debate for your counter argument: (2 minutes)

....

....

....

....

....

....

....

Water Exportation

[10] How has your initial stance on the issue changed or not changed as a result of the debate?

....

....

....

....

....

[11] What maKes this a difficult issue to debate?

....

....

....

....

....

APPROVED BY	

9 | Whose Water?

GRADE LEVEL
6-8

journal pages

FIRST NAME

LAST NAME

[12] Which group do you believe had the strongest argument? Explain why you feel it was strong.

[13] What made this debate work well?

[14] What aspects of the debate could be improved?

[15] Why is it important to learn about and listen to all sides of an issue?

[16] What are the main points you are making in your essay and/or letter about this issue?

APPROVED BY

9 | Whose Water?

FIRST NAME																			
LAST NAME																			

[1] If you do further research on Great Lakes water diversions, record the information below. Write down the source, title and author. Then write a three-sentence summary of each source.

a.   Source:
      Title:
      Author:
      Summary:

....

....

....

b.   Source:
      Title:
      Author:
      Summary:

....

....

....

c.   Source:
      Title:
      Author:
      Summary:

....

....

....

[2] What are the arguments presented in the articles? Be sure to pay attention to all sides of the issue!

....

....

....

....

....

APPROVED BY	

INVESTIGATE

10 | Global Climate Change

GRADE LEVEL
6-8

90 minutes

summary

Students participate in demonstrations and discussions about the greenhouse effect and global warming with regard to the Great Lakes.

objectives

- Explain the greenhouse effect and global warming.
- Design an experiment that demonstrates the greenhouse effect and global warming.
- Discuss the impact of global warming on freshwater in the Great Lakes watershed.

prerequisite

Water, Water Everywhere

vocabulary

Global warming: rise in the Earth's temperature which results from an increase in heat-trapping gases in the atmosphere

Greenhouse effect: natural phenomenon that keeps the Earth in a temperature range that allows life to flourish

setting

INDOORS

subjects

Social Studies, Geology, Ecology, Hydrology

standards

This Great Lakes in My World activity is aligned to the Common Core State Standards and to state learning standards in:

Illinois
Indiana
Michigan
Minnesota
New York
Ohio
Pennsylvania
Wisconsin

This alignment is available on your Great Lakes in My World CD in the "Standards" folder and on-line at http://www.greatlakes.org/GLiMWstandards.

materials

- Journals
- Pencils
- Articles on compact disc
- Two glass jars of same size with lids
- Clear container with lid (big enough to hold one of the smaller jars)
- Two thermometers
- Heat lamps

background

The Great Lakes basin contains 20 percent of the Earth's fresh surface water. A change in climate will alter water availability and quality in the Great Lakes, the region's groundwater and in the many wetlands, lakes, and streams in the region. Throughout this century, the region's climate is expected to become warmer in both summer and winter. Projected changes in seasonal precipitation are that winter and spring precipitation could increase, while summer rain could decrease by as much as 50 percent. Heavy summer downpours are likely to become more frequent, with dry periods in between, and lake levels are expected to drop overall. Some of these changes have already been detected in regional climate trends. The Great Lakes region depends on water for drinking, shipping, irrigation, and industrial processes.

Possible Changes

A change in the climate could cause a number of impacts in the Great Lake region:

- More heavy rainfall and flooding;
- Worsening water quality due to higher water temperatures and heavy run-off that transports pollutants, nutrients and sediment;
- Lower groundwater recharge rates;
- Less soil moisture in summer, which could harm crops, forests and ecosystems;
- Wetland and wildlife habitat losses and reduction of flood retention and water purifying functions;
- Drying up of smaller streams during the summer season as a result of earlier snow melt and lower summer water levels;
- Changes in fish distribution due to warmer lake and stream water temperatures; increased risk of dead-zones in lakes; and
- Lower lake levels due to higher evaporation and reduced ice cover.

What's Going On?

The Greenhouse Effect and Global Warming
The "greenhouse effect" refers to the natural phenomenon that keeps the Earth in a temperature range that allows life to flourish. The sun's energy keeps the Earth's surface and atmosphere warm. When this energy radiates from the Earth back toward space as heat, some of it is absorbed by heat-trapping gases (including carbon dioxide and methane) in the atmosphere, which creates an insulating layer. The greenhouse effect keeps the Earth's average temperature at 59 degrees Fahrenheit (15 degrees Celsius). Without it, the average surface temperature would be 0 degrees Fahrenheit (-18 degrees Celsius), a temperature so low that the Earth would be frozen and would not be able to sustain life. This is called the greenhouse effect because it is the same process that occurs in a greenhouse: the glass reflects some of the heat back into the room instead of letting it escape.

"Global warming" refers to the rise in the Earth's temperature which results from an increase in heat-trapping gases in the atmosphere. Global warming is caused when increased levels of greenhouse gases such as carbon dioxide cause additional amounts of the sun's energy to be reflected back to the Earth as heat.

What Causes Global Warming?

Scientists have concluded that human activities are contributing to global warming by adding large amounts of heat-trapping gases to the atmosphere. Our use of fossil fuels is the main source of these gases. We use fossil fuels when drive a car, use electricity from coal-fired power plants, or heat our homes with oil or natural gas. The second most important source of greenhouse gases is deforestation (forests hold and store carbon), and other land-use changes.

What Can We Do About Global Warming?

We can take action to reduce emissions of heat-trapping gases. Governments can adopt different options for reducing greenhouse gas emissions. They can:

- increase energy efficiency standards;
- encourage the use of renewable energy (wind and solar power);
- eliminate subsidies that encourage the use of coal and oil by making them artificially cheap; and
- protect and restore forests, which serve as important storehouses of carbon.

Individuals can reduce the need for fossil fuels and often save money. They can:

- drive less and driving more fuel-efficient and less-polluting cars;
- use energy-efficient appliances;
- insulate homes;
- use less electricity or choose environmentally-friendly power, when there is an option;
- plant a tree, as they store carbon and provide much needed shade in the summer, reducing energy bills and fossil fuel use; and
- let elected officials know you are concerned.

For more information, see: Union of Concerned Scientists
http://www.ucsusa.org/greatlakes/glsolutionsperson.html

Global Warming Diagram

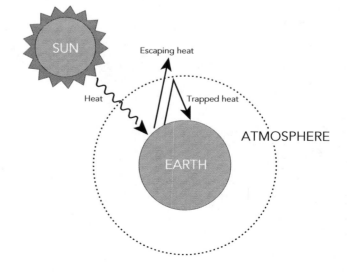

procedure

Depending on the time allotted for this activity, the articles could be assigned as homework prior to the class activity. If students read the articles in class, each student can be responsible for one article. Students can be placed in discussion groups of four, with each member of the group responsible for a different article. Both experiments for the greenhouse effect and global warming can be run simultaneously.

Part One

1. Discuss the greenhouse effect and global warming with the students. They can read the previous page and/or the fact sheets included on the compact disc for background information.

2. Show the students the jars and thermometers. Ask the student to design an experiment that uses jars and thermometers to test the difference in temperature of air trapped and not trapped by the greenhouse effect. What are students' hypotheses?

3. Here is one way to show the greenhouse effect: Place a thermometer in a glass jar and secure the lid. Put the jar near the window in the classroom. Place another thermometer next to the jar. Have students record the set-up in their journals. Record the initial temperatures and take two additional readings at timed intervals. If you need to do this activity in a shorter time frame, try using heat lamps in place of sunlight to speed the process. The temperature in the jar should be higher than the one outside of the jar. Ask students to record the temperatures in their journals.

4. Have students discuss with a partner the reason for the temperature difference. Students should understand that the jar represents the atmosphere. Allow a few students to share their ideas with the class. *This is the result of a greenhouse effect caused by the glass jar. Some of the heat from the sun is trapped inside of the jar, just as the atmosphere traps some of the heat from the sun. Be clear that this is a natural process that does not have a negative impact on the Earth's climate unless unusually high levels of gases in the atmosphere increase the effect. Explain that when more greenhouse gases are in the atmosphere, the greenhouse effect is enhanced, and the temperature of the Earth rises. This happens because there is more gas to reflect the heat back to Earth than there was before.*

5. Ask students how they might use the jar and thermometers to demonstrate global warming. What would be needed to increase the greenhouse effect in the jar? How would one know whether the temperature had increased or not—and what would be the basis for comparison? (Show students the available materials.)

6. Here's one way to show global warming: Place one thermometer in each of the glass jars and secure the lids. Place one of the jars inside of the larger glass/plastic container and close the lid. Place the jars next to each other near the window. Students should record this in their journals.

7. Record the initial temperatures and take two additional readings at timed intervals (depending on circumstances). As above, use a heat lamp to speed the process if necessary. The temperature inside the double jar should be warmer than the one inside the single jar. Have students record the temperatures again. During this time, students can be working on the questions and articles provided.

8. Have students explain to a partner the reason for the difference in temperatures and what the jars represent. Allow a few students to share their responses with the class and have all students record in their journals. *The jars represent the atmosphere. The double jar represents an increased level of greenhouse gases in the atmosphere. The temperature inside the double jar should be higher than the one in the single jar because the double jar prevented even more of the heat from leaving the atmosphere.*

9. Ask students what they think is the source of the additional carbon dioxide in the atmosphere that causes global warming. *The source is the burning of fossil fuels. Particularly, cars, coal-burning factories. Oil and coal store large amounts of carbon. When the oil and coal are burned, the carbon is released as carbon dioxide. The current rate at which we are burning fossil fuels is higher than it's ever been.*

10. Have students read fact sheets (included on compact disc). Break students into small groups. Have them brainstorm a list of possible effects of global warming. See background for additional information. Ask students if the temperatures are the same or varied across the globe. Where are the warmer areas and where are the cooler areas? Why? Ask students to discuss whether they think the temperature increase will be uniform around the globe, or if it will vary. *There are many factors that can influence climate, including latitude, ocean currents, wind currents and mountain ranges.* Ask students to discuss whether they think the changes in evaporation and precipitation will be uniform or will vary. *The rates will vary. Some areas will experience a loss of water, and others a gain. The Earth will still have approximately the same amount of water. What will be different is the location of the water—whether it is in the atmosphere, on land or in the ocean.* Have the groups share their ideas.

procedure continued

Part Two

1. In their small groups, have students discuss the fact sheets after they have read them. They should share their summary sentences and ask each other any questions they have about the articles.

2. Go back to the jars in the window. Place a bottle cap full of water in each jar. Again, one of the jars should be doubled, to represent increased levels of greenhouse gases in the atmosphere. Over time, you will be able to see the water from the caps evaporating and condensing on the glass. After one hour, check which cap has lost more water. The bottle caps of water represent freshwater supplies on Earth. Have students record in their journals, and explain the reason for the difference to a partner. *The atmosphere (jars) trapped heat, causing water to evaporate. The double jar, or atmosphere with increased gases, trapped more heat, which caused more water to evaporate.*

3. The increase in solar radiation drives the increase in evaporation. But where does this evaporated water go? Discuss. *Some stays in the atmosphere as water vapor, and some condenses and precipitates elsewhere. Freshwater for drinking comes from rivers, lakes and groundwater. If these freshwater sources are depleted through evaporation, can they be reconstituted somehow? Some of the water that evaporates will probably rain down into these freshwater sources. Some of the freshwater will end up in the ocean or in soil that cannot hold and preserve it like an aquifer does.*

wrap-up

1. What is the potential problem with this global climate change? Have students think back to Water, Water Everywhere. *With an increase in evaporation, more freshwater may become undrinkable, further reducing our drinking water supply.*

2. Ask students what impact this might have on the Great Lakes. *The water level in the Great Lakes may be reduced and the soils in the Great Lakes basin could decrease in moisture level. This could cause a shortage of drinking water for people in or around the basin. This could also have an impact on agriculture, which requires high amounts of water for irrigation.*

3. What impact does the global warming scenario have on the responsibility of the people who govern the Great Lakes? *It increases the need for the Great Lakes to be protected so they remain a viable source of drinking water. In addition, the governors of the Great Lakes will have the responsibility of managing the water. They will need to decide whether or not it is best to share the water outside of the basin, and what is a sustainable way to manage the water. Great Lakes governors can also take steps to reduce emissions of greenhouse gases.*

4. What impact does global warming have on the responsibility of individuals? *Individuals can do their part by reducing their own water and energy consumption.*

extension

Have students write an essay describing the impact of global warming on the Great Lakes and what they can do to help minimize it.

sources

Union of Concerned Scientists: Global Environment
http://www.ucsusa.org/greatlakes/

U.S. Environmental Protection Agency: Global Warming - Impacts
http://yosemite1.epa.gov/EE/epa/wpi.nsf/fa5b1c5d41f058f58525 66a20074f17c/0e4e53113f856d848525751b0070e6d3/$FILE/ Lindzen-12-9-08.pdf

Global Warming: Early Warning Signs
http://www.climatehotmap.org/impacts/greatlakes.html

 We value your thoughts and feedback on Great Lakes in My World. Please let us know about any oversights, errors or omissions you find, or if there are things you or your students particularly like.

Send your comments to: education@greatlakes.org

assessment

Rubric on page 465

10 | Global Climate Change

GRADE LEVEL
6-8

FIRST NAME																			
LAST NAME																			

Greenhouse effect

[1] Draw the set-up of the greenhouse effect demonstration. Include the thermometers, jars, and sun or heat lamps. Label the diagram and what each element represents.

[2] Record the temperatures on each thermometer.

Initial Reading: _____   _____

Temperature Reading #1: _____   _____

Temperature Reading #2: _____   _____

[3] What is the reason for the temperature difference?

....

....

....

....

[4] What is the greenhouse effect?

....

....

....

....

....

....

APPROVED BY	

10 | Global Climate Change

GRADE LEVEL
6-8

FIRST NAME																					
LAST NAME																					

GLOBAL WARMING

[5] Draw the set-up of the global warming demonstration. Include all of the materials, the sun, and the placement of the jars. Label what each element represents.

[6] Record the temperatures on both thermometers.

Initial Reading: _____   _____

Temperature Reading #1: _____   _____

Temperature Reading #2: _____   _____

[7] What is the reason for the temperature difference?

....
....
....
....
....

[8] What is global warming?

....
....
....
....
....

APPROVED BY	

10 | Global Climate Change

GRADE LEVEL
6-8

journal ≡ pages

FIRST NAME

LAST NAME

[9] What are the sources of the additional carbon dioxide in the atmosphere that causes global warming?

[10] What are some possible effects of global warming for the Great Lakes region?

[11] What are some possible effects of global warming for your state?

[12] Do you think temperature change due to global warming would be uniform or would vary around the globe? Why?

[13] Do you think changes in evaporation and precipitation would be uniform or would vary around the globe? Why?

APPROVED BY

10 | Global Climate Change

GRADE LEVEL
6-8

journal   pages

FIRST NAME																			
LAST NAME																			

[14] Draw the set-up of the evaporation demonstration. Include all of the materials, the sun, and the placement of the jars. Label what each material represents (for example, the jars represent the atmosphere).

[15] Record the water levels in the caps after one hour.

....

[16] What is the reason for the difference in water levels?

....

....

....

[17] What is the possible impact of global warming on freshwater supplies?

....

....

....

....

....

[18] What can you do about global warming?

....

....

....

....

APPROVED BY	

10 | Global Climate Change

GRADE LEVEL
6-8

FIRST NAME

LAST NAME

[1] Article Name_____

[2] Author_____ Date Written_____

[3] Write down the author's main point.

....
....
....
....

[4] Identify three pieces of evidence that support the author's main point from the article.

a. ....

b. ....

c. ....

[5] Article Name_____

[6] Author_____ Date Written_____

[7] Write down the author's main point.

....
....
....
....

[8] Identify three pieces of evidence that support the author's main point from the article.

a. ....

b. ....

c. ....

APPROVED BY

INVESTIGATE: FINAL PROJECT

11 | Geology of My Home

GRADE LEVEL

K-3

2 hours+

summary

Students use information from previous activities to create an educational piece that conveys the geologic history and present-day significance of the Great Lakes region to their own lives.

objectives

- Use a story to explain the process of the Great Lakes' formation.
- Give examples of the Great Lake's importance to students' own lives.

prerequisite

Looking at Landscape, Follow the Water and Big Changes

vocabulary

None

setting

INDOORS

subjects

Geology, Hydrology, History

standards

This Great Lakes in My World activity is aligned to the Common Core State Standards and to state learning standards in:

Illinois
Indiana
Michigan
Minnesota
New York
Ohio
Pennsylvania
Wisconsin

This alignment is available on your Great Lakes in My World CD in the "Standards" folder and on-line at http://www.greatlakes.org/ GLiMWstandards.

materials

- Research materials
- Journals
- Paper
- Art supplies

background

Most information should be in students' journals from previous activities.

....

procedure

1. Tell students they will make books that highlight the formation and significance of the Great Lakes landscape in their lives. Students' stories should be communicated through pictures and descriptive text.

2. Ask the class to name some of the things they have learned in the unit that they thought were exciting or important. *List may include things such as: the Great Lakes were formed by glaciers, the formation process took a long time, glaciers are very large, the water in the Great Lakes moves through the lakes and the water cycle, the Great Lakes landscape is important in my life.* Write the list on the board.

3. Ask students if they could tell their parents something about the formation of the Great Lakes, what it would be? It is important that students make the decisions about how the Great Lakes landscape ties in with their lives and what is relevant to include in their books. Included here are suggestions for the layout of the books and the details of the pages. Students should cover at least two of the concepts outlined in the suggestions below.

4. Allow time for some discussion about the list the students have created on the board. What memories do they have from the unit that stand out most and why? Which seem the most important? Which ones do they think should be included in the books?

5. Mark the items on the list that the class has chosen for their books. This is a guideline for what they might do. Some students may choose to make some changes to the list for their own books.

6. Provide paper and art supplies for the students to make the pages of their books. Choose a book binding method that works well for you. An easy method is to punch two or three in the sides of the pages, then tie the pages together with yarn, string, or ribbon once the books are complete. It may be easiest for the educator to punch the holes in the paper in advance.

7. Tell students to look back through their journals for ideas, pictures and information to help them along the way, but guide students through the creation of the book through discussion and questions.

Suggestions
Students should create pages for two of the following suggestions, and should make sure to include a page that addresses why they think the Great Lakes are important.

- Describe the Great Lakes landscape during glaciation. For this page, students should imagine what the glaciers looked like based on what they have seen and discussed during the unit. For example, students might draw ice and snow. Students could also include a page showing the size of themselves or their homes compared to the glacier to give an example of the scale.

- Describe the landscape as it is today (after the glaciation). For this picture, students may work from their journal pages from Looking at Landscape, or may go outside to create new pictures if time and location permits. Students can draw one picture that includes the lake and one picture that describe the landscape around their home or school.

- Show that water moves through the water cycle and through the five lakes. Students may choose to highlight a few parts of the water cycle or draw a map of the lakes with arrows showing the water flow.

- Convey the significance of the landscape in students' lives. Students may describe activities they do on/in the landscape such as bike riding, swimming, drinking water or sledding. These pages should include the activity and a particular place. For example, I ride my bike because it is flat, I sled in the park because it is hilly, or I swim in the lake.

....

wrap-up

1. Have students share their stories with the rest of the class (or another class) by reading them aloud and showing the pictures.

assessment

Rubric on page 466

INVESTIGATE: FINAL PROJECT

12 | Shaped by Geology

GRADE LEVEL
4-8

90 – 180 minutes

Developmental Modifications: Students in grades 6-8 can write an essay explaining what they have learned in the unit as a part of their final assessment.

summary

Students synthesize the information from previous activities to create an educational piece that conveys the geologic history, and the present-day significance of the Great Lakes region for their own lives.

objectives

- Explain the significance of the geologic changes in the Great Lakes areas.
- Document the process of geologic change in the Great Lakes basin.
- Work cooperatively in small groups.
- Create a book based on geologic facts.
- Evaluate other groups' work.

prerequisite

Timelines, Looking at Landscape, Landscape Changes

vocabulary

None

setting

INDOORS

subjects

Geology, Hydrology, History

standards

This Great Lakes in My World activity is aligned to the Common Core State Standards and to state learning standards in:

Illinois
Indiana
Michigan
Minnesota
New York
Ohio
Pennsylvania
Wisconsin

This alignment is available on your Great Lakes in My World CD in the "Standards" folder and on-line at http://www.greatlakes.org/ GLiMWstandards.

materials

- Research materials
- Journals
- Paper
- Art supplies

background

Students will work in small groups or individually to create a book geared towards students in kindergarten through second grade, or a travel booklet for tourists regarding the formation of the Great Lakes. Students highlight the significance of the Great Lakes, the geologic formation, glaciation and water flow.

Much of the necessary information should be in students' journals from previous activities, or can be done as part of this project. Research can be done through observation, the internet, community speakers, books, journals and field trips. Local nature centers and museums may be willing to work with students on their research.

procedure

1. Break students into groups of three to five to work on the project. In the groups, students answer the question: What is the significance of the formation of the Great Lakes? *Responses should include at least one personal reason and, among other things, that the Great Lakes are the largest supply of freshwater in the world.* The answers to the above question should guide students through completion of the book (or brochure).

2. The rest of the book should explain when and how the lakes were formed, and what they physically are like today. To strengthen inquiry, students can be asked to create additional questions and research them or incorporate information from Rock Songs.

3. The storybooks make take any format the students choose, including a travel brochure or children's book. The organization of content may take any format as well. For example, they may choose to cover the time period on one page, glaciation on another, etc; or they may wish to integrate the ideas throughout the storyline.

4. Students should review their journal entries from the unit and conduct any supplementary research as needed to find the information for their books or brochures. Students should take the time to illustrate their projects and may be as creative as possible since they want to attract an audience (younger students or tourists) to their stories.

5. As with any activity, show students the grading rubric so that the expectations are clear.

wrap-up

1. Have students evaluate another group's work.

2. Find opportunities for students to share their books to the intended audience. Hang up the completed storybooks in the school or classroom to share with other students. Students may wish to read their stories to each other or to other classes.

assessment

Rubric on page 466

 We value your thoughts and feedback on Great Lakes in My World. Please let us know about any oversights, errors or omissions you find, or if there are things you or your students particularly like.

Send your comments to: education@greatlakes.org

ELEMENTS	☆☆☆☆	☆☆☆	☆☆	☆
PERSONAL TIMELINE: Student's timeline contains 3-5 significant dates and the student is able to explain a timeline.	Addresses all of the components	Missing one component	Missing two components	Missing three or more components
EARTH'S TIMELINE: Student helps create a sign for a timeline event and marks timeline events in the journal pages. Student explains how her/his personal timeline fits into the timeline of geologic history and discusses the importance of the formation of the Great Lakes to present day inhabitants.	Addresses all of the components	Missing one component	Missing two components	Missing three or more components
PARTICIPATION: Student actively participates in the class discussion by raising her/his hand, making eye-contact with the speakers, referencing prior comments, and providing imaginative insights.	Addresses all of the components	Missing one component	Missing two components	Missing three or more components

CONNECT   2 | Looking at Landscape

ELEMENTS	☆☆☆☆	☆☆☆	☆☆	☆
LAND SKETCH: Student's sketch pays close attention to the details of the landscape. The sketch includes 2-4 different natural landforms. Student used appropriate coloring. The sketch is neat.	Addresses all of the components	Missing one component	Missing two components	Missing three or more components
LAND-USE SKETCH AND DISCUSSION: Student draws a picture of her/himself in the local landscape doing an activity. Student explains why the Great Lakes are important. Student provides a hypothesis as to how the Great Lakes were formed.	Addresses all of the components	Missing one component	Missing two components	Missing three or more components
PARTICIPATION: Student discusses different ways of learning by using senses. Student actively participates in the class discussion by raising his/her hand, making eye-contact with the speakers, and providing imaginative insights.	Addresses all of the components	Missing one component	Missing two components	Missing three or more components

EXPLORE   3 | Water, Water Everywhere

ELEMENTS	☆☆☆☆	☆☆☆	☆☆	☆
PERSONAL WATER CONSUMPTION LOG: Student fills out the log by indicating the type of use as well as the approximate amount of water. Student indicates ways s/he could change her/his habits to conserve water. Student correctly totals amount of water used and potentially saved and graphs the results. Graphs are neat and accurate.	Addresses all of the components	Missing one component	Missing two components	Missing three or more components
ESSAY QUESTIONS: Student thoroughly addresses all of the questions. Student notes trends and patterns in his/her personal water use. Student uses information provided to determine the governors and premiers' responsibility to the Great Lakes and the general public's responsibility. Student brainstorms specific ways s/he could preserve the Great Lakes watershed.	Addresses all of the components	Missing one component	Missing two components	Missing three or more components
PARTICIPATION: Student actively participates in the class discussion by raining his/her hand, making eye-contact with speakers, referencing prior comments, and providing imaginative insights that move the discussion.	Addresses all of the components	Missing one component	Missing two components	Missing three or more components

EXPLORE   **4 | Follow the Water**

ELEMENTS	☆☆☆☆	☆☆☆	☆☆	☆
GREAT LAKES WATERSHED MAP: Student labels the map using the words provided. The map is neat and well-organized.	Addresses all of the components	Missing one component	Missing two components	Missing three or more components
WATER CYCLE GAME: Students participates in the game and the discussion before and after the game. Students are able to explain the general movement of Great Lakes water. Students are able to name parts of the water cycle as it pertains to the Great Lakes.	Addresses all of the components	Missing one component	Missing two components	Missing three or more components
PARTICIPATION: Student participates in the hydrologic cycle stations by listening and following the directions. Student actively participates in the class discussion by raising his/her hand, making eye-contact with the speakers, referencing prior comments or ideas, and providing imaginative insights.	Addresses all of the components	Missing one component	Missing two components	Missing three or more components

EXPLORE   **5 | Water Flow**

ELEMENTS	☆☆☆☆	☆☆☆	☆☆	☆
GREAT LAKES WATERSHED MAP: Student labels and draws lines indicating the five stations to which her/his droplet went. The map is neat and well-organized.	Addresses all of the components	Missing one component	Missing two components	Missing three or more components
WATER FLOW STORY: The story reflects the student's understanding of the movement of water and retention rates. The story includes all five stations the student visited. The story notes that very little water moves into the Great Lakes. The story is original and imaginative.	Addresses all of the components	Missing one component	Missing two components	Missing three or more components
PARTICIPATION: Student participates in the hydrologic cycle stations by listening and following the directions. Student actively participates in the class discussion by raising his/her hand, making eye-contact with the speakers, referencing prior comments or ideas, and providing imaginative insights.	Addresses all of the components	Missing one component	Missing two components	Missing three or more components

EXPLORE   **6 | Landscape Changes: (K-3)**

ELEMENTS	☆☆☆☆	☆☆☆	☆☆	☆
JOURNAL PAGES: Student draws pictures to show the "before and after" effects of the glacier's movements.	Addresses all of the components	Missing one component	Missing two components	Missing three or more components
PARTICIPATION: Student participates in the glacier demonstration by listening and following the directions. Student actively participates in the class discussion by raising his/her hand, making eye-contact with the speakers, referencing prior comments or ideas, and providing imaginative insights.	Addresses all of the components	Missing one component	Missing two components	Missing three or more components
GLACIER OBSERVATIONS: Student explains how big a glacier is and how glaciers formed the Great Lakes. Students should include words with their pictures to aid the explanation.	Addresses all of the components	Missing one component	Missing two components	Missing three or more components

EXPLORE   6 | Landscape Changes (4-8)

ELEMENTS	☆☆☆☆	☆☆☆	☆☆	☆
JOURNAL QUESTIONS: Student thoroughly addresses all questions. Student compares how people and landscapes change over both shorter and longer periods of time. Student provides an example of how landscapes can change over time.	Addresses all of the components	Missing one component	Missing two components	Missing three or more components
SCALE DIAGRAM: Student uses the equations to correctly calculate the number of people it takes to equal the height of a glacier.	Addresses all of the components	Missing one component	Missing two components	Missing three or more components
GLACIER OBSERVATIONS: Student includes a "before and after" diagram detailing landscape changes as a result of the glacier. Student describes his/her observations and explains the formation of the Great Lakes using ideas and concepts introduced by the activity. The diagram pays close attention to details.	Addresses all of the components	Missing one component	Missing two components	Missing three or more components

EXPLORE   7 | Rock Songs

ELEMENTS	☆☆☆☆	☆☆☆	☆☆	☆
SONG: Student's song is accurate, clear and detailed. Student's song includes at least 3 concepts learned in the unit and is written on the journal pages.	Addresses all of the components	Missing one component	Missing two components	Missing three or more components
GROUP/INDIVIDUAL WORK: Student participates in group/individual work by creating a research question based on Great Lakes geology, and finding the appropriate answers. Student creates lyrics that reflect her/his research and rehearse the song prior to performance. Student performs the song with her/his group.	Addresses all of the components	Missing one component	Missing two components	Missing three or more components

INVESTIGATE   8 | Water in Motion

ELEMENTS	☆☆☆☆	☆☆☆	☆☆	☆
PARTICIPATION: Student participates in the discussion and brainstorm about water flow model. Student actively participates in the class discussion by raising his/her hand, making eye-contact with the speakers, referencing prior comments or ideas, and providing imaginative insights.	Addresses all of the components	Missing one component	Missing two components	Missing three or more components
GROUP WORK: Student works with group to choose one focus question. Student (and group) design an experiment that addresses the question and takes the scientific method, retention rates, elevation and lake volume into account.	Addresses all of the components	Missing one component	Missing two components	Missing three or more components
DEMONSTRATION/WRAP-UP: Student (and group) conduct experiment for the class, write it up in the journal pages and creatively display their data. Student creates a list of ways s/he can help keep the Great Lakes clean.	Addresses all of the components	Missing one component	Missing two components	Missing three or more components

INVESTIGATE 9 | Whose Water?

ELEMENTS	☆☆☆☆	☆☆☆	☆☆	☆
DEBATE PREPARATION: Student prepares for debate by listing elements of a good debate, completing summary of specific article, and preparing to debate based on a specific view and/or character.	Addresses all of the components	Missing one component	Missing two components	Missing three or more components
DEBATE: Student (and group) presents a two-minute focused summary of group's perspective. Summary includes supporting evidence. Student (and group) presents a counter argument that addresses other perspectives. Argument is based on facts, not opinions. Student (and group) concludes with a final defense that summarizes stance and responds to others' critiques.	Addresses all of the components	Missing one component	Missing two components	Missing three or more components
DEBATE REFLECTION: Student reflects on the effectiveness of debate and debaters. Student notes areas of strength and areas for improvement. Student discusses how his/her opinions evolved through research and the class debate.	Addresses all of the components	Missing one component	Missing two components	Missing three or more components
LETTER: Letter is appropriately addressed. Student summarizes the issue and presents his/her views with supporting details from reliable sources. Letter is persuasive, advocates for a specific point, has minimal spelling/grammar errors and follows a letter format.	Addresses all of the components	Missing one component	Missing two components	Missing three or more components
ESSAY: Essay has a central theme developed throughout. Student presents and critiques all sides of the issue fairly. Student concludes the essay with his/her personal opinion and supporting details. Essay has minimal spelling and grammatical errors. Sources are cited.	Addresses all of the components	Missing one component	Missing two components	Missing three or more components

INVESTIGATE 10 | Global Climate Change

ELEMENTS	☆☆☆☆	☆☆☆	☆☆	☆
GREENHOUSE EFFECT: Student draws the set-up accurately and labels each diagram. Student records temperatures for both jars and explains the difference in temperatures. Student defines the greenhouse effect as illustrated by the demonstration.	Addresses all of the components	Missing one component	Missing two components	Missing three or more components
GLOBAL WARMING: Student draws the set-up accurately and labels each diagram correctly. Student records temperatures for both jars and explains the difference. Student defines global warming, lists sources of carbon dioxide, determines possible effects of global warming, and hypothesizes about changes in temperature, evaporation and precipitation.	Addresses all of the components	Missing one component	Missing two components	Missing three or more components
ARTICLES: For each article, student identifies the author's main point. Student lists 3 supporting pieces of evidence for each main point.	Addresses all of the components	Missing one component	Missing two components	Missing three or more components
EVAPORATION: Student draws the set-up accurately and labels each diagram correctly. Student records the amount of water left after one hour and explains the difference in water levels. Student discusses the possible impact of global warming on freshwater supplies.	Addresses all of the components	Missing one component	Missing two components	Missing three or more components
ESSAY (extension): Student's essay explains and illustrates the concepts of the greenhouse effect, global warming and evaporation. Student describes at least 3 possible effects global warming could have on the Great Lakes. The essay has minimal spelling and grammatical errors. Sources are cited.	Addresses all of the components	Missing one component	Missing two components	Missing three or more components

INVESTIGATE **11 | Geology of My Home**

ELEMENTS	☆☆☆☆	☆☆☆	☆☆	☆
GETTING STARTED: Student contributes to the brainstorm list of what was learned in the unit. Student chooses 2 focus areas for the book and works to personalize and create the book structure.	Addresses all of the components	Missing one component	Missing two components	Missing three or more components
CONTENT AREAS: Storybook includes information from the 2 content areas chosen. Book includes relevant illustrations and words.	Addresses all of the components	Missing one component	Missing two components	Missing three or more components
WRAP-UP: After creating the storybook, student is able to explain its content and why the Great Lakes are important.	Addresses all of the components	Missing one component	Missing two components	Missing three or more components

INVESTIGATE **12 | Shaped by Geology**

ELEMENTS	☆☆☆☆	☆☆☆	☆☆	☆
GEOLOGIC TIME: The project includes an explanation of short and long-term scales. The project situates the formation of the Great Lakes in relation to the 4.6 billion years of time.	Addresses all of the components	Missing one component	Missing two components	Missing three or more components
GLACIATION: The project defines what a glacier is and illustrates how the Great Lakes were formed through the melting and receding of the glaciers. The project notes the different materials that contributed to its formation.	Addresses all of the components	Missing one component	Missing two components	Missing three or more components
WATER FLOW: The project demonstrates how water flows through the Great Lakes watershed. There is an explanation of how very little water moves into the Great Lakes. The project notes why this source of freshwater is significant.	Addresses all of the components	Missing one component	Missing two components	Missing three or more components
STORYLINE: Student developed an age-appropriate storyline that is both imaginative and informative. The project also engages others through its illustrations and is neat and creative.	Addresses all of the components	Missing one component	Missing two components	Missing three or more components

Great Lakes in My World
Resource List

Books (K-5) (alphabetical by title)

Lake Unit
The Freshwater Alphabet Book, *Jerry Pallotta*
What is a Fish?, *Bobbie Kalman*
What are Food Chains and Webs?, *Bobbie Kalman*
What's on the Beach? A Great Lakes Treasure Hunt,
    Mary Blocksma
Who Eats What? Food Chains and Webs, *Patricia Lauber*

Sand Dune Unit
Discovering Great Lakes Dunes,
    Elizabeth Brockwell-Tillman, Earl Wolf
The Legend of Sleeping Bear, *Kathy Jo Wargin*
Sand Dunes of the Great Lakes, *C.J. and Edna Elfont*
Sand on the Move, *Roy A. Gallant*

Wetlands Unit
Coming Out of Our Shell, *Canadian Department of*
    Fisheries and Oceans
A Freshwater Pond, *Adam Hibbert*
From Tadpole to Frog, *Wendy Pfeffer*
In the Small, Small Pond, *Denise Fleming*
Insect Metamorphosis, *Nancy Goor*
A Ladybug's Life, *John Himmelman*
A Luna Moth's Life, *John Himmelman*
A Pill Bug's Life, *John Himmelman*
Plants That Never Ever Bloom, *Ruth Heller*
Pond Life: Cycles of Life, *David Stewart*
Pond Year, *Kathryn Lasky*
The Reason for a Flower, *Ruth Heller*
The Salamander Room, *Anne Mazer*
A Salamander's Life, *John Himmelman*
A Slug's Life, *John Himmelman*
The Trip of a Drip, *Vicki Cobb*
Wally and Deanna's Groundwater Adventure: To the Saturated
    Zone, *Waterloo Center for Groundwater Research*
What's it Like to be a Fish?, *Wendy Pfeffer*

Communities Unit
Eastern Great Lakes/Western Great Lakes: State Studies,
    Thomas and Virginia Aylesworth
Urban Roosts: Where Birds Nest in the City, *Barbara Bash*
Where Does Garbage Go?, *Paul Showers*

History Unit
By Canoe and Moccasin, *Basil Johnston*
Great Lakes and Great Ships, *John Mitchell and*
    Tom Woodruff
Great Lakes Ships We Remember, *Peter J. Van Der Linden*
Indians of the Great Lakes, *John Mitchell and Tom Woodruff*
Indians of the Northeast: Traditions, History, Legends and Life,
    Lisa Sita
Lake Michigan, *Ann Armbruster*
Lake Superior, *Ann Armbruster*
Mail by the Pail, *Colin Bergel*
Michigan, an Illustrated History for Children,
    John Mitchell and Tom Woodruff
Native Americans of the Great Lakes, *Stuart A. Kallen*
The Ojibwa, People of the Great Lakes, *Anne M. Todd*
People of the Northeast Woodlands, *Linda Thompson*
The Potowatomi, *James A. Clifton*
Shingebiss: An Ojibwe Legend, *Betsy Bowen*
Songs of the Chippewa, *John Bierhorst*
Woman of the Green Glade: *The Story of an Ojibway Woman*
    on the Great Lakes Frontier, Virginia M. Soetebier

Historical Fiction Books by Janie Lynn Panagopoulos
(a selection):
Calling the Griffin
Erie Trail West
Journey Back to Lumberjack Camp
Madame Cadillac's Ghost
Mark of the Bear Claw
The Runes of Isle Royale

Geology Unit
Ancient Life of the Great Lakes Region, *J. Alan Holman*
The Big Rock, *Bruce Hiscock*
Down Comes the Rain, *Franklyn M. Branley*
A Drop Around the World, *Barbara Shaw McKinney*
Everyone Needs a Rock, *Byrd Baylor*
Glaciers, *Roy A. Gallant*
Icebergs and Glaciers, *Seymour Simon*
Paddle to the Sea, *Holling C. Holling*
The Pebble in My Pocket: A History of our Earth,
    Meredith Hooper
Prehistoric Great Lakes, *John Mitchell and Tom Woodruff*

Books (6-8 and Educators)

Borne of the Wind: *An Introduction to the Ecology of Michigan's Sand Dunes, Dennis Albert*

Discovering Great Lakes Dunes, *Elizabeth Brockwell-Tillman and Earl Wolf*

The Dynamic Great Lakes, *Barbara Spring*

Encyclopedia of Mammals, *David Macdonald*

Eye Witness: Pond and River, *Steve Parker*

Field Guide to Lakes, *Jacob Verduin*

Great Lakes Atlas, *United States Environmental Protection Agency*

Great Lakes Dune Ecosystems, *Michigan State University Extension*

Great Lakes Nature: *An Outdoor Year, Mary Blocksma*

Great Lakes Water Levels, *Great Lakes Water Levels Communications Centre*

Guide to the Study of Freshwater Biology, *Needham and Needham*

A Guidebook to Groundwater Resources, *Great Lakes Commission*

How to Know Immature Insects, *H.F. Chu*

Illinois Native Peoples, *Andrew Santella*

The Inland Seas: A Journey Through the Great Lakes, *Paul Vasey*

The Living Great Lakes, *Jerry Dennis*

Maritime Chicago, *Theodore Karamanski and Deane Tank Sr.*

On the Brink, *Dave Dempsey*

People of the Lakes, *editors of Time-Life Books*

Pond and Brook: a Guide to Nature in Freshwater Environments, *Michael Caduto*

Stories From Where We Live: The Great Lakes, *Sara St. Antoine*

Wild Lake Michigan, *John & Ann Mahan*

Great Lakes Field Guides

Amphibians and Reptiles of the Great Lakes Region, *James H. Harding*

Animal Tracks of the Great Lakes, *Chris Stall*

Dune Country: *A Hiker's Guide to the Indiana Dunes*

A Field Guide to Great Lakes Coastal Plants, *Michigan Sea Grant*

Fish of Lake Michigan and Fish of Lake Superior, *Sea Grant*

Guide to Common Invertebrates of North America

Insects of the Great Lakes Region, *Gary A. Dunn*

Mammals of the Great Lakes Region, *Allen Kurta*

Additional Field Guides

Audubon Field Guides

Fandex Family Field Guides

Golden Guides

Newcomb's Wildflower Guide, *Lawrence Newcomb*

Peterson Field Guides

Pocket Naturalist Series

Take Along Guides

Song Books and Albums

Bunyan and Banjoes: Michigan Songs and Stories, Great Lakes Songbook *by Kitty Donohoe*

Distant Shores, Picture Book and Music Cassette *by Bluestem Productions*

Folk Songs of the Great Lakes *by Depot Recordings*

Lake Rhymes: Folk Songs of the Great Lakes, *Lee and Joann Murdock (curriculum)*

Romp in the Swamp, an Album *by Billy Brennan*

Underwater Land, a Children's Album *by Pat Dailey and Shel Silverstein*

Additional Great Lakes Books

River Road Publication, Inc., *www.riverroadpublications.com/*

Magazines

EEK! (online): Wisconsin Department of Natural Resources, *http://www.dnr.state.wi.us/org/caer/ce/eek/*

Tracks Magazine, Michigan United Conservation Clubs *http://www.mucc.org/youth/tracks/index.php*

Web sites

Resources and Organizations

Alliance for the Great Lakes, *www.greatlakes.org*

Center for Great Lakes Environmental Education, *www.greatlakesed.org*

COSEE Great Lakes, *http://www.coseegreatlakes.net/*

Environment Canada: Great Lakes Kids and Our Great Lakes, *http://www.on.ec.gc.ca/greatlakeskids/*

Environmental Education Association of Illinois, *http://www.eeai.net/*

Environmental Protection Agency Region 5 Office, *www.epa.gov/region5/*

The Globe Program, *www.globe.gov/globe_flash.html*

Grand Valley State University, Annis Water Resources Institute, Education Resources, *http://www.gvsu.edu/wri/education*

Great Lakes Atlas, *http://www.epa.gov/glnpo/atlas/index.html*

Great Lakes Aquarium, *http://www.glaquarium.org/*

Great Lakes Directory, *www.greatlakesdirectory.org/*

Great Lakes Fisheries Education Resources, *http://www-personal.umich.edu/~zintmich/GLFT/*

The Great Lakes Green Book, *http://www.glu.org/english/restoration/files/greenbookweb6-11.pdf*

Great Lakes Image Collection, *www.epa.gov/glnpo/image/*

Great Lakes Information Network, *www.great-lakes.net*

Great Lakes National Programs Office, *www.epa.gov/glnpo/*

Great Lakes Research and Education Center, *www.nps.gov/indu/Research_Education/education.htm*

Great Lakes Sea Grant, *www.greatlakesseagrant.org/about.html*

Great Lakes United, *www.glu.org/*

Illinois-Indiana Sea Grant: Education Resources, *http://www.iisgcp.org/education/topics_education.html*

Inland Seas Education Association, *http://www.schoolship.org/*
International Joint Commission, *www.ijc.org*
John G. Shedd Aquarium, Shedd Educational Adventures:
    http://www.sheddaquarium.org/sea/
Lake Superior Youth Symposium, *http://wupcenter.mtu.edu/*
    education/lake_superior_symposium/
Lakewide Management Plans, *www.epa.gov/glnpo/gl2000/*
    lamps/

Michigan Department of Environmental Quality, Education
    Resources, *http://www.michigan.gov/deq/0,1607,7-135-*
    3307_3580---,00.html
Michigan Environmental Council, *http://www.*
    environmentalcouncil.org/
Michigan Environmental Education, *http://www.*
    michiganenvironmentaled.org/
Michigan Sea Grant: Education Resources, *http://www.*
    miseagrant.umich.edu/education/index.html
Michigan United Conservation Clubs: Education Resources,
    http://www.mucc.org/youth/tracks/index.php

Michigan United Conservation Clubs: Tracks Magazine, *http://*
    www.mucc.org/youth/tracks/index.php
Minnesota Environmental Education Resources, *http://*
    www.d.umn.edu/ceed/
Minnesota Sea Grant: Education Resources, *http://www.*
    seagrant.umn.edu/education/index.html
National Wildlife Federation, *http://www.nwf.org/kids/*
National Wildlife Federation: eNature, *http://www.enature.com/*

National Wildlife Federation: Happenin' Habitats,
    http://happeninhabitats.pwnet.org/index.php
National Wildlife Federation: Schoolyard Habitats and
    Resources, *www.nwf.org/schoolyard/*
New York Sea Grant, *http://www.seagrant.sunysb.edu/*
The Notebaert Nature Museum, Education Resources: *http://*
    www.naturemuseum.org/index.php?id=36
Ocean Arks International, *http://www.oceanarks.org/*

Ohio Sea Grant, *http://www.ohioseagrant.osu.edu/*
Pennsylvania Sea Grant: Education Resources, *http://seagrant.*
    psu.edu/education/resources.htm
Pier Wisconsin, *http://www.pierwisconsin.org/*
TEACH Great Lakes, *www.great-lakes.net/teach*
TEACH Great Lakes, *Education Resources, http://www.great-*
    lakes.net/teach/links/

Union of Concerned Scientists: Great Lakes Communities and
    Ecosystems at Risk, *www.ucsusa.org/greatlakes/*
US Fish and Wildlife Service, *www.fws.gov/*
Wisconsin Sea Grant: Education Resources, *http://www.*
    seagrant.wisc.edu/education/
Departments of Natural Resources by States and Provinces
Wisconsin Department of Natural Resources, *www.dnr.state.*
    wi.us

Michigan Department of Natural Resources, *www.michigan.gov/*
    dnr
Michigan Department of Natural Resources- Plants and Animals,
    www.michigan.gov/dnr/0,1607,7-153-10370_12145---,00.
    html
Wildlife Educational Resources, Michigan Department of
    Natural Resources, *http://www.michigan.gov/dnr/0,1607,7-*
    153-10369-57667--,00.html
Minnesota Department of Natural Resources, *www.dnr.state.*
    mn.us
New York State Department of Environmental Conservation,
    http://www.dec.ny.gov/

Ohio Department of Natural Resources, *www.dnr.state.oh.us*
Indiana Department of Natural Resources, *www.in.gov/dnr*
Illinois Department of Natural Resources, *www.dnr.state.il.us*
Ontario Ministry of Natural Resources, *http://www.mnr.gov.*
    on.ca/en/index.html

Wetland Sites by States and Provinces
Illinois Wetlands, *www.twingroves.district96.k12.il.us/Wetlands/*
    Wetlands.html
Indiana Wetlands, *www.in.gov/wetlands/*
Michigan Wetlands, *www.glhabitat.org/mwac/*
Michigan Environmental Council, *http://www.*
    environmentalcouncil.org/
New York State Wetlands Forum, *www.wetlandsforum.org*

Ontario Wetlands, *http://www.ec.gc.ca/tho-wlo/default.*
    asp?lang=En&n=06269065-1
Wisconsin Wetlands Association, *http://www.wisconsinwetlands.*
    org/
Wisconsin Department of Administration Coastal
    Management Program, *http://www.doa.state.wi.us/section.*
    asp?linkid=65&locid=9
The Ohio Wetlands Foundation, *www.ohiowetlands.org/*

Sand Dune Sites
Indiana Dunes National Lakeshore, *www.nps.gov/indu/home.*
    htm
Sand Dune Park Geology Tour, *http://www.nature.nps.gov/*
    geology/tour/sanddune.cfm
Sand Dune Ridges and Dunes in the Calumet Region, *www.*
    newton.dep.anl.gov/natbltn/700-799/nb709.htm
The Unofficial Sleeping Bear Dunes Home Page, *www.leelanau.*
    com/dunes/dunes/
Preserve the Dunes, *http://www.sosdunes.org/*

Save the Dunes Council, *www.savedunes.org/*
Parks in the Great Lakes, *www.great-lakes.net/tourism/rec/parks.*
    html
Indiana Dunes National Lakeshore, *www.nps.gov/indu/home.*
    htm
Sleeping Bear Dunes, *www2.nature.nps.gov/geology/parks/slbe/*

Curricula

ESCAPE: Exotic Species Compendium of Activities to Protect the Ecosystem, Illinois/Indiana Sea Grant, *http://www.iisgcp.org/catalog/ed/esc.htm*

Exploring the Great Lakes: A Logbook of Adventures, Patricia Westfield and Nan Soper, *www.riverroadpublications.com/HTML/StateStudies.html*

Fresh and Salt, COSEE Great Lakes, *http://coseegreatlakes.net/curriculum/*

Great Lakes in My World, *http://www.greatlakes.org/glimw*

Great Minds? Great Lakes!, United States Environmental Protection Agency, Great Lakes National Programs Office *http://www.epa.gov/glnpo/monitoring/great_minds_great_lakes/*

Greatest of the Great Lakes, COSEE Great Lakes *http://www.coseegreatlakes.net/news/20070402*

Lake Rhymes: Folk Songs of the Great Lakes (includes a cd), Lee and Joann Murdock, *http://www.leemurdock.com/lm_html/music/lakerhymes.htm*

L.A.P.'s Great Lakes Unit, Michigan Department of Natural Resources, *www.outdoorexplorersclub.com/flash/OECKids/KidsMain.html*

Learning to Give: A Day at the Beach, *www.learningtogive.org/lessons/unit85/overview.html*

Life of the Lakes: A Guide to the Great Lakes Fishery Education Materials, Michigan Sea Grant Extension, Michigan State University, *http://www.miseagrant.umich.edu/store/cart.php?m=product_detail&p=2*

Michigan Department of Environmental Education Curriculum Project (5 units), *http://www.michigan.gov/deq/0,1607,7-135-3307_3580_29678---,00.html*

This Land is Your Land: Lesson Plans for Land Use, Michigan State University Extension, *http://www.uwsp.edu/cnr/wcee/PDF/Bibs/LandUse.PDF*

Working With Water: Wisconsin Waterways, Teacher's Guide and Student Materials, Wisconsin Historical Society, Office of School Services, *http://www.wisconsinhistory.org/whspress/books/book.asp?book_id=242*

Ohio Sea Grant Publications (ES-EAGLS)

Land and Water Interactions in the Great Lakes, Great Lakes Climate and Water Movement, Great Lakes Shipping, Life in the Great Lakes, Great Lakes Environmental Issues, *http://earthsys.ag.ohio-state.edu/pubs07htmlumich.edu/flow/index.html*

Paddle-to-the-Sea: Supplemental Curriculum Activities, *http://earthsys.ag.ohio-state.edu/project/pubs/Paddle.html*

Project Flow, Michigan Sea Grant Extension, Michigan State University, *http://www.miseagrant..*

Poetry

Great Lakes Rhythm & Rhyme: A New Poetry Collection, Denise Rodgers, *http://thepoetrylady.com/*

Visual Media

The Great Lakes Research and Education Center has a video loan service available to educators. To borrow a kit, call: 219-929-1707. Available videos include:

Common Miracles
It's All Connected
The Rise and Fall of the Great Lakes
Dunes to Forest "The Indiana Dunes"
The Geology of the Indiana Sand Dunes

Succession: From Sand Dunes to Forest
Paddle-to-the-Sea
Fresh Water: Resources at Risk
Great Lakes Alive! The Great Experiment
Great Lakes Alive! To the Last Drop

Great Lakes Alive! Restoring the Balance
Waste Water: An Environmental Resource
The Life of the Lakes: The Great Lakes Fishery

Additional Videos

Bugs Don't Bug Us, *Bo Peep Productions*
Creatures of the Great Lakes, *Brauer Productions*
Great Lakes, Fragile Seas, National Geographic Society
St. Lawrence: Stairway to the Sea, *the National Film Board of Canada*
Too Much Mussel, *Ohio Sea Grant*

Compact Discs

Biodiversity Around the Great Lakes, US EPA Great Lakes National Programs Office
Exploring the Great Lakes, US EPA Great Lakes National Programs Office
Wetlands Educational Curriculum, US EPA

Contact the Alliance for the Great Lakes if you know of additional resources that should be added to this list: education@greatlakes.org

Great Lakes in My World
Activity Index (Alphabetical)

Great Lakes in My World
Activity Index (by Topic)